CW00829504

THE BEE-EATERS

THE BEE-EATERS

by C. H. FRY

Illustrated by JOHN BUSBY
and with colour plates
by the author

T & A D POYSER

London

ISBN 0 85661 037 2

First published in 1984 by T & A D Poyser Ltd
Town Head House, Calton, Waterhouses, Staffordshire, England

First reprint 1991 by T & A D Poyser Ltd
24–28 Oval Road, London, NW1 7DX

United States Edition published by
Academic Press Inc., San Diego, CA 92101

Printed in Great Britain by
Mackays of Chatham PLC, Chatham, Kent

Colour plates by Wood Westworth & Co. Ltd.
St Helens

Contents

   Geographical differentiation among the bee-eaters—The fact
   of evolution—Monotypic and polytypic species—Patterns in
   allopatry: subspeciation—Patterns in allopatry: speciation—
   Superspecies—Evolving sympatry: the species-group—Rate of
   evolution—Two problem bee-eaters—The Family's roots

For Kathie

Preface

Exactly one hundred years ago there was published in London a sumptuous treatise which has remained until now the only work in any language devoted exclusively to bee-eaters. It was *A Monograph of the Meropidae, or Family of the Bee-Eaters* by H. Dresser, and is nowadays a collector's item. The text is ample, and yet to the modern ornithologist it has hardly anything of interest to say. I mean no disrespect to the memory of Dresser, a great ornithologist in his day—if his monograph expounds little it is for the simple reason that when it was written practically nothing was known about the birds except what could be gleaned from museum specimens and their collectors' scant field notes. Of only one sort was anything more than the most rudimentary details of its natural history known, the sole species breeding in Europe: *The* Bee-eater, or the European Bee-eater*.

Recently, European Bee-eaters have been studied intensively, because the way they hunt makes them ideal subjects for research upon the energetic 'cost' of foraging. Some Australian and African bee-eaters have attracted even more intensive investigations, because of their extraordinary societies with 'helpers' joining parents in rearing the young: Red-throated and White-fronted Bee-eaters are now amongst the best studied of all African birds.

It has seemed to me that the time is ripe for this second book about bee-eaters, to set down what is known and to identify some of the many areas where further effort in the field is likely to pay rich dividends. My first aim is like that attributed to my illustrious predecessor by a reviewer of his *Monograph*, in the *Ibis* of 1886, to "summarize all that can be gathered together concerning a set of birds which are not generally very well

*'European Bee-eater' is unconsciously jingoistic too—what a pity that the neutral and aesthetic 'Golden Bee-eater' was never adopted, which Russians use in distinction from their Blue-cheeked Bee-eater.

known". My second is to describe how races and species originate and to explain the significance of the small differences in plumage, size, shape and society which distinguish them: in a word, their evolution. If this book had been addressed to biologists only, I would have entitled it *Evolutionary Biology of the Meropidae*; but it is intended for a broader readership and I have tried to write it accordingly, avoiding jargon and attempting to put across the one or two taxing biological concepts in everyday terms.

The evolutionary emphasis reflects my own interest, but the bee-eaters do in fact demonstrate a number of evolutionary principles very well indeed. It is my hope that students and bird-watchers who have been puzzled by the multiplicity of similar birds around them (one has only to open an American, African or Australian field guide for a host of examples), will find some explanation for it here—or at least that they will finish with a better understanding about species' adaptations and the unending diversity of nature. At the same time I mean to publicize these admirable birds, that others may come to enjoy them too, and be prompted to seek for themselves the pleasures of study and the rewards of discovery.

'Admirable' is the word for bee-eaters. Being birds of the sun, none live in Britain and so they have never been accorded the special place in English traditions and affections of the Swan or the Swallow, or indeed of that distant cousin the Kingfisher. Yet thoroughly attractive birds they undoubtedly are—sleek and graceful, melodious, restrainedly colourful, tractable, confiding and sociable; and wherever the various kinds occur they are regarded (except by bee-keepers!) with affection. In southern Australia the arrival of their bee-eater, the Rainbowbird, is taken to herald the spring; throughout Africa villagers take proprietary pride in any nearby colony of Carmine Bee-eaters; while a clamorous nesting colony of 50,000 Rosy Bee-eaters is one of the seven wonders of the ornithological world. I shall forego the satisfaction of rhapsodizing any further, and let the birds speak for themselves.

Acknowledgements

It is humbling to think what a small proportion of this book is the result of my own unaided effort. From the kindling of my interest in bee-eaters twenty years ago I have had to count on the help of others in almost every endeavour, so the travelling companions, hosts, string-pullers, charitable foundations, technicians, museum and university colleagues, and correspondents to whom I am heavily indebted must by now number hundreds. I have already had the satisfaction of offering my thanks publicly, in previous publications, to many of these; but I would like here to repeat the names of those to whom I feel especially beholden.

First there are John Elgood, Emeritus Professor of Zoology at Ibadan University, who supervised my doctoral research at Ahmadu Bello University, and Michael Dyer and Humphrey Crick whose bee-eater researches, also in Nigeria, I in turn supervised, from Aberdeen University. We have shared weeks of sweated labour in the African bush and I have benefited greatly not only from my mentor's experience but also from my students', for between academic generations learning spills in one direction no less bounteously than understanding flows in the other. Dr Dyer and Dr Crick have each been unstinting in allowing me to draw on their dissertations (of 1979 and 1984 respectively), and I am most grateful too to Dr Robert Hegner for letting me have a copy of his 1981 Cornell University thesis on a Kenyan bee-eater. Michael Dyer spent the austral summer of 1982–1983 studying bee-eaters nesting in Western Australia, and with much generosity has made his findings available to me for publication here.

Then there are those many people who, residing in bee-eater domains in three continents, over the years have made it possible for me to spend days and weeks pursuing studies in the field, and to each of the following I again extend my deep appreciation of their hospitality, kindness and expertise: Mrs and the late Mr Rudyerd Boulton, Dr and Mrs Joe Charles, Mr Chum Cunningham-van Someren, Mr and Mrs John Deeming, Mr Robert Dowsett, Mrs Billy Gill, Mrs Dale Hanmer, Dr and Mrs David Happold, Prof and Mrs Brian Harris, Mr and Mrs Geoffrey Harrison, Mr and Mrs James Hendrick, Mr Tony Hopson and Dr Jane Hopson (at Lake Chad and later Lake Turkana), Mrs Jennifer Horne, Mr and Mrs Desmond Jackson, Mr and Mrs Philip Marshall, Mr and Mrs Robert Sharland, Mr and Mrs Bernard Walker, Dr and Mrs David Wells, Dr and Mrs Roger Wilkinson and Mr John Wilson.

During the preparation of the book I have profited immeasurably from the special knowledge of numerous correspondents. In answering my queries they have sent me field notes, photographs, tabulations, skins, manuscripts and a wealth of information for which—as well as for their time—I extend to each my warmest thanks: Dr J. S. Ash, Mr D. R. Aspinwall, Mr M. L. Avery, Dr D. B. Baker, Dr P. S. Baker, Lt-Col H. L. Bell, the late Mr C. W. Benson, Mr P. Bergier, Mr O. Biber, Mr K. D. Bishop, Ms M. Blakers Mr J. Boswall, Mr P. L. Britton, Mr R. K. Brooke, Mr P. W. P. Browne, Mr M. D. Bruce, Dr D. M. Bryant, Mr G. Bundy, Dr P. J. K. Burton, Ms C. Buxton, Sr E. Callegari, Mr G. S. Cansdale, Mr C. Carter, Dr J. Charles, Mr P. A. Clancey, Mr G. E. Clapp, Mr C. F. Clinning, Mr P. Colston, Mr R. A. Conant, Prof P. S. Corbet, Ms N. Coulthard, Mr S. Cramp, The Earl of Cranbrook, Mr B. Cropp, Mr G. R. Cunningham-van Someren, Mr G. Debout, Mr J. C. Deeming, Dr R. J. Douthwaite, Mr R. J. Dowsett, Mr R. D. W. Draffan, Prof Dr W. Drescher, Mr P. J. Dubois, Dr J. Dyck, Dr M. Dyer, Mrs M. Dyer, Prof J. H. Elgood, Dr S. T. Emlen, Mr G. Field, Mr O. FitzGerald, Dr M. Fogden, Mr J. M. Forshaw, Mr I. C. J. Galbraith, Dr E. I. Gavrilov, Mr L. Gillard, Mr P. J. Ginn, Dr U. Glutz von Blotzheim, Mr D. Goodwin, Mr M. E. J. Gore, Dr V. Hahn, Mrs D. B. Hanmer, Dr C. J. O. Harrison, Dr R. M. Harwin, Dr R. J. Hayward, Mr J. Hendrick, Mr R. Hindmarsh, Mr M. C. Hodgson, Mr P. Hogg, Mr D. A. Holmes, Mr P. Holmes, Mrs J. Hopson, Mr M. Horwood, Mr J. H. Hosken, Mrs K. Hough, Mr S. Howe, Mr J. D. Huckabay, Mr B. J. Huntley, Dr A. M. Hutson, Mr M. P. S. Irwin, Mr M. Jaeger, Mr M. C. Jennings, Dr R. A. C. Jensen, Mr S. Keith, Dr A. Kemp, Dr J. R. Krebs, Mr B. Lamarche, Mrs P. Lorber, Dr M. Louette, Mr I. A. W. Macdonald, Dr J. Mackinnon, Dr G. L. Maclean, Mr G. C. Madoc, Mrs F. S. Miles, Dr G. J. Morel, Mrs I. C. Morris, Mr K. A. Muller, Mr P. Neophytou, Mr G. Nikolaus, Dr P. A. Orkin, Mr H. Pager, Dr D. J. Pearson, Dr D. E. Peters, Mr W. W. A. Phillips, Mr S. K. Priklonskiy, Dr D. Purchase, Mr D. Read, Mr J. C. Reid, Mr E. Risley, Mr T. J. Roberts, Mr G. P. Robinson, Mr D. V. Rockingham-Gill, Prof F. Ruttner, Dr R. Schodde, Prof R. Shotter, Mr R. H. N. Smithers, Mr D. A. Smith, Dr D. W. Snow,

Mr R. Stjernstedt, Mr J. J. Swift, Mr M. Thévenot, Dr J. M. Thiollay, Dr D. Thomas, Dr I. Tutman, Prof E. K. Urban, Dr J. Ursprung, Dr J. P. Vande weghe, Mr C. R. Vardy, Dr J. Verschuren, Dr C. Violani, Mr J. F. Walsh, Mr M. P. Walters, Mrs F. E. Warr, Dr R. Watling, Mr P. Watson, Dr D. R. Wells, Prof F. N. White, Dr R. Wilkinson, Dr J. G. M. Wilson, Mr M. Wilson, Prof J. M. Winterbottom, Mr S. Woldhek and Dr A. Zahavi.

I wish to express my indebtedness to the Trustees and staff of the British Museum (Natural History) Sub-Department of Ornithology for study facilities afforded to me on numerous occasions; to Mrs Inge Allen and Dr Eva Crane and the International Bee Research Association for bibliographic assistance; to Mr Carl O'Callaghan, Mr Colin Willock and Survival Anglia Limited for allowing me to view films; to Prof Roy Siegfried and the Percy FitzPatrick Institute of African Ornithology for supplying nest record data, and to Zoology staff of Ahmadu Bello University, Bayero University and University of Malaya for technical and other help. At Aberdeen University I have become much indebted for translation to Mr Clive Liddiard (Russian, Ukrainian) and Dr Heinz Richner and Dr Iain Marr (German), to Mr Bernard Möbus for information about honeybees, Mr Andy Lucas for his photographic expertise, Ms Edna Watson for converting appalling manuscript into faultless typescript, Dr Bryan Nelson and Dr Mark Young for valued discussion, Dr H. Crick for critical reading of Chapters 6 and 7, and to successive heads of the Zoology Department, Prof Vero Wynne-Edwards, Prof George Dunnet and Prof William Mordue, for facilities therein and for their sympathetic interest in my work.

Without a number of research awards and travel grants my field experience of bee-eaters would be insignificant and this book could not have been contemplated, and I acknowledge with gratitude financial support from the Aberdeen University Fund for Travelling Allowances, the Carnegie Trust for the Universities of Scotland, the Frank M. Chapman Memorial Fund of the American Museum of Natural History, the Natural Environment Research Council (GT4/78/TLS/7), the Royal Geographical Society, the Royal Society, and the Science Research Council (GR/A 99312).

I should like to say last, how much I value John Busby's illustrations. Small land birds are a new departure for him, yet his skilful and evocative drawings have captured the very essence of bee-eaters, and depict their *jizz* much better than I have found words to describe.

Aberdeen, November 1983

NOTE: The abbreviation *pc* is used throughout the text to mean *personal communication*.

1 : Introduction

According to my reckoning there are 24 species of bee-eaters, falling into three genera with an essentially tropical distribution in the Old World, and the taxa* which I recognize are set out in the list later in this chapter. Eleven species are monotypic and seven others have only two subspecies (races) each. Of the remainder easily the most variable geographically is the Little Green Bee-eater *Merops orientalis*—its populations differ amongst themselves quite sharply in head colours and tail-streamer lengths, but by and large the polytypic bee-eaters each exhibit little plumage variation. In total I admit 52 taxa, the species and most of the subspecies being readily separable and only a few races needing critical examination in the museum for their determination. All the world's bee-eaters are portrayed in the eight colour plates except ten poorly differentiated races—42 kinds altogether.

In a distinctive and rather close-knit family of animals showing only a small amount of subspecific variability, one would expect to find correspondingly little distinction between the species themselves. A glance at the Plates will show that in the Family Meropidae, however, several kinds are highly distinctive in appearance. Most are grass-green above, buff or pale blue-green below with bright, contrasting throats, a black mask, dark gorget, black trailing edge to the wing, and rufescent green tails with long streamers; but none of those characters is universal. The most obvious departures are the Red-bearded Bee-eater *Nyctyornis amicta* with its bilious plumage together with the other rainforest forms shown in Plates 1 and 2, and the shocking-pink birds in Plate 8. The low intra-specific and high inter-specific variation means either that bee-eaters do not differentiate

* For the non-biologist there is a glossary of technical terms in Appendix 1.

readily or (contradictory as it may sound) that they are differentiating so rapidly that in no evolutionary time at all their races have become good, distinctive-looking species. In fact it is my belief that some bee-eater lineages have 'stuck' but that others are evolving fast (Chapter 3).

In the field bee-eaters—at least most kinds of *Merops*—come over as alert and vivacious birds: it is one of their more appealing characteristics. True to their name, they do indeed feed mainly on bees and related Hymenoptera. Such insects fly fast or are manoeuvrable, or both, which dictates that their avian predators shall prey on them in open situations— it follows that bee-eaters are conspicuous birds, perching in the open and often darting out after a passing insect. They spend the greater part of the day hunting, and their eminent watchability is enhanced by their generally permitting close approach. Carmine Bee-eaters *M. nubicus* frequently forage not from a perch but high in the sky, sailing around on the acute triangles of their wings in a leisurely-looking way and, with a few quick beats, effortlessly twisting after an insect. A few other large bee-eaters hunt likewise, and even the smallest ones, flycatching from their look-out perches, have the same enviable mastery of flight (although by no means are their sallies always successful). Continuous small postural movements show that a perched bee-eater, when not engaged in preening or interacting with others of its kind, is ever searching for food: looking to right and left, cocking an eye to the sky, following with turning head the flight of an insect at grass level, or starting forward with quarter-opened wings (an 'intention movement') before deciding better of it.

Those lucky enough to have watched birds in Africa or to have encountered bee-eaters in Europe, Asia or Australasia will know that these attractive birds are lively not only in pursuit of prey but also in interactions with others of their species. In even the least gregarious sort, singletons are rarely found and occurrence in pairs or family parties is the rule. A bird keeps close company with its fellows; they habitually perch close, even huddled up against each other, and pursue the same activity all together, wheeling round, preening, feeding or bathing. In the execution of commonplace daily activities they seem to show a degree of mutualism, as if seeking security in numbers and comfort in the reciproca-tion of behaviour.

Although without any great variety of expression they are quite vocal, the common voices being contact-calls pleasing to the human ear, rolling *pruuik-pruuik*'s and the like. High-flying flocks of migrants and the hubbub of a large nesting colony can be heard a kilometre away. At colonies much of the noise is of greeting and strident bickering, yet for all their rivalries and aerial chases they never inflict any physical damage upon one another, and in fact a much more evident feature of bee-eater society is the tenacity of individual bonds. A notable characteristic of many species, and one that has been the principal target of recent researches on the Meropidae, is the co-operation at the nest between the parents and one or several helpers, which undoubtedly ameliorates the often precarious lot of the nestlings.

A large number of birds, as well as a few mammals, are known to eat social bees and wasps from time to time, not only the stingless males or drones but also the stinging and often highly dangerous sterile females or workers; to justify the risks involved—risks if the predator knows the danger—the rewards are probably high with the bee or wasp a money-for-jam meal. In warm climates ants, wasps, bees and suchlike hymenopterans, many venomous, are abundant and they form a high proportion of daytime-flying insects. But surprisingly few birds have evolved in any sense as professional bee and wasp predators, and paramount amongst them are the bee-eaters of the Old World tropics and, in the New, the unrelated but extraordinarily convergent jacamars (Galbulidae). Whether the last have any obvious ways of devenoming bees is not known; but bee-eaters certainly have. Except for Carmines, which sometimes evidently de-sting bees without breaking flight, bee-eaters always return with a captured bee to their perch. There they deftly juggle it until it is held crosswise at the tip of the mandibles, near the end of the abdomen. Bouts of hitting the head end of the insect to one side of the perch alternate with rapid rubs of the tail with its sting to the other, like somebody vigorously using an india-rubber. I call it bee-rubbing and it is peculiar to the treatment of stinging Hymenoptera.

Even at distance it is easy to see if bee-rubbing is included in the immobilization treatment of an insect and, in the field, that provides a ready means for reckoning the proportions of Hymenoptera (or strictly of stingers) in a bird's diet. Close at hand a smooth perch can sometimes be seen to be wetted because rubbing causes the bee or wasp to discharge its bowel-fluid and poison; at times the sting is torn out and sticks into the perch, although more often a bee is swallowed with its sting still intact.

For the researcher studying their food biology a further convenient habit of bee-eaters is that several times a day they regurgitate a neat, black, odourless pellet of the indigestible remains of their prey. The fresh pellet is compact, 1–3 cm long, and easy to find below favoured perches. On stubbly or broken ground I have gone so far as to pin down sheets from which the day's harvest of pellets can be collected in a few seconds; but under roosts and near nests a mass of pellets can generally be obtained whatever the terrain. They can readily be dissected and analyzed, rendering it quite unnecessary to subject bee-eaters to the more brutal techniques like the use of emetics, sometimes applied to other birds.

All bee-eaters nest in earth holes. They excavate new holes each season or much less commonly they use a previous year's nest. Excavating, done with the beak and feet, is a powerful compulsion; it seems that both sexes need to perform a certain minimum of digging before they can successfully enter into the next phase of reproduction. In the immediate environs of the definitive nest-hole two or three 'false starts' are usually to be found, incomplete tunnels anything from a few centimetres long to almost full length, which are not so much diggings which failed when an obstruction was encountered, or soil of the wrong consistency, as the evident dissipation of a behavioural drive. In some instances false starts seem to be the product mainly of supernumeraries or helpers at the nest. Colonial bee-eaters have their nesting cliffs riddled with holes, but fewer birds comprise the colony than might be supposed, since maybe half of the holes are false starts or otherwise abandoned.

It is not difficult to locate bee-eater nests, solitary or aggregated.' The birds make little effort to conceal their visits, which are particularly frequent and obvious after the eggs have hatched. Some bee-eaters prefer to use cliffs, generally between one and five metres in height, often but by no means always by water, others may use sloping or flat ground. In Africa, Red-throated Bee-eaters *M. bullocki* and White-fronted *M. bullock-oides* nest only in cliffs, digging nearer to its top than its foot, so that in high cliffs the nest entrances are as difficult of access for the investigator as those of some cliff-nesting seabirds. Little Bee-eaters *M. pusillus* use low cliffs of a metre high or less, and sometimes a hoed ridge in a pepper-field or even a dried-out hoof depression will suffice for tunnelling to begin. Interestingly this bird will also use a very specialized site: the sloping roof of Aardvark burrows, with the nest-hole entrance a half-metre or more into the cavernous mouth of this large mammal's lair. Of all species the Rosy Bee-eater *M. malimbicus* makes the closest approach to being exclusively a flat-ground nester. It breeds in spectacular colonies of tens of thousands on sand-bars in the great West African rivers; only four or five such colonies have ever been discovered, yet the birds can be so abundant that from 10 km away it needs only a morning and a little luck to home onto the nesting site.

In some migratory forms, pair-bonding and helper-bonding occur before the prenuptial migration, in others after. Excepting that splendid sub-Saharan bird the White-throated Bee-eater *M. albicollis*, courtship does not amount to anything much, but greeting ceremonies (the same as in the initial courtship) continue throughout the nesting season. After tunnelling finishes and little mounds of fine soil have grown in front of the nest entrance the pair, with helpers if they have any, start roosting in the egg chamber, a low-ceilinged oval expansion at the end of the 1–3 m long tunnel. European Bee-eaters *M. apiaster* winter in Africa and on their return, after digging the nest, they lose no time in laying eggs at 1–2 day intervals until the clutch is complete in about six days. Red-throated Bee-eaters in the savannas of West Africa, sedentary birds, encounter an unusual difficulty: toward the end of the long dry season when they lay, the ground has dried to a concrete hardness. They obviate the problem simply by excavating their nest holes some four months in advance when, at the end of the previous wet season, the earth is moist and workable. (We need not credit them with foresight and intelligent problem-solving; the operation of natural selection will account for their behaviour.)

In all species incubation starts at the time the first or second egg is laid, so that hatching—after some 20 days—is sequential too. As in most cavity-nesting birds the eggs are subspherical and immaculate white, and they have a delicate pink translucence when new-laid. There is no nest material as such, but some protection from breaking against the hard earthen floor is afforded to the clutch by an accreting carpet of insect remains from pellets trodden underfoot. At first the egg chamber keeps dry and wholesome; but adults defaecate in the nest and so of course does the brood. Dropped whole insects go bad and any youngster which dies is left to rot. Predictably, an ammoniacal stench pervades the air around a large colony as if it were a gullery. It is all the more surprising that from this pestilential squalor there emerges at the end of four weeks a succession of fledglings, graded in size according to their differing ages, in perfect, unsullied plumage.

Again reminiscent of some seabirds, the frequency of feeding the brood falls sharply a few days before they fledge. Going hungry probably prompts them to fledge; but when they do leave the nest the parents and helpers—which are usually their one-year-old brothers—solicitously resume feeding them. For many sorts of birds the days and weeks after fledging are a difficult time, fraught with the dangers of a novel and hostile world. For a specialist like the bee-eater that is particularly true, since it must learn not only how to catch sufficient daily fare but also how to immobilize its prey and (if a stinger) to render it innocuous. To the young bee-eater a worker honeybee must represent a formidable adversary as well as a potential meal.

I once reared a Red-throated Bee-eater from a few days of age and was fascinated to find that the rudiments of bee-rubbing emerged spontaneously. When presented with its first honeybees, treatment was unrefined and irregular and the wretched bird was obviously stung several times in its mouth and gullet. But the tail-rubbing and head-beating components of the bee treatment behaviour were clearly there and when in the following days I interspersed more bees in an otherwise innocuous diet of meal worms and grasshoppers, it bee-rubbed and ate all of them without further distress. Thereafter its skill continued to improve until, seven or eight weeks after it hatched and at the age when in nature it would have been out of the nest for weeks, it unhesitatingly dealt with all worker honeybees by bee-rubbing them and tossing them to the back of its throat with all the polish and aplomb of an adult.

Further study would be needed to unravel the parts played by instinct and by learning in the maturation of bee-rubbing behaviour, but it does seem to be perfected by way of learning and I think that the long weaning period of six weeks or so, when the fledgling is normally closely accompanied by adults which often feed it, trains it to graduation in bee-eating proficiency. Even adult bee-eaters are occasionally stung (or at least stings barb the gullet, which does not *necessarily* mean that venom has been injected) and the known toxicity of honeybee venom for small birds makes it very likely that bee-eaters have partial immunity. In fact a surprising variety of birds will eat bees, evidently without attempting to de-sting them. Swifts, for instance, engulf bees whole and cannot possibly avoid being stung—two *Chaetura* swifts shot raiding an apiary contained 400 honeybees between them and dozens of detached stings pricked their gullets[432]. Bee stings may not affect birds as badly, on the whole, as one might have imagined. That might be why bee-eaters can on occasion afford to get careless. Raiding beehives, they gobble up bees voraciously always bee-rubbing them first—but so perfunctorily that the stings are not jettisoned, and probably it is at such times that the birds get stung. Clearly they find it worth it: good luck to them.

A half-dozen species are found in the tropical rainforest regions of Africa and southeast Asia but only one, the Red-bearded Bee-eater, confines itself to the dank, tenebrous depths of forest proper. The others keep mainly to better-illuminated places, where a stream breaks the tree canopy, or glades, secondary growth in felled forest, and adjacent wooded farmland. They are the Blue-bearded Bee-eater *Nyctyornis athertoni* of India and Burma to one side of the Red-bearded's range and the Celebes Bee-eater *Meropogon forsteni* to the other, and in Africa the Black-headed, Blue-headed and Black Bee-eaters *Merops breweri*, *M. muelleri* and *M. gularis*. Like most small tropical forest birds they are difficult to locate let alone to watch for any length of time (although mostly they seem to be quite common, for instance with 10–20 Red-bearded Bee-eaters per square kilometre), so it is not surprising that little is known about any of them. In 1980 and 1981 several nests of the Black-headed Bee-eater, a handsome denizen of African rainforests and in some ways a meropid curiosity, were found in Nigeria—the only ones since nests were first discovered in Zaire twenty years earlier. During a few days' incarceration in a broiling hide strategically placed between two of them I had the good fortune to learn as much about it as I know of many a much commoner bee-eater.

A few other kinds occupy regions where rainforest is the dominating

climax vegetation, but their nesting habitat is open, unforested country—
in the case of Malaysia's Blue-throated Bee-eater *M. viridis* gardens,
pasture and sandy clearings. They may move to forest after breeding;
Rainbowbirds *M. ornatus*, nesting all over Australia, migrate to forested
New Guinea and in Africa Rosy and White-throated Bee-eaters winter in
the rainforest zone, hawking from emergent trees for insects well above the
canopy. It must be a radical change for such birds, for their breeding
season habitat could not be more different—the borders of the Sahara in
the case of the White-throated. These and all of the remaining bee-eaters
are really birds of light and sunny places, thinly wooded savannas and
farmland, bushy watercourses, swamps and green lakeshores. Several
inhabit arid steppe, even pretty unremitting desert: the Rainbowbird,
White-throated, Somali *M. revoilii* and in particular the Blue-cheeked
Bee-eater *M. persicus*.

I hope that these many bee-eater names are not confusing. Frequent
reference to the colour Plates and the facing distribution maps should
enable the reader to sort out the birds without too much difficulty. In later
chapters discussion will revolve in large part around the European and
the Red-throated, but I shall have to make frequent reference to the other
kinds too and the reader's lot will be easier if he or she has by that point an
identifying image of each bird. At first mention of a species I am giving
both its approved English name and its scientific, but thereafter the
scientific names will usually be dropped. Fortunately most English names
are quite good ones; there is a nice decisive ring to Black, Carmine, Rosy,
Boehm's (*M. boehmi*) and Swallow-tailed Bee-eaters (*M. hirundineus*) and to
the Rainbowbird, and there is no mistaking the birds themselves.
Place-named ones are distinctive too: European, Celebes, Somali and
Madagascar (*M. superciliosus*). But beware Little and Little Green;
White-fronted (*M. bullockoides*) and White-throated; Red-throated and
Red-bearded; and the *six* birds (counting the distinct Oriental version of
the Madagascar Bee-eater) which are Blue-somethinged (see list below).

To return to habitats. In Asia you would be lucky ever to find more
than three kinds of bee-eaters living in the same area. In Africa, by
contrast, with a bit of judicious field-craft you can place yourself within
sight and sound of five species together in many countries. Six is my
record, in Nigeria. Camping on the banks of the great River Niger, where it
flows majestically through pleasant wooded hills and cultivated vales with
tributary streams, I had a large colony of Carmines with a dozen
Red-throated Bee-eater nests tacked onto its end in a sand cliff cut clean
by the river; pairs of Little Bee-eaters every 100 metres along both banks;
an immense colony of Rosies nesting an hour's canoe-trip downstream
and never less than fifty birds hawking near the camp; three Swallow-tails
in residence about a burnt field not far away; and scattered parties of

White-throated Bee-eaters around all week, migrating to Saharan breeding grounds from their forest winter quarters near the coast. Had I but
known it at the time I could probably have added Blue-cheeked Bee-
eaters, for the following year the first Nigerian colony was discovered no
great distance upstream.

Where congeneric birds are found together there are generally marked
differences between them in their diets and foraging strategies; think of the
inland and seashore (but essentially sympatric) *Larus* gulls, for instance,
or Song Thrushes *Turdus philomelos* catching mainly worms and snails
where Blackbirds *T. merula* go more for berries and insects. But with few
exceptions the 21 bee-eaters of the genus *Merops* have diets and also
foraging behaviours which are much alike. The species reduce mutual
competition by differing in body size up to a factor of four, and
ecologically, by taking different if overlapping habitats and breeding
times. The various specific habitats are more difficult to diagnose and
describe than in practice to identify; that is to say, with experience one can
get the feel of bee-eaters' habitat requirements to the extent of being able

THE SPECIES AND SUBSPECIES OF BEE-EATERS

Red-bearded Bee-eater	NYCTYORNIS amicta	
Blue-bearded Bee-eater	N. athertoni	*athertoni*
		brevicaudata
Celebes Bee-eater	MEROPOGON forsteni	
Black-headed Bee-eater	MEROPS breweri	
Blue-headed Bee-eater	M. muelleri	*mentalis*
		muelleri
Black Bee-eater	M. gularis	*gularis*
		australis
Little Bee-eater	M. pusillus	*pusillus*
		ocularis
		cyanostictus
		meridionalis
		argutus
Blue-breasted Bee-eater	M. variegatus	*loringi*
		variegatus
		bangweoloensis
		lafresnayii
Cinnamon-chested Bee-eater	M. oreobates	
Swallow-tailed Bee-eater	M. hirundineus	*chrysolaimus*
		heuglini
		furcatus
		hirundineus
Red-throated Bee-eater	M. bullocki	*bullocki*
		frenatus

White-fronted Bee-eater	M. bullockoides	
Somali Bee-eater	M. revoilii	
White-throated Bee-eater	M. albicollis	
Little Green Bee-eater	M. orientalis	*viridissimus*
		flavoviridis
		cleopatra
		cyanophrys
		najdanus
		beludschicus
		orientalis
		ferrugeiceps
Boehm's Bee-eater	M. boehmi	
Blue-throated Bee-eater	M. viridis	*viridis*
		americanus
Blue-cheeked Bee-eater	M. persicus	*chrysocercus*
		persicus
Madagascar Bee-eater	M. superciliosus	*superciliosus*
		alternans
Blue-tailed Bee-eater	M. superciliosus	*philippinus*
Rainbowbird	M. ornatus	
Bay-headed Bee-eater	M. leschenaulti	*leschenaulti*
		andamanensis
		quinticolor
European Bee-eater	M. apiaster	
Rosy Bee-eater	M. malimbicus	
Carmine Bee-eater	M. nubicus	*nubicus*
		nubicoides

Most of the familiar names are now standardized in the English-speaking world. Nomenclatural problems arise in varying treatments of species boundaries in the *M. persicus-superciliosus* complex and with *lafresnayii*, which some authorities regard as a race of *M. oreobates*.

to make good predictions as to which species will be encountered where, in a given area. All the same, any one species is likely to live in such a variety of situations throughout its range that defining its habitat requirements in anything but general terms is a daunting task.

At that location on the River Niger the six *Merops* in a sense shared the same habitat and they were most certainly competing for its food resources. At the same time, none of them was 'out of habitat', ie in a habitat abnormal for it, and the generalization still stands that Carmine Bee-eaters inhabit plains with scattered trees, Red-throateds wooded watercourses in dissected country, Littles grassland, Rosies wide forested rivers, Swallow-tails mature savanna woodland, and that White-throated Bee-eaters *on migration* are catholic in their habitat tastes. It was also the case that at the time of my visit in May, Red-throated Bee-eaters were a fortnight fledged, Little Bee-eaters had young in the nest, Carmine Bee-eater eggs were only just hatching, while the late-breeding Rosy Bee-eaters downstream were still digging their nests. All the same, in some situations bee-eaters show no readily discernible ecological differences; Little and Blue-breasted Bee-eaters *M. variegatus*, for instance, are very closely allied, similar-looking birds which often live side-by-side in the same marsh. They seem to defy the ecological principle of competitive exclusion, and so they sorely need investigation.

So far as I know, rainforest bee-eaters—like rainforest birds in general—are entirely sedentary. In the genus *Merops* migration becomes a more obvious phenomenon, broadly speaking, with increasing latitude away from equatorial forest in both hemispheres. Admittedly at least one savanna form, the Red-throated Bee-eater, is rigidly sedentary throughout most of its range, north as high as latitude 15°N. But other savanna bee-eaters are in large part migratory even if their movements have not been well worked out. In West Africa, White-throateds are one of the best-known intra-tropical migrants of all, flying by day in large and noisy flocks and travelling a thousand kilometres or more between nesting grounds along the southern border of the Sahara and wintering grounds in and near the rainforest zone. Rainbowbirds, moving much greater distances within Australia and between Australia and islands to the north from the Lesser Sundas to the Solomons, must experience a comparable change of habitat from sandy plain to closed forest. Since these species sit *on* rather than *in* the vegetation, I suspect the change makes little difference to them and they will be perfectly happy as long as the airspace around and above them harbours an adequacy of insects.

Easily the longest-distance migrants are, predictably, those two species nesting furthest from the Equator, the European and Blue-cheeked Bee-eaters. Both breed at 47°N on the north shore of the Caspian in the estuary of the river Ural, and the European Bee-eater nests up to 8° of latitude further north, both west and east of the Ural Mts. Blue-cheeked Bee-eaters cross Arabia and the Red Sea and winter in Africa south to near the Equator; but European Bee-eaters go further and many winter in South Africa, so that some individual birds may move as much as 10,000 km. It needs no great feat of imagination to understand why they vacate their breeding grounds: their hymenopteran prey, in common with most other insects, simply disappear in autumn. Only the mated queens of bumble-bees and vespid wasps survive the winter (and they are underground) while what is left of the summer colony of honeybees overwinters in the hive. Doubtless intra-tropical migrations are regulated by the same sort of consideration, although through lack of field work hard evidence is not easy to find. The ecological changes which make Cinnamon-chested

Bee-eaters *M. oreobates* forsake their nesting places 3,000 m high in Kenya, or Bay-headed Bee-eaters *M. leschenaulti* withdraw from their subtropical Indian breeding grounds, would make a valuable investigation for some local student.

Spectacular concentrations of European Bee-eaters can occur during migration. They move principally by day and although often flying high, they are among the more conspicuous of migrants. In the autumn— mainly within the fortnight from the end of August—30 to 40,000 cross the Straits of Gibraltar. Thereby they seem largely to avoid the depredations of Eleonora's Falcon, a bird virtually confined to the Mediterranean which fattens its young on daytime autumn migrants; but over the Red Sea the other autumn-breeding falcon, the Sooty, gives bee-eaters a terrible time, with Blue-cheeked Bee-eaters its commonest prey by far.

That concludes an introductory purview of the living bird. Several aspects of the natural history of this engaging Family which I have touched upon will be dealt with at greater length in later chapters. In the following section the birds are treated species by species, and it may be found useful if I precede it with some remarks about relationships, which will also prepare the ground for readers treating Chapter 2 as for reference only and turning directly to Chapter 3.

For long, bee-eaters have been classified in the Order Coraciiformes together with hornbills, rollers, kingfishers, hoopoes and some other Families. The mutual affinities of these Families, and indeed their proximity of relationship with some Families in the piciform assemblage of birds (woodpeckers, toucans, barbets, jacamars etc, Order Piciformes), have long been open to question. The latest anatomical studies indicate forcefully that the two Orders should be reconstituted into three[101] or five Orders[201]. So far as the coraciiform Families are concerned, five of them including the Meropidae may now be held to constitute their own Order Alcediniformes, or else the same five may be given subordinal status (Alcedines) in a revised Order Coraciiformes to emphasize their distant kinship with another five Families (Coracii). In the latter classification bee-eaters would appear as on p. 26 (note that this scheme includes the 'piciform' puffbirds and jacamars and the 'trogoniform' trogons[395A] and excludes the 'coraciiform' hoopoes, wood-hoopoes and hornbills[101]).

If I were asked to judge from field characters whether the bee-eaters were closest to the trogons or to the kingfisher-motmot-tody assemblage I should unhesitatingly opt for the latter. Nothing about trogons is in the least bit bee-eater-like. Among the Alcedinoidea, I am not well ac- quainted with motmots and do not know todies at all, although field studies[332,447] do suggest some behavioural similarities with bee-eaters, but I do lay claim to some authority on kingfishers[237]. Like the bee-eaters, they

ORDER CORACIIFORMES

Suborder	*Superfamily*	*Family*
Coracii	Coracoidea	Coraciidae, rollers Brachypteraciidae, ground-rollers Leptosomatidae, cuckoo-rollers
	Galbuloidea	Bucconidae, puffbirds Galbulidae, jacamars
Alcedines	Alcedinoidea	Alcedinidae, kingfishers Momotidae, motmots Todidae, todies
	Meropoidea	Meropidae, BEE-EATERS
	Trogonoidea	Trogonidae, trogons

comprise a very distinctive Family: despite great diversity there is never any doubt whether a bird, in field or museum, is or is not a kingfisher. In nature they lead lives radically different from those of bee-eaters, as hovering fishers and sit-and-wait predators of ground-dwelling arthropods and small vertebrates; yet from time to time I have been struck by resemblances between the two Families. Although, generally speaking, there could be no greater contrast than that between a flock of bee-eaters actively feeding, wheeling aloft in excited pre-roosting flocks, or coming and going at a breeding colony, and the solitary kingfisher sitting stolidly for a couple of hours before dropping to the ground for a crab, some affinity between them can be discerned. Both Families are long-beaked, large-headed, short-necked, very short-legged and weak-footed perching birds, and two or three times I have caught sight of a single bird and been momentarily confused as to its identity, whether kingfisher or bee-eater. They are all basically insectivorous (or so I have argued for the kingfisher Family[237,238]) and a few kingfishers have the bee-eaters' aptitude for catching flying insects, even the occasional stinging bee. The converse, bee-eaters fishing, happens too, as I found only recently and much to my surprise (Chapter 4), and I dare say that bee-eaters catch fish at least as often as kingfishers catch bees. Moreover one bee-eater, the White-throated, feeds at times on grounded insects and small vertebrates in the manner of many terrestrial kingfishers. Finally, to complete the comparison, bee-eaters and kingfishers (in common with other coraciiform and piciform Families) are hole-nesters and some aspects of their nidification are much alike.

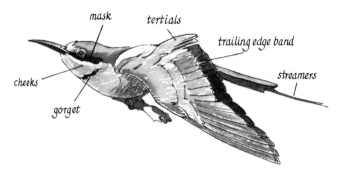

mask · tertials · trailing edge band · cheeks · streamers · gorget

2: Species accounts

My intention in this section is to set down the known salient biological characteristics of every bee-eater species, the foundation for later generalization and discussion. The observations are partly my own but mainly an amassment of other people's, drawn from the literature and from correspondence. Sources are acknowledged throughout by superscript references to a bibliography at the end and by the notation *pc* (personal communication).

Species sequence is the same as shown in the Table in Chapter 1 (from 'primitive' to 'advanced', by my conception). Subspecies sequences are also the same: usually geographical, from west to east and from north to south. Topic coverage varies a little with circumstance from one species to the next. The European Bee-eater *Merops apiaster* is dealt with at much the greatest length, partly because of the substantial literature about it, and I have given a fairly detailed account of every aspect of its biology. To avoid repetition and verbosity in accounts of the other species I have made only passing reference to, or even omitted, some biological detail common to them all. For instance, so far as I can tell, nest-digging behaviour is identical in all bee-eaters in which it has been observed and is almost certainly the same in the remainder, so I describe it minutely only under one species (the European). With due discretion the reader can legitimately apply much of the information given for *M. apiaster* to its congeners. In point of fact, although the best *knowledge* we have is undoubtedly anent the European bird, arguably the best *understanding* is of the Red-throated/White-fronted Bee-eater superspecies, as may emerge in later chapters.

No-one will read this section word for word; nor is that intended. Descriptive passages are largely in a terse, telegraphic style with verbs and articles omitted; yet not, I intend and hope, to the point of these basic biological data being totally unreadable.

Nomenclatural history, at the beginning of each account, gives the name, author, date, reference and type locality of each taxon which I recognize, and some other key names. Plumage descriptions, abridged in FIELD CHARACTERS and detailed in ADDITIONAL DESCRIPTION, use the standard terminology[16] with the following six terms (see Figure) for bee-eater peculiarities. The *mask* is the lores, line of feathers below the eye, and ear coverts, black in all *Merops* species except *M. leschenaulti*. *Cheeks* are that area, bordering the mask below, which commonly contrasts in colour with the chin and throat. The *gorget* is the striking black or blue pectoral area between throat and breast in nine species, a narrow transverse line or a broad obtuse triangle. In the wing the conspicuous black tips of the flight feathers form the *trailing edge band*, and *tertials* are the innermost feathers of the series, never black tipped. I call the central pair of tail feathers *streamers* whenever they are attenuated and elongated.

Measurements are in mm, of the nominate race and from prepared skins unless otherwise specified. *Weights* are in g. Average values are given, with range then sample size in parenthesis. *Beak* lengths from tip to forehead feathering and also to skull (naso-frontal suture) are given, the latter being a more accurate measure than the former. Beak depths are the greatest distances which can be calipered from fusion point of left and right jaws (usually a pronounced convex angle or bulge at proximal end of gonys); in a few species depth at nostrils is given also. *Wing* length is the flattened chord. *Tail* length is from shaft root to tip of the central pair, or in taxa with streamers to the tip of the adjacent feather. Tail feathers are numbered centrifugally, so that the outermost is the sixth. Wing shape is dealt with under *Structure* by indicating the longest primary, and shortfalls of the remaining primaries and 1st secondary; in most instances these measurements were taken from no more than five non-moulting specimens. Secondaries are numbered 1–13 from the outermost inward and primaries 1–10 from the innermost outward, and identified as p5, p10, s1 and so on (bee-eaters have the outermost or 10th primary reduced and in several species it is vestigial, a mere 10–15 mm long).

TECHNICAL DIAGNOSES*

ORDER CORACIIFORMES

An assemblage of five well-defined Superfamilies which may be grouped into two Suborders (see Table p. 26). Superficial differences between the ten Families (in plumage, size, beak shape, comportment) are

---

* Based on those of F. E. Beddard in Dresser (1884–1886[172]), and Witherby *et al.* (1938[607]) updated by the work of Sibley & Ahlquist (1972[518]), Feduccia (1977[201]) and Burton (1982[101]). The ordinal diagnosis is good for the Order Coraciiformes as constituted in the Table on p. 26.

considerable. Plumage usually brilliant with structural greens and blues predominating. Eggs immaculate white (tinted in Trogonidae and Leptosomatidae). Nidicolous; young hatch blind and naked (downy in Galbulidae and Leptosomatidae), often prognathous and with heel pads. Legs short, feet weak, toes zygodactyl (Todidae, Galbulidae, Bucconidae) or syndactyl with the three forward-directed toes united basally and the outer pair (third and fourth) united for most of their length. Arrangement of flexor tendons of toes similar to that of swifts and nightjars. Palate desmognathous, without basipterygoid processes, or ambiens muscle. Quadrate with deep, prominent medial condyle and a broad orbital process having a long medial edge. Large cartilaginous entoglossum and short basihyal. *M. branchiomandibularis* originates far forward on mandible. *M. tracheohyoideus* has an origin on clavicle. Sternum with four lateral notches. Pelvic muscle formula AXY (or AX in some kingfishers).

SUPERFAMILY MEROPOIDEA AND FAMILY MEROPIDAE

Lightly built Coraciiformes (see above) feeding primarily on Hymenoptera. Beak long, slender, laterally compressed, decurved, with both mandibles sharp pointed. Tongue long, slightly brush-tipped. Plumage soft and compact; little or no sexual dichromatism, but males have slightly longer wings and tails than females and markedly longer tail streamers; eutaxic. Feathers without aftershafts[412]. Pterylosis, described by F. E. Beddard[172], very like that of rollers (*Coracias*). The meticulous W. DeW. Miller stated in 1924[411] that there is a very vestigial 11th primary in bee-eaters other than the "Meropinae" (presumably meaning the genus *Merops* only); I have carefully re-examined *Nyctyornis*, *Meropogon*, and *Merops* (*Bombylonax*) *breweri* and dissected the last, and find no indication at all of such a primary in any of them. Feather barbs with separate cloudy and melanized medullary cells; in the cortex, uniquely, only surface cells are basiphilic, the remainder being acidophilic[23] (L. Auber pc). *Expansor secundariorum* muscle present. Tarsus very short and foot weak; 2nd and 3rd toes united along proximal phalanx only, and 3rd and 4th toes united except along distal phalanx; nails hooked, sharp and rather long, particularly 3rd. Skin thin but tough. Preen gland naked. Probable partial immunity to Hymenoptera venom. Fifteen cervical vertebrae. Sternum with long *spina communis* and deep indentations. Stapes with large bulbous footplate fenestrated on posterior aspect, a large hollow fossa, and stapedial shaft at periphery of footplate. Caeca long. A single, left, carotid in *Merops*, paired carotids in *Nyctyornis*. *M. hypoglossus medialis* present; *Mm. pygmaei* present in *Merops*, absent in *Nyctyornis*. Ovomucoids a dense band cathodal to ovalbumins, which migrate fast. Excavate own nest holes in earth. Hatchlings prognathous; nestlings

naked at first then spiny before long-sheathed feathers break open; nestlings shuffle on papillate heel pads. Opinion is divided as to whether Meropidae are most closely related to Alcedinidae[436,516,517], to Todidae and Momotidae[518], to those three Families equally and to Trogonidae[101,201], or to Coraciidae[117,132,172] (Meropidae and Coraciidae share a genus of feather-lice, *Meromenopon*).

Genus Nyctyornis
Nyctyornis Swainson MS. Jardine and Selby 1830, Illustrations of Ornithology, 2. Addenda, sign. D 2. Type, by diagnosis, *Merops amictus* Temminck.
Nyctiornis Swainson, Zool. Illustr. (2), 2, 1831 in text to plate 56 which was lettered *Nyctinomus amictus*.
Cf. sub nom. *Bucia* Hodgson, 1836, in Stuart Baker, Fauna Brit. India, ed. 2, Birds, 4, 1927, p. 242–244 and sub nom. *Alcemerops* Geoffroy Saint-Hilaire, 1832, in Delacour and Jabouille, Ois. Indochine Franç., 2, 1931, p. 305–306.
Nyctyornis is the correct name by priority although the spelling *Nyctiornis* is preferable.
Large, rather sluggish birds, weight >80 g. Beak robust, culmen ridged and grooved, nostrils screened by feathers. Elongate, pendant throat feathers. Paired carotids[172]. Six ribs[409]. *Mm. pygmaei* absent. Round winged, 7th and 8th primaries longest, 10th >50 mm long. Tail long, square, not streamered, underside yellow. Hoarse voice. Two species, in south and southeast Asian forests.

Genus Meropogon
Meropogon Bonaparte 1850, Conspect. Genera Avium, 1, p. 164.

Beak like *Merops*, slender, culmen not ridged nor grooved, nostrils not screened. Long feathers on throat often erected, with shorter ones on sides of neck, to form a ruff. Seven ribs[409] (one vestigial), five with uncinate processes. Wings round, proportions like *Nyctyornis*, unlike *Merops* except *M. breweri* which it almost exactly resembles. Tail with streamers. Voice unlike *Nyctyornis*, not much like *Merops*. One species, in Sulawesi rain-forest.

Genus Merops
Merops Linnaeus 1758, Systema Naturae ed. 10, 1, p. 117. Type, by tautonymy, *Merops apiaster* L. (*Merops*, a pre-binomial specific name in synonymy). (Re defined here so as to include the genera *Bombylonax* Heine, J. Orn., 7, 1859, p. 434, *Melittophagus* Boie, Isis von Oken, 21, 1828, col. 316, *Dicrocercus* Cabanis and Heine, Mus. Hein., Th. 2, 1859–60 (1860), p. 136, *Meropiscus* Cassin, Proc. Philadelphia Acad. Sci., 1857, p. 37, *Aerops* Reichenbach, Handb. spec. Orn., Meropinae, 1852, p. 82, and *Philothrus* Cabanis and Heine, Mus. Hein., Th. 2, 1859–60 (1860), p. 137.)

Characters those of the Family (qv). More lightly built and active birds than *Nyctyornis* or *Meropogon* and probably more specialized on dietary Hymenoptera; weight <75 g Beak slender, robust or usually delicate, culmen decurved, not ridged nor grooved, gonys either decurved or (nearly) straight. Nostrils bare. Throat feathers short, or if a little long not pendant. Six ribs[409] (one incomplete), four with uncinate processes. *Mm. pygmaei* present. Wings vary from short and round (10th primary 30-<50 mm, 8th or rarely 7th longest) to long and pointed (10th primary 10–15 mm, 9th or rarely 8th longest). End of 10th primary rounded or sharp-pointed. Tail square-ended, or with central pair of rectrices elongated into short or very long streamers, or slightly or markedly forked. All species but one have black mask, commonly made conspicuous by contrasting superciliary and cheek streaks. Chin and throat usually in colour contrast with breast, accentuated by intervening black gorget. Melodious voices. 21 species, mainly inhabiting open country and prone to hunt in long sorties.

Red-bearded Bee-eater   *Nyctyornis amicta*   (Plate 1)

Merops amicta Temminck 1824, Nouv. Rec. Planches Color. d'Ois., livre 52, pl.
310 (Bencoolen, Sumatra).

FIELD CHARACTERS

A rather inactive bird of south-east Asian forests, easily overlooked if
distinctive voice unknown. Length 27–31 cm (about 11–12 in). Solitary or
in pairs (the Malay name *bĕrek tunggal* means solitary bee-eater). Grass
green with lilac forehead and crown (male) and vermilion-red lores, chin
and throat; in female forehead is vermilion and forecrown lilac. Red
'beard' puffed out when bird calls. Belly pale green. Underside of rather
long tail mustard yellow with 2-cm terminal black band. Juvenile green,
with yellowish belly and dusky undertail. In flight head drawn in and
beak points slightly upward.

HABITAT

Lowland evergreen mixed dipterocarp forest, and disturbed forest up to
1,370 m altitude or even 1,500 m. Frequents the middle storey and lower
part of the canopy. In Burma prefers woods where larger trees are
scattered and plenty of sunlight penetrates. Forested banks of large
streams and borders of swamps and shallow lagoons surrounded by forest.
Exceptionally in gardens and about houses. Nests in burrows in the
ground.

DISTRIBUTION AND STATUS

Map opposite Plate 1. Sedentary. Throughout lowland Borneo and
usually common. Sumatra including Bangka Island, but absent from
Java. Formerly throughout Malay Peninsula from Johore north to
Moulmein (at Salween river mouth, 16° 25′N) and Dawna Range in
Tenasserim (Burma) where fairly common, and Petchaburi District in
southwest Thailand. Penang Island. Doubtless now absent from large
swathes of its former range where dipterocarp forest has been replaced by
oil-palm and rubber plantations, eg Perak, Selangor, Negri Sembilan,
Malacca and Johore States of Malaysia and much of peninsular Thailand.
Density of 4 birds per 20 ha in Bornean primary lowland forest (M.
Fogden pc), or about 2 per 20 ha in peninsular Malaysia (D.R. Wells pc).

FOOD AND FORAGING

Airborne insects: wasps, hornets, bees, cicadas, beetles, crickets and ants[537]; bees include carpenter-bees *Xylocopa*. Hunts from a leafy perch, partly hidden from view and not conspicuously exposed as are *Merops* species, and flies out after passing insects, returning often to a different concealed perch*. Sits for long periods without feeding, moving in the vegetation to a new vantage point from time to time. Often (usually?) hunts next to a clearing, stream, forest path, etc, where insects can probably be more readily seen and pursued. At times drawn into the open to exploit eg a swarm of flying termites, which are caught in brief and efficient sortie-flights (G.C. Madoc pc).

VOICE AND CALLING BEHAVIOUR

Commonest call a loud, gruff, hoarse *chachachacha* or *quo-qua-qua-qua* or KAK, *kak-ka-ka-ka-ka* on a descending scale, tailing off in volume, uttered at irregular intervals. "When one calls it is usually answered by its mate . . . when uttering its note the bird leans forward, stretches out its neck, and puffs out the feathers of its throat, and at each syllable of its note bobs its head up and down"[308]. Also, the crown feathers are raised. Usually quiet; at times calls incessantly. Occasionally calls on clear nights within two hours of dusk. "The bird has a curious habit, when calling, of jumping a few steps sideways and then turning right round in a single hop"[263]. When the pair is together near the nest one bird utters a very deep *kwow* as approach or warning note, and the tail is always fanned. The other responds with a rattling *kwakwakoogoogoo*, and the tail is flicked regularly. There is also a very deep guttural *kwok* issued by either bird at any time[537]. Alarm note, a distinctive growling *krerkrer*.

BREEDING

During courtship of a female by two males, their tails were bent downwards and forwards and then fanned, making the yellow-black pattern conspicuous; one male frequently took flight, circled and dived low over the others (G.C. Madoc pc). Excavates nest hole in earth, in roadside banks, sandy soil or stiff soil of small streams in dense forest, and low banks cut by man (eg sawyers' pits). Burrows are about 1.2 m (4 ft) long. Eggs found in Borneo in January, and one of five burrows dug in the

---

* In an account of this bee-eater in Birds of the World magazine 5 (7) p. 1531 I wrote in 1968 that "In Borneo one individual was watched probing for beetle grubs in rotten wood, while others were seen to take small centipedes and, on one occasion, a small scorpion". These observations were not my own and, embarrassingly, I now have no record as to their source. Recent enquiries have thrown no light on the matter and in the absence of comparable authenticated observations I must reluctantly conclude that somewhere wires were badly crossed, and ignore the information. Hume and Davison in 1878[308] stated categorically that the species lives entirely on insects which it takes on the wing.

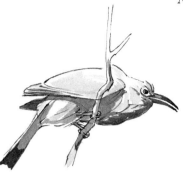

side of an archaeological pit inside Great Cave, Niah, had one fresh egg in February. In Malaysia two eggs were taken from a nest in Pahang in late August. A pair nested on Fraser's Hill (Selangor/Pahang) in February and the young probably fledged in mid March (G.C. Madoc pc). Clutches of 3, 5 and 5 eggs said to have been taken near Taiping, Perak, in mid February. A recent fledgling was collected on Bangka and two young seen attended by an adult, in June. In Tenasserim breeds in March and April. A female was caught on one of the Taiping nests and a male on another, so both sexes probably incubate. The above is virtually everything on record about the breeding of this bee-eater.

ADDITIONAL DESCRIPTION

Monotypic. ADULT ♂ Lilac of crown an extraordinary hue, intense and with a pearly sheen, very rare in birds (how the colour is produced in *N. amicta* has been explained by L. Auber[23]). Lilac merges into mauve toward hindcrown. Bases of lilac feathers are buff tending toward scarlet; and from underside, tip of feather appears red, not lilac. A narrow border of small, thin, stiff, forward-curved feathers around base of beak is pale azure. Eyelid featherlets caerulean blue, forming a very narrow blue eye ring. Basally, long throat feathers grey and dark olive green; only feather tips, with their long radiating barbs, are red. In places dark green feather centres (darker than green sides of breast) show through red 'beard'. Green tertials do not seem to bleach blue, as they do in *Merops*. Underside of wing uniform warm buff. Rectrices rather stiff with shafts wide proximally and conspicuously ivory or pale yellow. ADULT ♀ Like ♂ but forehead vermilion, and lilac of crown restricted, replaced by green at line between eyes. Eye ring nearer green than blue. JUVENILE A few powder-blue feathers around base of beak, otherwise plumage uniform grass green except for warm buff underside of wings, yellowish underside of tail, empire yellow belly and yellowish wash on breast and undertail coverts. BARE PARTS Beak black with proximal quarter of lower mandible lead grey; tongue and inside of mouth yellowish; iris yellow, orange or red-orange in adult ♂ (also adult ♀?), grey-brown in juvenile; legs and feet dull lead grey with blueish tinge in juvenile and olive tinge in adult. WEIGHT 80 g (average of 4[213]). MEASUREMENTS *Beak* to feathers 47 (45–52, n = 20), to skull ♂ 53.1 (50–56, n = 10), ♀ 49.3 (46–53, n = 10), depth ♂ 11.9 (11.3–13.0, n = 10), ♀ 10.6 (9.7–11.4, n = 10). *Wing* ♂ 131.2 (125–141, n = 10), ♀ 123.7 (119–129, n = 5). *Tail* ♂ 117.0 (110–119, n = 10), ♀ 114.3 (112–119), n= 5). *Egg* 24.9 × 28.8 (23.2–27.0 × 28.0–30.5, n = 13). STRUCTURE The beak is the most massive, arched and decurved of all bee-eaters; see figure, p. 251. Primaries project up to 20 mm beyond tertials in folded wing. Wings very rounded; p8 = p7 longest, p10 50–57 long and 36–43 shorter than p8–7, p9 7–10, p6 0–3, p5 8–13, p4 17–24, p3 23–29, p2 26–30, p1 27–31 and s1 27–30 shorter than p8–7.

Blue-bearded Bee-eater   *Nyctyornis athertoni*   (Plate 1)

Merops athertoni Jardine and Selby 1830, Illustr. Orn., 2, pl. 58 and text (India).
Bucia nipalensis, Hodgson, J. Asiatic Soc. Bengal, 5, 1836, p. 361.
Alcemerops athertoni brevicaudata Koelz 1939, Proc. Biol. Soc. Washington, 52, p. 79 (Hainan).

FIELD CHARACTERS

The largest bee-eater, length 31–35 cm (about 13 in); with grass green head, back, wings, tail and breast, the belly pale buff with soft streaks; pale blue forehead and pale blue 'beard'—a quite narrow line of feathers from chin to lower breast which droop down or are puffed out when the bird calls. Iris orange. Underside of tail dusky mustard yellow, blackish distally, feather shafts pale yellow. Tail square and rather long. Beak less stout and smaller than that of its smaller congener the Red-bearded Bee-eater. Unobtrusive, quiet and shy; solitary or in pairs. Inhabits forest in India and Indochina. Sails out from leafy cover after passing insect; flight deeply undulating, a few quick beats followed by a nose-dive with closed wings.

HABITAT

Moist deciduous and deep secondary evergreen forest; moss forest; forest clearings with scattered trees and native gardens; thin deciduous hilltop jungle, near spaces made by eg rock outcrop. Mainly frequents middle storey; comes to ground to nest. At all elevations up to 2,200 m (D. Wells pc); commonest in foothills dissected by ravines.

DISTRIBUTION AND STATUS

Map opposite Plate 1. Probably sedentary; but in Shan Hills said to be particularly common at beginning of the rains[536]. In foothills of Himalayas, from Uttar Pradesh through Nepal, Sikkim, Bhutan, Assam, and Burma from Kachin State south through Chin range (Nagaland, Manipur) and Shan States to Kawthoolei State; not in Yunnan, but to the southeast throughout Indochina (Thailand; Laos, Cambodia, Cochinchina, around Gulf of Tongking; Hainan). Described as fairly common in Lower Himalayas (westernmost record: Kotgarh, c 31°18′N 77°29′E), sparingly distributed in Burma (southernmost record: Kyaikkami (= Amherst), on coast at 16°03′N), and uncommon in Thailand (absent from Central and Peninsular regions[335]). South of Himalayas, throughout Assam and Bangladesh; occurs more locally in West Bengal, Bihar, Orissa, Madhya Pradesh and Andhra Pradesh. Very locally in Western Ghats from Gujarat Satpuras and Tapti river south through western parts of Maharashtra, Mysore, Tamil Nadu (Patni Hills) and Kerala[3,4,484].

Essentially parapatric with the Red-bearded Bee-eater, but their ranges evidently overlap by 60 km between Moulmein and Kyaikkaimi on Tenasserim coast of Burma.

FOOD AND FORAGING

Insects hawked in flight, chiefly bees and large beetles, also dragonflies (field observation; no pellet analyses). Beats insect against perch before swallowing it. "It feeds little on the wing, searching the leaves and flowers of trees and shrubs for insects, and clambering about with slow, awkward movements ... the *letpan* tree in flower attracts them ... observed perched on the roof of a house in Maymyo catching bees that flew right up to them; this confirms the belief that the bees mistake the bird's blue 'beard' for a flower and are attracted by it" (Smythies, 1953[536]). Nobody has observed this bird critically and I have never seen it at all, yet I am inclined to think that the "clambering about" is more likely to be by way of changing vantage points from time to time, as Red-bearded Bee-eaters do, than searching for insects. On the other hand the Blue-bearded *has* occasionally been observed at nectar-bearing flowers, such as *Erythrina*[67] and *Salmalia*[6], where it might be gleaning insects.

A large 'midden' of insect remains below a nest hole in Thailand in 1981 consisted exclusively of beetles, nearly all large scarabs with a few passalids, up to 40 mm long (D. Wells pc). Evidently only abdomens had been eaten, and head, thorax, legs and elytrae—all articulated—discarded.

VOICE AND CALLING BEHAVIOUR

Hoarse guttural croaks or chortles *kor-r-r, kor-r-r*[6], or a harsh double croak ending in a chuckle. When calling, the head is held low and blue 'beard' feathers stand away from throat and breast. With each succeeding note the head is said to be raised until the beak is pointing straight up as the last note is sounded[536]. Also calls on the wing. Voice not particularly loud, yet audible at a surprising distance.

BREEDING

Courtship display in front of another bird, and voice, "like a roller (*Coracias*)"[1]. Tunnels are dug in sandy banks of streams, precipitous alluvial banks of forest ravines, in roadside cuttings and landslips, or more commonly in banks made where paths are cut through hilly jungle. Holes are sited from 0.5 m to 6 or 8 m high. Tunnels stated variously to be 5–6 and 9–9.5 cm diam.; they are 1.4–3.0 m long and widen into a terminal egg chamber about 13 cm high and 20 cm diam. Nests are unlined but the floor fills with insect remains from pellets, since both adults roost in the nest before and during egg-laying and incubation. Nests are always solitary although numerous 'false starts'—"as many as a dozen or twenty"—are dug nearby. Excavation commences up to a month before egg-laying, and is by both sexes. During incubation, also by both sexes, much food is brought into the nest. Completed clutch nearly always six, rarely only five eggs (Assam). Egg-laying is mainly in April-May and in Assam clutches have been found additionally in February, March and August. In Burma nests have been discovered in April, May and October. In Nepal it breeds in April-May but "the principal season is undoubtedly October"[63]. (Details of nidification mainly from Baker, 1934[26].)

SUBSPECIES

(1) *N. a. athertoni* Range as for the species, except Hainan. Peninsular

Indian birds have clearer, less dark green upperparts and paler cheeks than birds from Himalayas and southeast Asia. Eastern birds are more richly coloured, with heavier-striped underparts[1].

(2) *N. a. brevicaudata* Hainan. Differs from nominate race only in size, ♂ tail averaging 10 mm shorter[392].

ADDITIONAL DESCRIPTION

ADULT ♂, ♀ Fresh plumage green, fades or bleaches blueish on crown, nape, mantle and tertials. Forehead pale azure or powder blue when fresh. Lores and eyelid featherlet ring green. 'Beard' feathers dark caerulean (or turquoise or purple-blue depending on angle of view) grading to pure azure on long, radiating barbs. Sleeked, 'beard' appears pale blue but dark blue feather centres often show irregularly through. Underlying breast feathers green with concealed yellowish-buff bases. Belly feathers and undertail coverts yellowish-buff, the former with olive centres. Wing lining warm buff. JUVENILE Plumage said to be exactly like adult; nestling undescribed. BARE PARTS Beak dark horn brown, with proximal third of lower mandible lead grey; mouth greyish pink; iris varies from brown (?immature) to bright orange; legs and feet yellowish grey or dull green. MOULT Post-juvenile moult, and single annual adult post-nuptial moult, about May–October. WEIGHT ♂ 85, 93, ♀ 84 g. MEASUREMENTS *Beak* to nostrils[392], ♂ 36.5 (33–40, n = 12), ♀ 34.9 (29–41, n = 13), to skull ♂ 50.2 (46–54, n = 6), ♀ 47.6 (42–51, n = 10), depth at nostrils ♂ 10.4 (9.8–10.8, n = 10), ♀ 10.5 (9.9–11.5, n = 10). *Wing* ♂ 139.5 (135–143, n = 12), ♀ 134.5 (130–138, n = 13). *Tail* ♂ 135.2 (127–140, n = 12), ♀ 129.8 (127–136, n = 13)[392]. *Egg* 28.0 × 30.0 (25.4–29.0 × 28.5–32.9, n = 50)[26]. STRUCTURE Beak shorter and more attenuated than that of *N. amicta* (see figure p. 251), wing and tail (of nominate race) respectively 6–8% and 14–15% longer. Wings rounded; when folded primaries project 4–20 mm beyond tertials. P7 longest, p10 52–62 long and 41–45 shorter than p7, p9 8–9, p8 0–5, p6 0–1, p5 4–8, p4 18–20, p3 24–26, p2 25–28, p1 and s1 27–30 shorter.

Celebes Bee-eater   *Meropogon forsteni*   (Plate 1)

Meropogon forsteni Bonaparte 1850, Conspect. Genera Avium, 1, p. 164 (Sulawesi).
Meropogon forsteni centralis, Meyer, Notes Leyden Mus., 23, 1903, p. 186.

FIELD CHARACTERS*

An alert and lively-looking bird with rather heavy, undulating flight on rounded wings, without gliding, and, when perched, a vertical stance with thick-necked profile. Length 26 cm (10 in) excluding 6 cm streamers. Under the usual conditions of bright overcast, plumage looks blackish; in sunlight it is seen to be mainly grass green above with dark ultramarine face and throat backed by dark vinous brown nape and sides of neck. Wags tail conspicuously (particularly upon perching) and almost continuously, forward and backward through wide arc about the vertical; the effect is like an inverted metronome. Tail rather long and the short streamers are inconspicuous. Hunts from prominent perches in woods and forest edges, in middle storey or near ground; in the field reminiscent of *Nyctyornis* (M.D. Bruce pc, R. Watling pc), but unlike that genus·it is evidently not a bird of deep forest. Flight calls given often, but otherwise rather silent. Eye dark. Long, dark blue throat feathers are not pendulous like those of *Nyctyornis*; rather they form a ruff or cape at front and sides of neck, puffed out most noticeably when the bird scratches its head (with the foot, overwing). The blue feathers form a tract not on their own but along with their bordering brown ones; ie, blue and brown feathers are puffed out together and equally. Sexes similar. Found in pairs and fours. Apart from thick-necked look with rather mobile ruff, emphatic tail-wagging and deep undulating flight, the Celebes Bee-eater is much like typical bee-eaters, *Merops*, in appearance and behaviour.

* Few naturalists have seen this bird. These notes are made from a short film by John Mackinnon in my possession, supplemented with his, Murray Bruce's and Dick Watling's field notes, and Jaroslav Klapste's paper[337]. The figures are drawn from stills from the film. It has recently been named the Purple-headed Bee-eater[595].

HABITAT, DISTRIBUTION AND STATUS

Map opposite Plate 1. Openings and clearings in primary and successional forest in Sulawesi (formerly Celebes), Indonesia, at all altitudes up to 1,850 m. Edges of lowland, montane and elfin moss forests; occasionally in farmland with plenty of timber (R. Watling pc). Locally distributed in northern, north-central, central and southeastern parts of the island. Early records from Tondano, Masarang crater, Mahawu Massif, Mengkoka Range, Mongondo, Takala Mts (at 1,600 m), Rurukan (900 m), Wawo (50 m), Masembo (550 m), Tanke Salokko (300 m and 1,500 m); recently found to be not particularly rare in Tangkoko and Ambang Mountain Reserves and present in Dumoga-Bone, Lore Lindu and Morowali Reserves, near Rantepao (1,200 m) and in several other forests in central Sulawesi. Shuns sunny places near the ground but does forage in the open, usually at mid and upper canopy levels, perching on a tree top or exposed limb. Said by natives to move near to coast for the rains, returning inland to breed in the dry season[542].

FORAGING

Makes tree-top sallies like *Merops* bee-eaters, but for short distances only. On the lookout for prey it twists and turns its slender-beaked head, searching in all directions; it makes pursuit flights with an audible wing flutter, and uses a limited number of favoured, prominent perches. Prey are mostly bees and wasps, also beetles and large dragonflies[337]. An insect is mandibulated with the beak inclined upward at 45°, and is then swiped against the perch a few times to each side before being swallowed. Occasionally a bird wipes its beak spontaneously and vigorously against the perch.

VOICE

A quiet but shrill and high-pitched *szit* or *peet*, at intervals (J. Mackinnon pc), perhaps the same as 'a low, soft, repeated *sip-sip*'[337]. Parties of four make a high-pitched double piping call (R. Watling pc).

BREEDING

Nests in holes which it excavates in steep banks of forest streams, where they cut through the Mahawu Massif; also in cliffs by Masarang crater[542], land-slips and banks by a well-maintained forest path and a new road cutting; one tunnel was 40 cm long (R. Watling pc). Another was 90 cm long, horizontal, with entrance 90 mm wide and 35 mm high[337]. Occupied nests recently found in July (two) and September (one), a just-fledged bird in September, a nestling in December and a juvenile in January (R. Watling pc). There are old records of a nest with two young in April, and two fledglings collected in October.

ADDITIONAL DESCRIPTION*

Monotypic. ADULT ♂, ♀ Forehead and crown blackish, feathers with ultramarine fringes; eyebrow clear ultramarine blue. Lores blue-black; ear coverts, nape and sides of neck chocolate or dark vinous brown. Chin, throat, centre and sides of breast ultramarine, feather centres and bases blackish. Belly dark grey with green wash; flanks green; undertail coverts cinnamon broadly edged green. Mantle dark green, back, rump, uppertail coverts and wings clearer green. Folded tail appears green above; central rectrices wholly green, others russet narrowly edged and tipped green, outer vane of outer feather being entirely green. Below, tail dull russet with ochreous shafts. Wing lining silvery grey, axillaries white. BARE PARTS Beak black; iris dark brown; legs and feet black or dark grey, nails black. MEASUREMENTS Beak to feathers 42, to skull 48, depth 8.0, 8.2 mm. *Wing* ♂ 113–116, ♀ 114, 116, 119. *Tail* 109, 121 excluding streamers up to 61 mm (which are probably longer in ♂s than in ♀s[337]). STRUCTURE Beak shape like that of *Merops superciliosus*, rather slender and not strongly decurved. Depression in which external nostrils lie is carried forward as shallow groove nearly to tip of beak. Primaries project 4–12 mm beyond tertials in folded wing. P8–p7 longest, p10 45–46 long and 40–43 shorter than p8–7, p9 9–10, p6 0–2, p5 10, p4 22, p3 30, p2 31, p1 32 and s1 33 shorter.

* Only two specimens examined: British Museum 88.10.12.184 and Liverpool Museum 15912, both adults. Juvenile plumage not known.

Black-headed Bee-eater   *Merops breweri*   (Plate 2)

Meropogon breweri Cassin 1859, Proc. Philadelphia Acad. Sci., p. 34 (Ogobai River); *idem*[118].
Bombylonax breweri, Peters, Check-List Birds World, Vol.V, 1955, p. 238; *idem*[594].
Merops breweri, Sharpe, Cat. Birds Brit. Mus., 17, 1892, p. 86; *idem*[159,226].

FIELD CHARACTERS
A rather large, solitary bee-eater of open secondary growth in the African rainforest zone, foraging at mid or low levels in and around woods. Length 25–28 cm (10–11 in) excluding 8 cm (3 in) streamers. Not shy, but silent and sluggish and so easily overlooked. Active in short pursuit of flying insect, which is taken to a perch and vigorously battered; otherwise it flies little, sailing slowly on rounded wings. Head including nape and throat dull black; rest of upperparts, wings and closed tail grass green, fanned tail showing rich cinnamon; breast and belly yellow ochre merging to red ochre in a band bordering the black of throat, broader at the sides. Eye crimson. Beak does not look particularly stout in the field. Juvenile has green crown, and green wash over rest of black head.

HABITAT
Open secondary growth and plantations in and near rainforest, particularly by rivers and streams, also bordering footpaths and villages. Gallery forest by rivers; wooded mid-river islands. In Nigeria moist thickets and disturbed woods, open secondary growth around cultivated land, occur-

ring especially where earth-workings provide nesting places (eg dug-over fields and sandy roadside drainage cuts).

DISTRIBUTION AND STATUS

Map opposite Plate 2. The rainforest zone, in the north of Congo basin where probably not uncommon on Sanga and lower Ubangui drainage and along Uele river[566]; the length of Congo river; Cabinda, Gabon, Congo proper, and Zaire southeast at least to 5° S, 23° E. Near Mankrong (06°41′N 00°19′W) on Affram river, Ghana (an area now inundated by Lake Volta) a pair, and a singleton a few miles away, were recorded in 1952[306 and pc]; there are out-lying populations in disturbed mature forest/oil palm forest/farmland mosaic on Igalaland plateau at 300–350 m altitude in southeast Nigeria, where sparse, and near Bamingui and on Haute Pata near Ndélé, northern Central African Republic, where said to be common[385]. A flock of about 40 was said to have been seen in west Congo basin, "sans doute en migration"[74].

FOOD AND FORAGING

Airborne insects caught in short sallies at low and mid levels (1–5 m high) in light woods, sometimes so tangled that bird has little clear air-space for pursuit. Occasionally snatches an insect from ground layer of vegetation, checking in flight but not landing. Probable grubs seen fed to nestlings. Food carried into nest was mainly cicadas and hawkmoths, including *Cephanodes hylas* and *Nephele comma* with fewer butterflies and beetles. Of 560 insects salvaged from nest litter, half were Hymenoptera (honeybees, *Megachile*, *Sphecodes*, *Ropalidia*, *Eumenes*, *Belanogaster*, *Philanthus* etc), and 42% were beetles, mainly the chafer *Plaesiorrhina recurva* and dung-beetle *Onthophagus tridens*[182,249A]. Some dragonflies were very large, and one wasp *Chlorion maxillosum* was larger than all but one in the collection of 500 specimens in the British Museum.

VOICE

Most commonly heard voice is the alarm, a repetitive *wic*, rather like low-intensity flight call of Red-throated Bee-eaters, but shorter and less loud. Food delivery at nest always accompanied by quiet *pfuruk-p'r'k*. The only other note is a recognition or greeting call, rarely given when one bird lands next to another: a "short bubbling"[294] or a very subdued, whispered *churruk-churruk* and a hard-to-describe soft musical trilling (M. Dyer pc).

BREEDING

Nests were first discovered in 1962, near Bwamanda (03°10′N 19°15′E), Zaire[503,384]. A nest in Igalaland, Nigeria in 1980[294] and three there in 1981 at Alade (07°21′N 07°11′E) and Elubi (07° 35′N 07°26′E)[182] are the only ones found subsequently (the species has also been seen in this region on west bank of the Niger near Idah, 07°07′N 06°40′E, and in Mamu Forest, 06°10′N 07°10′E[512]). Breeds in pairs and trios. Nest burrows sited in sloping heaps of soft lateritic earth beside unsurfaced motor roads, in bare or grassy flat sandy ground in a cultivated field with scattered standing dead trees or by rivers, and once in a shoulder-high termite mound with the burrow entrance 60–75 cm above ground level. Nests solitary, or two 10 m apart. Burrows decline at about 20° to horizontal, more or less straight, 7–9 cm diam., 110–190 cm long (average of six, 152 cm), with egg chamber sharply angled to one side, oval and 25 cm long. Flat-ground nests have chamber floor 25–50 cm below ground level. Excavation is in January, laying in February, hatching in early to mid March, and fledging in the first half of April, in Nigeria and Zaire. Clutch 2–3, usually 3. Nestlings fed by both or all three adults, and in one nest were near in size (34, 40 and 43 g at about 10–14 days old).

ADDITIONAL DESCRIPTION

Monotypic. ADULT ♂, ♀ Entire head, nape, ear coverts, chin and throat black; rest of upperparts including folded wing and closed tail grass green, the tertials blueing in worn plumage. Cinnamon breast band narrower in centre than at sides where, if bird tucks bend of folded wing away, cinnamon feathers conceal it. Breast and belly rich burnished ochreous with lime-green wash; undertail coverts more olivaceous. Axillaries and wing lining warm buff or ochreous. Tail ventrally dull dark cinnamon. Above, median pair of rectrices green, next one broadly tipped and narrowly edged green (broader at base), and remainder dark cinnamon brown with green tips 3–6 mm broad with outer vane of outer feather wholly green. Shafts dark brown above and light brown below. JUVENILE Like adult but black feathers of forehead, crown and nape broadly fringed green, black feathers at sides of neck and around gorget less broadly fringed green (in some individuals there is a distinct green moustachial streak). No cinnamon band over breast, which is quite heavily green-washed in fledglings, particularly at sides. Fledglings also have broad green outer edges to all rectrices. BARE PARTS Beak black, inside mouth horn and flesh, iris brilliant crimson, legs and feet dark grey, soles pale yellow, nails black. WEIGHT 54 g (one bird; another, starved for three days, was 41.5 g but that weight is exceeded by half-grown nestlings). MEASUREMENTS *Beak* to feathers 40.7 (34–42.5) and to skull 49 (41–59), depth 9.6 (8.7–10.1, n = 6). *Wing* 120 (117–125, n = 31). *Tail* 113 (107–119, n = 6) with ♀ streamers up to 41 and ♂ up to 64 mm longer (n = 11[118]), and 83 mm longer in an unsexed Nigerian bird. *Egg* 22.0 × 24.6 (21.1–22.5 × 23.3–25.5)[503]. STRUCTURE Beak more massive than in any bee-eater other than *Nyctyornis amicta*, 10–11 mm deep at

nostril, with culmen arched and curved and tapering less acutely than in
N. athertoni. Tongue with distal 10 mm translucent, tip with 2.5 mm-long
fringe. Folded wing tip projects 3–23 mm beyond secondaries. P7 longest,
p10 46–51 long and 40–45 shorter than p7, p9 7–15, p8 0–4, p6 0–1, p5
5–7, p4 15–16, p3 20–22, p2 24–25, p1 29–30 and s1 33 shorter.

Blue-headed Bee-eater   *Merops muelleri*   (Plate 2)

Meropiscus Mülleri Cassin 1857, Proc. Philadelphia Acad. Sci., p. 37 (Muni
    River, Gaboon).
Merops mentalis Cabanis, 1889, J. Orn., 78, p. 78 (Cameroun).
Melittophagus mulleri yalensis van Someren, Bull. Brit. Orn. Cl., 40, p. 26 (Nyaron-
    do, Kenya).

FIELD CHARACTERS
   A small, silent and confiding bee-eater of West and Equatorial Africa
forest regions, found on edges of clearings rather than deep in primary
forest. Length about 19 cm (7½ in); in good light unmistakable, the
plumage mostly ultramarine blue, with back and wings rich dark russet
brown. A small patch of scarlet on chin and upper throat, surrounded by
black on cheeks and lower throat. The belly is a paler, caerulean blue, and
in the Congo race (ranging west to Cameroun) the crown is mid blue
paling to white on forehead. Iris red. Tail rather short, square in the
Congo race and with short, blunt streamers in the West African race
(Cameroun westward). Wags tail up and down through a small arc. In
prevailing poor light of the forest zone it can be confused with the Black
Bee-eater which, however, has a black back and contrasting azure rump,
and azure-streaked belly.

HABITAT
   Small clearings and glades within and at edges of rainforest; along

well-lit broad tracks through forest and around open areas cleared for farming. Very much an edge species, preferring to forage from exposed perches in dead and open vegetation within 4 m of the ground and occasionally moving adjacently 100 m or more into a burnt and tilled clearing with only a few dead trees left standing, and conversely into thick growth (both low down and also toward the canopy).

DISTRIBUTION AND STATUS

Map opposite Plate 2. Entirely sedentary. Probably ranges continuously throughout African rainforest zone, except for Togo-Benin forest gap and elsewhere where the land is deforested, from Sierra Leone or western Guinea east to Ruwenzori and Kivu Province, but is common hardly anywhere and in Ivory Coast and Nigeria is decidedly rare. Absent from Ruzizi valley, Rwanda and Burundi (J.P. Vande weghe pc); quite common in Bioko (Fernando Po), up to 1,200 m. A small outlying population in Kenya between Kavirondo Gulf and Mt Elgon, now probably restricted to Mt Elgon and Kakamega Forest. Also found along northern border of the rainforest zone; and in the south to about Ogooue river, Gabon, to Kwamouth on Congo river and to 6°S in Kasai (about Kananga = Luluabourg). Judging from the number of locality records[538] and from the considerable skin holdings in the Tervuren Museum, mainly from Zaire, the abundance of this species is only about one-third that of Black Bee-eaters there. In Nigeria it is even sparser, recorded certainly from only four localities[185].

The species has been seen recently in dense gallery forest on Bafing river south of the well-watered Mandingo Mts in southwest Mali, an astonishing $5\frac{1}{2}°$ further north than any other record (B. Lamarche pc). But intervening Guinea is one of the most poorly explored countries in all Africa, ornithologically, and it is quite likely that this and the following bee-eater (qv), together with many more forest birds, habitually occur far north of the conventionally-shown rainforest boundary, in Guinea and adjacent parts of Mali.

FOOD AND FORAGING

Three birds which I watched in Kakamega Forest alternated active feeding with bouts of inactivity. They foraged by flycatching from 3 m high perches in dappled shade or full sun, sweeping low after a passing insect, seizing it and wheeling back to the same tree (but seemed rather unparticular about perches). They fed mainly on bees, captured 1.5–12 m above the ground and then beaten and bee-rubbed. A pellet contained a worker honeybee, a small ichneumon-fly and a large typical fly (?Tabanidae). The birds were netted and the beak of one was sticky with juice smelling characteristically of honeybee venom.

VOICE

Infrequent and weak; a high-pitched tinkling or squeaky *tsee-sup*. An occasional contact call between perched birds (distant or side-by-side) is a quiet *sip* or almost disyllabic *s(l)ip*, like that of the Little Bee-eater. An annoyance call, when disturbed by an arboreal squirrel, is *slip-slip* run into a short trill. Netted birds, in separate cloth bags, uttered muffled monosyllabic noises much like the contact call of undisturbed Red-throated Bee-eaters in the nest at night. A woodpecker-like trill *triiii triiii*[202]. Does not call when assembling for or flying to roost.

BREEDING

Very few nests found. A burrow was dug into the vertical side of a sawyer's pit in forest at Kumba, Cameroun; it was 55 cm long and the terminal oval chamber contained two incubated eggs in mid January[510]. Also near Kumba a bird was flushed from a half-made tunnel in a roadside bank 20 m from the forest edge in late January. From a third Cameroun burrow, again 55 cm long, two nestlings were taken in February. In Kakamega, Kenya, egg-laying was imminent in the second week of March, as evidenced by cloacal condition and high weight of a captured female.

Usually seen in pairs or trios, never in flocks. The three birds which I studied for three days in Kakamega were a female and two males and behaved as if a pair with a helper. They stayed within sight and sound of each other all the time, the female and a male often side-by-side, occasionally joined by the presumed helper. Both males courtship-fed the female and once an insect was passed from the first bird to the second then from the second to the third, which ate it. Copulation was not seen although laying appeared imminent.

SUBSPECIES

(1) *M. m. mentalis* Sierra Leone east to about Douala, Cameroun[378].

(2) *M. m. muelleri* From about Douala, Cameroun, south and east through the Congo basin. Differs in having forehead white, not ultramarine; no blue suborbital cheek streak; a more intense shade of chestnut; blue of belly not so pale, and in less contrast with breast; and central rectrices not streamered. Kenyan birds, described as *M. m. yalensis* (van Someren 1919) are to my eye indistinguishable.

ADDITIONAL DESCRIPTION

(Nominate race). ADULT ♂ Wings, back, mantle and rump vary from russet brown to rich, deep chestnut. Secondaries rufous, obscurely edged and tipped blackish. Wing lining pale rufous. Blue of nape, uppertail coverts, tail and breast varies from caerulean with a greenish wash to ultramarine with a purplish wash, paling towards belly and undertail coverts. Closed tail appears blue above, but concealed parts of rectrices are black. Tail black below. Iris brown to dark red-brown. ADULT ♀ In some cases chestnut suffused with olive and blue parts with green, and iris wine red, and red throat patch smaller than in ♂; but none of these apparent differences may in fact be constant. JUVENILE Chestnut parts of the plumage more ochreous than adult, and blue parts more a dusky turquoise. Crown, cheeks, nape and mantle with decided olive wash. Recently-fledged birds have chin and throat blue with only a few russet or reddish feather-barbs, barely discernible in the field. BARE PARTS Beak black; iris brown to wine red; legs and feet black when wet and grey when dry. WEIGHT ♂ 22.4 (17.4–25.0, n = 17), ♀ 22.9 (22.0–25.0, n = 7) and one near laying weighed 30.0 g. MEASUREMENTS *M. m. muelleri* Beak ♂ to feathers 31 (30–32), to skull 35 (34–36, n = 4), ♀ to feathers 29, to skull 35 (n = 2), depth 5.7 (5.2–6.3, n = 10). *Wing* 85.9 (83–88, n = 7). *Tail* 75.3 (73–79, n = 7). *M. m. mentalis Beak* to skull ♂ 36.0 (35–38, n = 7), ♀ 35.7 (33 38, n = 5). *Wing* ♂ 87, 89 (n = 2). *Tail* 73.3 (68–79, n = 9) excluding streamers up to 15 mm in ♂ and 12 in ♀. *Egg* 20.1 × 23.2 and 20.0 × 23.7 (n = 2). STRUCTURE Beak slighter than that of Black Bee-eater. Red chin feathers are stiff and narrow, the barbs not radiating but paralleling the shaft. Primaries project 2–6 mm beyond tertials in folded wing. Wing rounded; p8 longest, p10 28–35 long and 31–36 shorter than p8, p9 4–5, p7 1, p6 1–3, p5 10–12, p4 15–16, p3 20, p2 22, p1 25 and s1 25 shorter. Streamer tips of *mentalis* lyre-shaped.

Black Bee-eater   *Merops gularis*   (Plate 2)

Merops gularis Shaw 1798, Nat. Misc., 9, text to plate 337 (Sierra Leone).
Melittophaga gularis australis Reichenow 1885, J. Ornith., 33, p. 222 (Angola and
    Congo).
Meropiscus gularis australis, Reichenow, J. Ornith., 33, 1885, p. 468.
Melittophagus gularis, Shelley, Ibis, 1890, p. 167.

FIELD CHARACTERS
An African rainforest zone species with striking colouration: mainly
black plumage contrasting with large, scarlet throat patch and with
brilliant, pale azure rump and belly. Length 19–20.5 cm ($7\frac{1}{2}$–8 in) or
barely longer than Blue-headed Bee-eater, the only species with which
confusion is possible: but the Black Bee-eater is longer-winged, much
heavier and altogether more robust. Square-tailed. Like the Blue-headed
Bee-eater, shuns interior of forest and frequents glades and clearings and
forest-edge next to tracks and rivers; also in adjacent evergreen savanna
woodlands. In pairs; or rarely in flocks of up to ten. Feeds by flycatching
higher up than Blue-headed Bee-eater, often at canopy height. Quiet; not
particularly tame; flirts tail when perched. Nests are solitary, or two or
three may be aggregated into loose colony. May momentarily spread and
quiver wings when another bird perches adjacently (M. Dyer pc) as
shown in above heading.

HABITAT
High forest edge next to cleared land, by plantations and waterways;
larger clearings in forest; but only rarely encountered deep within forest
proper[202]. Secondary and fringing forest, oil-palm 'bush', and moist
savanna woodlands with well-formed canopy, and edges of gallery forest
in savanna. Perches mainly between 3 and 25 m high[610], on open rather
than leafy branches, often using dead trees, also telegraph wires.

DISTRIBUTION AND STATUS

Map opposite Plate 2. Range encompasses that of Blue-headed Bee-eater (except that Black Bee-eaters are absent from Kenya). Occurs in partially cleared land throughout the rainforest zone, and also 100–200 km into adjacent moist savanna woodlands, mainly following gallery forests along watercourses. So far recorded in Guinea only between Guékedou and Macenta near Liberian border; in Sierra Leone scarce west of Jong river but generally distributed east of it and southeast of Tingi Plateau[202]; throughout Liberia, and fairly common in Ivory Coast, but in Ghana only locally common in forested Fanti and Ashanti regions[29]; quite frequently encountered in Nigerian rainforest zone from Lagos to Niger delta and Calabar[185], but rarer in the adjacent derived savanna zone, north to Lokoja (07°48′N). Widespread in forested coastal lowlands of Cameroun, north to about 6°N and to an altitude of about 1,500 m[511], and throughout Congo basin north to Oubangui and Uele rivers, east in western Uganda to Bugoma, Bunyoro[387], Impenetrable Forest, Kigezi, Kibale[329], and Bwamba Forest (where numerous[220]), south to Kivu, Lulua and Kasai rivers at about 7°S, the length of River Congo and also found in evergreen and gallery forests of northern Angola from Cuango river to Cabinda, Cuanza Norte and northern Luanda Provinces[565]. Absent from Rwanda and Burundi (J.P. Vande weghe pc).

Probably mainly sedentary, some birds evidently highly so, a group keeping in a particular spot for years. But at one locality on Mt Nimba, Sierra Leone, which a group inhabits all year, numbers diminish in November and December and increase in February and March, when in one 2-hour period many flocks of 10–30 birds were seen flying west[135A]. It is seasonal in Bo district, Sierra Leone (present February to May[29]) and in Liberia, on Mt Nimba in wet season only (A. Forbes-Watson pc)—this may represent only local dispersal after breeding[202]. A sight record of two at Sikasso, 11°07′N, 05°35′W in Mali is exceptionally far north (B. Lamarche pc).

FOOD AND FORAGING

Airborne insects including bees, butterflies[389] and odonates[118]. Eight gizzards at Lamto, Ivory Coast, contained 218 insects in the proportions Hymenoptera 81%, Coleoptera 6%, Diptera 6%, Lepidoptera 3%, bugs, a cricket and a grasshopper 4%[556]. The Hymenoptera were one-quarter honeybees *Apis mellifera* and one-fifth flying ants *Crematogaster* sp. (J.M. Thiollay pc). Two gizzards from Léssé river, Central African Republic, had 30 insects: two bees, a wasp, a fly and 26 platypodine bark beetles. Feeds like other small and medium-small bee-eaters, keeping watch from an elevated perch and dashing out after a passing insect, curving back to its perch with more leisurely, sailing flight to treat and consume it.

Forages from perches often as high as 12 m, sometimes higher.

VOICE

Rarely calls[254]; the only call that I have heard is a monosyllabic *wic*, like that of Red-throated Bee-eater. According to Mackworth-Praed & Grant[382] there is a sharp shrill cry *tzik-tzik-tzik* and a 'pleasant quavering song'.

BREEDING

Poorly known. In Ghana and Nigeria nest excavation starts in January and "eggs are not laid before mid March"[30]. A clutch of three was found in early April in an oil-palm plantation, in a 38 cm burrow in the side of a planting hole; other nests in similar locations had single nestlings in early April and mid May[513]. Another Nigerian clutch of two fresh eggs was in mid May, at the end of a 45 cm tunnel. Two undated clutches in Cameroun were also of two eggs each[38,39]. In Congo basin the breeding season is protracted: from January to April north of the Equator in Ituri[118], laying inferred to be at the beginning of June at Basongo (4°30'S on Kasai river), while at Lukolela (0°30'S on River Congo) a bird was flushed from a tunnel sloping slightly downward into the base of an old termite hill in mid September[118]. Another burrow was "in the loose soil at the side of a shallow ditch in my rubber plantation. The hole ran into the ground 21 inches, amongst small roots of the rubber trees, first sloping upwards a little . . . and then downwards to the pocket where the eggs were"[39]. In Sierra Leone and Liberia the Black Bee-eater nests in small colonies, excavating its tunnels in sandy roadside and river banks[29,202]; at one locality in Liberia 12 adults had between them at least two nests in March 1979 and eight nest-holes in March 1981[135A]. But elsewhere it is evidently always solitary; and Bates stated emphatically that the species never congregates[39].

SUBSPECIES

(1) *M. g. gularis* From Sierra Leone east to Nigeria, probably about Cross river (although the distinction is not sharp, some southeast Nigerian and west Camerounian birds showing intermediate and mixed characters).

(2) *M. g. australis* From about Cross river, Nigeria, south-eastward through Congo basin, and in north Angola. Only a few forehead feathers are blue, or greenish blue, and it lacks blue superciliary stripe of nominate race. Azure streaks on breast are often and on belly sometimes red-tipped.

ADDITIONAL DESCRIPTION

(Nominate race) ADULT ♂, ♀ In freshly moulted plumage the ground colour is jet black, without much gloss, relieved as follows: a narrow azure band of feathers over forehead and above lores and eye; rump, upper- and undertail coverts brilliant azure, at least as vivid as the azure blue of many kingfishers; remiges dark rufous with blackish tips making a broad black band over trailing edge of wing (outer vane of outer primaries blackish, and outermost two primaries entirely blackish); wing coverts and secondaries narrowly edged green and tertials broadly tipped greenish or blue; central pair of rectrices broadly edged greenish; chin and throat scarlet; breast with small azure tear-drop streaks, which become broader and congruous toward belly; wing lining dull rufous. In worn or bleached plumage exposed black parts acquire a greenish wash and tertials and central rectrices are caerulean blue. JUVENILE Nestling and fledgling are like adults except that chin and throat are oily dark green, breast dull black, and belly and undertail coverts less brightly azure. In nestlings, azure uppertail coverts grow faster than black retrices, transiently concealing them when tail is still very short. A few reddish barbs appear in throat before fledging, and a month afterwards chin and throat are dull greenish black in some birds, dull reddish in others. BARE PARTS Beak black; iris dark red or crimson; legs and feet purplish black. MOULT In West Africa from August to October[556]. *Weight* ♂ 27.25 g (23.3–33.0, n = 18), ♀ 27.4 (22.0–32.0, n = 13) (Liberia A. Forbes-Watson pc, Ivory Coast J.M. Thiollay pc, and Central African Republic, September–December). MEASUREMENTS *M. g. gularis Beak* to feathers[29] ♂ 29–32 (n = 7), ♀ 28–30 (n = 7), to skull ♂ 34.6 (31–38, n = 3), ♀ 33 (31–35, n = 3), depth 5.7 (5.2–6.3, n = 10). *Wing* ♂ 90.5 (88–92, n = 7), ♀ 86 (83–93, n = 7). *Tail* ♂ 70 (68–75. n = 7), ♀ 71 (69–78, n = 7). *M. g. australis Beak* to feathers[29] ♂ 31–33 (n = 11), ♀ 29–32 (n = 9), to skull ♂ ♀ 38.6 (32–39, n = 17), depth 5.9 (5.6–6.4, n = 10). *Wing* ♂ 92.6 (90–99, n = 21), ♀ 91.3 (88–97, n = 15). *Tail* ♂ 67.7 (63–71, n = 21), ♀ 69.8 (67–72, n = 15). *Egg* 20.0 × 23.5 (19.0–21.0 × 21.0–26.0, n = 4) and 18.1 × 21.4 (17.9–18.5 × 21.0–22.2, n = 3[513]). STRUCTURE The scarlet throat feathers have basal portion of the vane dark grey and diamond-shaped, giving rise to non-interlocking scarlet barbs 10 mm long. A white zone between grey base and scarlet barbs, which are aligned nearly parallel with the shaft rather than radiating. On the chin grey and white feather bases show through the scarlet. Uppertail coverts long and undertail coverts exceptionally long, reaching to within 25 mm of tail tip. Primaries project 2–10 mm beyond tertials in folded wing. Wings less rounded than in *M. muelleri*; p8 longest, p10 27–35 long and 33–38 shorter than p8, p9 0–3, p7 1, p6 10–11, p5 17–20, p4 23–25, p3 26–28, p2 29–31, p1 33–34 and s1 35 shorter.

Little Bee-eater   *Merops pusillus*   (Plate 3)

Merops pusillus P. L. S. Müller 1776, Natursyst., Suppl., p. 95 (Senegal).
Merops cyanostictus Cabanis 1869, in von der Decken's Reisen Ost-Afr., 3, Abth. 1, p. 34 (Mombasa and Dschagga).
Melittophagus meridionalis Sharpe 1892, Cat. Birds Brit. Mus., 17, p. 45 (Natal).
Melittophagus pusillus ocularis Reichenow 1900, Orn. Monatsb., 8, p. 86 (Kordofan).
Merops pusillus argutus Clancey 1967, Bull. Brit. Orn. Cl., 87, p. 166 (Nata, Botswana).

FIELD CHARACTERS
Found throughout sub-Saharan Africa, usually common and probably the most numerous of all bee-eaters. Also, at 14–15 g, the smallest species (except the Somali Bee-eater?); length 15–17 cm (6–6½ in). In pairs and family groups in all main habitats except rainforest; usually near water. Tame, lively and 'conversational'. Above, burnished grass green, the central tail feathers and tertials fading blueish; bright yellow throat, triangular black gorget bordered behind by chestnut brown sides of breast, which merge into lime-washed buff lower breast and belly. In flight, wings appear largely rufous with broad black trailing edge band, and distal half of tail is black (not central rectrices). Wings not very long; feeding sallies a short chase with a gliding return to perch, longer flights undulating or slow sailing. Tail incipiently forked.

Adult Little Bee-eaters look and behave much like the other bee-eaters figured in Plate 3, particularly Blue-breasted Bee-eaters which, however, have a purple gorget (purple-black in one race) and white cheeks. Juvenile lacks black gorget and is mainly pale green below; distinguishable (with care) from juvenile Blue-breasted and Cinnamon-chested Bee-eaters by its lack of white cheeks and from juvenile Swallow-tailed Bee-eater by its green-and-rufous, not blue tail.

HABITAT

Grassy places seldom far from water. In the dry season marshes, lake-shores, river banks, streams; but in the rainy season also in cultivated land, lightly and sometimes heavily wooded savannas, grassy clearings in forest, bushy sand-dunes, grassed granitic outcrops, and treeless plains. Particularly fond of drying-out marshes with waist-high grasses and sedges interspersed with woody *Mimosa pigra* thickets. Quick to spread into areas cleared of forest, where grasses like *Panicum* are starting to invade. Forages up to 20 m above ground, from trees tops, but far more commonly low down, perching on grass stems and hawking just above the soil[167].

DISTRIBUTION AND STATUS

Map opposite Plate 3. Africa, from lower Senegal river, inland delta of River Niger, Lake Chad, the Nile at Khartoum, and about 16½°N in Eritrea south to Cunene river, Lake Ngami, southeastern Botswana, Vaal River (east of about 26°E), and lowland Natal to about Mzimkulu river. From coasts up to at least 1,800 m (in Ethiopia and Rwanda). Absent from Bioko (Fernando Po), Zanzibar and Pemba Islands. Throughout the rainforest zone, but only in cleared land and along rivers.

Generally quite common. Sedentary or locally dispersive and sporadic; many observers have recorded periodicity at a given locality[eg 390], for in any dry season it tends to concentrate on marshes and rivers, but there is no satisfactory evidence for regular, long-distance migrations anywhere. The best evidence comes from Nigeria, where I concluded a review by remarking "The evidence for the movements of this species is unsatisfactory, and in the absence of ringing returns it is not easy to decide whether there is an overall tendency to move southwards for the dry season (which would accord with what happens in other bee-eater species), or whether seasonal changes in abundance merely represent local movements of a few miles"[186].

Throughout its vast range it is common in suitable habitats by permanent water, and thinly but widely distributed elsewhere (but in western Zambia commoner in woodland than on the Zambezi[77]).

POPULATION

With the use of large-scale air photographs of 100 km² of terrain around Zaria, Nigeria, I estimate that some 580 birds inhabit the area prior to the breeding season. The African range of the species is 14.8 million km², so the total population will be 85.8 million or, to place it within reasonable limits, dividing and multiplying that value by $\sqrt{10}$, between 27 and 270 million birds.

For such a small bird survival is good, and Mrs Dale Hanmer has shown[282] that in Malaŵi at least 60% of Little Bee-eaters survive each of their 2nd to 5th years of age; the true value could well be higher. The greatest longevity she recorded was 7 years.

FOOD AND FORAGING

Small flying insects (4.5–30 mm long, generally <0.2 g), mainly Hymenoptera (bees, ants, digger, spider-hunting and true wasps, ichneumonflies, chalcidoids and scolioids). Hymenoptera vary from 40% to 75% of a food sample and average 57%. Beetles, flies and odonates comprise 33% and crickets, pigmy mole-crickets, bugs, butterflies, mayflies and antlions 10%; also termites and cockroaches[556]. Prey is diverse—1,500 insects eaten embraced 115 species, easily the most frequent being honeybees (16% of the food), sweat-bees (*Trigona*) and halictid bees (Appendix 5). Flies (10%) feature more commonly than in all other bee-eaters but Boehm's, and Little Bee-eaters are known to take tsetse-flies (*Glossina*). Odonates may feature importantly on occasion[167].

Little Bee-eaters 'flycatch' from a median perch-height of 1 m in sparse grassy vegetation (and 10 m in dense woodland). Most insects are caught within a few metres of the perch. One-third of forays are successful and on average 12 insects are caught per hour[167].

VOICE

Commonest call a quiet *sip*, monosyllabic or with suggestion of a disyllable as in *slip*. It may be repeated: *sip, sip*, or *sip-sip-sip* used in greeting a bird newly perched close by. High-intensity greeting is *siddle-iddle-ip, d'jeee* of c 1 sec duration, the last syllable alternatively *ooo* or French *eu* and almost devoid of initial consonant. That syllable may also be given on its own. A pair foraging alone may call only a few times an hour, but from a small feeding or pre-roosting flock there is an almost continuous conversation. Alarm: *ts'p, ts'p, ts'p*.

BEHAVIOUR

Monogamous, and helpers at the nest have never been reported*. Breeds solitarily, a pair every 100 m along best river banks. Pair-bonded birds forage and roost together all year, and after fledging a family party is similarly gregarious. The spacing of pairs and (family) parties in a marsh suggests that they are territorial, but no studies have been made. Adjacent pairs often meet without apparent conflict, and loose flocks of seven birds before the breeding season might either be last season's family party or be unrelated pairs. Colonies have been reported[64] perhaps in confusion for a nest being surrounded by false-start holes; a nesting colony of 200 holes

---

* Three adults took turns in alighting beside a nest and tugging the protruding tail feathers of a honeyguide which had just entered; it suggests a pair with a helper[111].

was reported in The Gambia[29], but probably in error for Red-throated Bee-eaters. Roosts in thickets in flocks up to 10 birds except during nesting season, when roosts in nest, solitarily or the pair together.

Courtship seems, from casual observation, just like that of Red-throated Bee-eater, qv. Whatever were the weird antics once described in South Africa, with a bird flying with another hanging from its beak[399], they were not "probable courtship"!

Grooming behaviour is like other bee-eaters, ie sunning with raised mantle-feathers and in 'broken-necked' posture (see Red-throated Bee-eater), dust-bathing[569], and diving onto water. Preens often, scratching head with foot overwing, and stretching one wing at a time backward while fanning tail to that side.

BREEDING

Nest holes are most commonly sited in a riverside sand cliff about 1 m high. Also in high cliffs, close to colonial bee-eaters' nest-holes; in weathered lateritic talus, in sides of drainage ditches and plough furrows, and in gently sloping soil or even flat ground, usually in lee of tussock or dried herbivore dung. Nests solitarily. Where Aardvarks are common, a favoured site is the sloping roof just inside their lairs. Said also to dig burrows into anthills (ie termite-hills) and to use old holes of rodents[382].

In the northern tropics digging starts in January (Zaire) and February (Senegal, Sierra Leone) or later, and laying in early March but mainly from late March to June[17,202,267,363,425]. Exceptionally early clutches in Mali were near Bamako in January and February (B. Lamarche pc). In Nigeria breeding starts later at higher latitudes, with most laying in March, April, May, and early June about latitudes 9°, 11°, 12° and 13–14° N respectively[176,186,231]. Laying is thereby towards the end of the cool dry season and fledging when the rains are getting into full swing. In East

Africa clutches have been found in every month except January, and data suggest a peak of laying about September in the region that includes Nairobi[92]. In the southern tropics laying in Zambia is mainly in September–October, in Zimbabwe mainly in October (57% of records), also September (16%), November (17%), December (7%) and January–February (3%)[312], in Malaŵi from September to December and mainly in October; while in the subtropics of South Africa it is from September to November and, again, mainly in October[56,59,401,535]. In other words, everywhere the breeding season commences in the relatively cool and dry season, shortly before the rains commence.

The clutch is 4–6 eggs, in Nigeria averaging 4.4. Incubation begins with the first egg laid; the first and second eggs hatch within hours on the same day, the third egg some 19 hours later and the fourth egg 24 hours after that[176]. The incubation period is 18–20 days (M. Dyer pc) and nestling period 23–24 days.

SUBSPECIES

(1) *M. p. pusillus* Northwestern savannas (see map). Forehead and eyebrow green. Merges with *ocularis* in a narrow zone about longitude 29° E[380] (G. Nikolaus pc).

(2) *M. p. ocularis* Eritrea through northwestern Ethiopia to Equatoria (Sudan), northwest Uganda and Upper Uele river (Zaire). Forehead green; a narrow ultramarine eyebrow.

(3) *M. p. cyanostictus* Somalia, arid eastern and northern Kenya. Wide ultramarine eyebrow, extending to forehead; purple-blue line across front of gorget.

(4) *M. p. meridionalis* Southern Congo basin, Albertine Rift, Uganda (except northwest) and western Kenya, intergrading with *cyanostictus* in highlands, south to Angola and Natal. Like *ocularis* but darker below and with eyebrow slightly more pronounced; a narrow blue-white band across front of gorget.

(5) *M. p. argutus* Border of South West Arid Zone, from south-western Angola to southwesternmost Zimbabwe, and Botswana. Like *meridionalis* but paler above and below and with smaller black gorget[128].

Racial boundaries in the map give a spurious impression of accuracy: there is sure to be a broad band of intergradation wherever adjacent races meet. In Ethiopia, for instance, where the species has been recorded almost everywhere, there is yet a 200 km gap between 'safe' records of *ocularis* and *cyanostictus* (J.S. Ash pc).

ADDITIONAL DESCRIPTION

(Nominate race). ADULT ♂, ♀ Closed wing appears green with edges of secondaries forming a rufous wedge. Outer primaries are olive with dusky tips, inner ones rufous (washed olive on outer webs) with well-defined blackish tips, and secondaries rufous with narrow pale buff tip and 8 mm broad subterminal black band. Wing lining rufous-buff. Central pair of rectrices green; the next one green-edged rufous, with a 3 mm pale tip and 13 mm black subterminal band over both webs; thereafter rectrices diminish in intensity of rufous and in extent and intensity of black, the outer feather being pale rufous and olive, with 5 mm dusky oval ending inner web and a small dusky tip to outer web. From centre of tail outward, feathers are successively 0.5 mm longer, and outer web of outermost feather is a further 1.5 mm longer than the inner web, and somewhat hooked, like a drongo *Dicrurus*. Underside of tail pale rufous with brown-black tips. JUVENILE Pale yellowish buff chin and throat merge into light green breast and buff flanks and belly; breast faintly streaked; upper breast washed with brown. BARE PARTS Beak black; iris pale orange to blood red; legs and feet dark brownish grey with paler soles. MOULT[281,327] Primary moult begins about ten weeks after fledging time in adults and juveniles; it is regular, descendant, and of duration about 134–152 days (Botswana) or 119–134 days (Malaŵi). The outer four secondaries moult ascendently starting halfway through primary moult; inner secondaries moult descendently, after third primary has grown fully. Tail moult is outward from median rectrix and also inward from outer one, the latter starting with or slightly before R3 to give moult sequence R1–2–6–3–4–5 (often 1–2–6–3–5–4). Tail and body moults are usually complete before innermost primary is fully grown. WEIGHT Means vary with time and place from 13.1 to 14.6 g (Ethiopia, J.S. Ash pc) and from 14.4 to 14.8 g (Malaŵi and Mozambique[281]) (total n = 500; range 11.2–18.1 with 90% of birds within 12.0–16.5 g). MEASUREMENTS (*M. p. meridionalis*) *Beak to feathers*[281] 26.9 (24–29, n = 225) in non-breeding birds and 24.6 (20–29, n = 52) in breeding birds, to skull ♂ 29.0 (26–32, n = 10) and ♀ 28.6 (26–32, n = 10), depth 4.9 (4.6–5.3, n = 10). *Wing*[281] 80.1 (74–86, n = 265). *Tail* 61–69 (n = 35[401]) and (*M. p. pusillus*) ♂ 57–60 (n = 12), ♀ 53–60 (n = 12)[29]. *Egg* 15.8 × 18.7 (14.4–17.0 × 17.0–20.5, n = 100[401]). STRUCTURE Short but strong rictal bristles, differing from all preceding and resembling all following species. In folded wing primaries project 1–4 mm beyond tertials. P8 longest, p10 28–30 long and 27–32 shorter than p8, p9 1–3, p7 2–3, p6 8–10, p5 14–15, p4 19–21, p3 21–22, p2 22–24, p1 25–27 and s1 26 shorter.

Blue-breasted Bee-eater   *Merops variegatus*   (Plate 3)

Merops variegatus Vieillot 1817, Nouv. Dict. Hist. Nat., 14, p. 25 (Malimbe).
Melittophagus variegatus loringi Mearns 1915, Proc. U.S. Nat. Mus., 48, p. 393 (Lake Albert).
Melittophagus variegatus bangweoloensis Grant 1915, Bull. Brit. Orn. Cl., 35, p 55 (Luena District).
Merops Lafresnayii Guérin 1843, Rev. Zool., p. 322 (Ethiopia).

FIELD CHARACTERS

Much like Little Bee-eaters in appearance, voice and behaviour; to be distinguished with care, since ranges and habitats of the two species often overlap. Blue-breasted Bee-eaters are larger: length 15.5–17.5 cm (6–7 in) or in the Ethiopian race *lafresnayii* 18–19 cm (7½ in); and weigh 50–60% more. They live in wetter and more open, or montane country, and all races except *bangweoloensis* can be told from Little Bee-eaters by having purple-blue gorgets. Blue-breasted Bee-eaters look larger-headed, and brighter. In the Zambian race, *bangweoloensis*, the gorget is only washed purple and can often look black in the field, like Little Bee-eaters; but it and other races of the Blue-breasted all differ further from Littles in having white cheeks below the black mask. White cheeks are visible only at close quarters, but at a distance they have the effect of making the throat appear a brighter yellow[85]. In Ethiopia the large Cinnamon-breasted Bee-eater also has white cheeks; Blue-breasted Bee-eaters there can be distinguished by gorget and also forehead colour. In pairs and (in Ethiopia) small flocks. Like other bee-eaters, wags tail irregularly forwards and backwards through small arc, as shown in heading above.

HABITAT

Reedy lakeshores and papyrus beds, marshes, grassy hillsides, rank grass savanna bordering the forest zone up to 2,100 m altitude; forest glades[219]. Broadly sympatric with Little Bee-eater in Ethiopia, Uganda and Zambia; where they occur at the same localities they generally seem to be segregated by habitat: Blue-breasted in open, permanently wet areas and Little in wet or dry places having plenty woody growth[76]. In Burundi Little Bee-eaters are abundant and widespread, but never occur in swamps occupied by Blue-breasted Bee-eaters (J.P. Vande weghe pc). But at Usengi, Lake Victoria, I found two adjacent pairs of Blue-breasted Bee-eaters and 100 m away two pairs of Little[see also 82]. One pair of Blue-breasted lived mainly in a wet reed-mace (*Typha*) bed, also feeding from a grove of 2 m tall bushes and above grazed grass sward with scattered low *Cassia* shrubs serving as perches, and the other pair inhabited beaten-down sedges between lakeshore reedbeds, feeding equally there and in dry cow pasture. Both pairs of Little Bee-eaters had nests, 70 m from each other, in the pasture and all the time kept to 50 cm high thorn hedges around patches of cultivation. The Blue-breasted Bee-eaters ranged much more widely and one pair liked to perch in the very centre of one Little Bee-eater's home range, only 20 m from their nest; yet in two days I saw no interaction between the two species.

Another population, which many people make conspecific with Cinnamon-chested Bee-eater (*M. oreobates*), inhabits Ethiopia (extending into Sudan on Boma hills) about the same altitudes as in Cameroun. It inhabits lightly wooded steep slopes, and on the Plateau open, grassy edges of coffee and *Eucalyptus* plantations[519,530].

DISTRIBUTION AND STATUS

See map facing Plate 3. Sedentary. An upland bird, sparingly distributed from Cameroun montane at levels between 1,100 m and 2,100 m[510] (and just into Nigeria on Obudu and Mambilla Plateaux*), in humid grass savannas across north of Congo basin rainforest zone—necessarily at < 1,000 m—to Mbomu river in northeastern Zaire, Uganda northeast to Kidepo valley, and northeastern shores of Lake Victoria; south to about the mouth of River Congo (where fairly common) and 7°S in Kasai river drainage, just entering northern Angola, thence east across southern Congo basin savannas and northeastward to west shore of Lake Victoria. In the Congo basin it occurs in low-lying swamps and large-river margins, not in forest proper. A discrete population is found on Bié Plateau of west-central Angola and is evidently very sparse. From the Zambezi drainage above 1,000 m in eastern Angola[565] and Zambia another race ranges eastward in most parts of Zambia east into Kafue National Park and to Muchinga Escarpment, intervening Zaire and Lake Upemba, and just into Tanzania on Ufipa Plateau and also 600 km north at Kibondo near the Burundi border; it inhabits damp plains and is everywhere very local[58,79].

* A sight record at Sapele near the Niger delta[185] is surely in error for Little Bee-eaters. Sapele is 400 km west of the Obudu Plateau and 2,000 m lower.

FOOD AND FORAGING

From an examination of 25 pellets from Zambia and three gizzard contents from Cameroun, the diet appears to be almost exactly the same as that of Little Bee-eaters, which is to be expected from their foraging methods seeming to be identical. Out of 235 prey items nearly 50 insect species were involved; the usual selection of Hymenoptera comprised 86%, flies 5%, beetles 7%, and bugs, grasshoppers and odonates 2%. Halictid bees, flower bees *Anthophora* and honeybee workers amounted to more than half of the Hymenoptera, and the wasps *Campsomeris* and *Cerceris* and buprestid beetle *Agrilus* were taken in good numbers. Pellets which I collected on the papyrus-fringed Kenyan shore of Lake Victoria contained over 100 insects—honeybees 19%, other hymenopterans 33%, beetles 22%, flies 16%, odonates and a grasshopper 10%, while one pellet contained remains of a small fish (see p. 221).

VOICE

Harder than that of Little Bee-eaters, some notes containing short trills recalling the trilling component in voices of larger bee-eaters: *pip*, *tup-tup* and *trrip*. What might be described as a song, from a perched bird with a food morsel to be courtship-fed to its mate: *trrrp p'ti p'ti p'ti*.

BREEDING

Nests have not often been found nor described in any detail. Appears always to nest solitarily, excavating in grassy hillsides or a small ridge in shelving ground near a lakeshore. Breeds in March in Cameroun and northern Zaire[118,510], October and December in Tanzania[92], September and October in Zambia[58], and about January in Ethiopia[519].

SUBSPECIES

(1) *M. v. loringi* Cameroun[378 see map 28] to Uganda and Kisumu (Kenya), south to near Equator (see map) where it intergrades with nominate race, differing in having a better marked blue eyebrow stripe. A poor race, barely distinct from the next.

(2) *M. v. variegatus* From Cameroun[378 see map 28] and Gabon through Kasai, and just into north Angola. Eyebrow green (ie not distinct from crown) or indistinct green-blue.

(3) *M. v. bangweoloensis* Central Angola through Zambia to westernmost Tanzania. Eyebrow green or, if blue, small and indistinct; gorget purple-washed black, almost sooty black in some individuals.

(4) *M. v. lafresnayii* Ethiopia, just into Sudan. Much larger than other races, with deep blue forehead and eyebrow, darker underparts with

greater extent of cinnamon on breast and much wider black subterminal band in tail. The evolutionary relationship of this form with the rest of its species and with the Cinnamon-chested Bee-eater is of interest and is discussed briefly in Chapter 3.

ADDITIONAL DESCRIPTION

ADULT and JUVENILE (*loringi, variegatus, bangweoloensis*) Apart from characters already mentioned, plumage is almost exactly the same as Little Bee-eaters'. Details of remex and rectrix colouration the same. ADULT (*lafresnayii*) Upperparts slightly brighter green; remiges narrowly fringed green so that their rufous vanes are barely visible in folded wing; white tips to rectrices broader. JUVENILE (*lafresnayii*) Like juvenile of nominate race, ie like juvenile Little Bee-eater, but breast greener. BARE PARTS (all races) Same as Little Bee-eater. WEIGHT (*bangweoloensis*) ♂ 21.5 (20–25, n = 4), ♀ 21 (n = 3)[76], (*loringi*) 20.3 (one), (*lafresnayii*) 22.5 (19.5–28.4, n = 66) (J.S. Ash pc). MEASUREMENTS *Beak* to feathers 28.7 (28–31), to skull ♂ 33.5 (30–36, n = 10) and ♀ 32.8 (30–34, n = 10), depth 5.7 (5.4–5.9, n = 10). *Wing* ♂ 88.2 (84–91, n = 20), ♀ 85 (84–86, n = 10). *Tail* 68.4 (57–72, n = 15). *Egg* One 18.6×22.9[510]. STRUCTURE Primaries project 2–3 mm beyond tertials in folded wing. P8 longest; p10 24–30 long and 34–41 shorter than p8, p9 3–6, p7 2–3, p6 10–12, p5 16–18, p4 21–22, p3 23, p2 26, p1 26 and s1 26 shorter.

Cinnamon-chested Bee-eater   *Merops oreobates*   (Plate 3)

Melittophagus oreobates Sharpe 1892, Ibis, p. 320 (Mt Elgon).
Melittophagus lafresnayii oreobates Peters, Check-List Birds World, V, 1945, p. 231.
Merops lafresnayii oreobates White, Revised Check-List Afr. Non-Pass. Birds, 1965,
   p. 234.

FIELD CHARACTERS
In Ethiopia (if it occurs there) liable to confusion with Blue-breasted
Bee-eaters, but elsewhere distinctively different from its congeners. Like
Little Bee-eater in plumage but much larger: length 21 cm (8 in) and twice
as heavy. Grass-green upperparts; outspread wings and tail mainly green
with broad black trailing edge band in wing and tail tip; black mask with
red eye; white cheek stripe, bright yellow throat, black gorget, cinnamon
breast merging to buff belly with bright lime green wash. Highland
forest-edge habitats characteristic. Distinguished from Blue-breasted Bee-
eaters by black, not purple-blue gorget and virtual absence of blue in
forehead and eyebrow. Nests in small colonies; at other times lives in pairs
or family parties, rather quiet and easily overlooked since it perches and
forages largely at forest-canopy height.

HABITAT
Wooded hillsides, forest edges, cedar forest[218], clearings overgrown with
bracken and elephant grass, gardens and plantations, never very far from
humid forest. Nests in earth cuttings, quarries and high earth cliffs of
streams at edges of forest, the sites always having immediate access to
open sunny places. Commonest between 1,800 m and 2,300 m and breeds
as high as 3,000 m. Lower limit 1,300 m[118].

DISTRIBUTION AND STATUS
See map. Sedentary, vagrant and locally migratory. East African

highlands, in the north from Lolibat and Nangeya Mts on Sudan-Uganda border, Mt Elgon on Uganda-Kenya border, Mts Nyiru and Kulal, Cherangani hills, Maralal, Mt Marsabit and Meru through highlands of west and central Kenya to Crater Highlands of Tanzania, Arusha National Park, Mt Kilimanjaro, Pare Mts, West Usambara and East Uluguru ranges. In mountains of Albertine Rift it occurs from highlands of northeastern Zaire (northwest of Lake Mobutu = L. Albert), through Ruwenzoris and southwestern Ugandan highlands, Rwanda and Burundi, south to about 5°S on the west side of Lake Tanganyika and to Kifunzo, Gombi Stream Game Reserve and Mt Mahari on the east side. At 3,000 in Mau Narok, Kenya, it is a breeding visitor from October to April[79], with several colonies at Lengibere (2,750 m)[64]. Sight records from Ethiopia, around Lakes Shala and Shamo, Nuara, the lowland Ilubabor salient, and lower Omo river are probably all referable to the Blue-breasted Bee-eater. Recently recorded also from Bangangai Forest at 730 m altitude (southwest Sudan, 04°51′N, 27°45′E), a major extension of known range[299A].

FOOD AND FORAGING

V. G. L. van Someren studied this bee-eater in his Nairobi garden[577]: "I usually became aware of them by hearing the sharp snapping of their bills as they seized some prey in mid-air. Searching for them, I would see them perched on some exposed high branch. They sit with their heads drawn in between the shoulders, bodies almost upright and tails wagging slowly up and down, pendulum fashion. Suddenly one will dart out—a swift glide, a rapid bank, a click, a turn, and so back to the outlook stance. . . . The accuracy with which they make these sallies is a treat to watch. Many of the insects are not discernible to the human eye, but the birds spot them; then swoop, bank, snap! There is a short *fruu fruu* of wings as they turn and dive sharply, then sail upward to their stance."

He counted the insects they caught and found that 95% were Hymenoptera, mostly honeybees, 2% "Diptera, recognizable as such", and 3% butterflies (*Terias, Belenois*). Hatchlings only a few days old were fed honeybees but not butterflies. Later, nestlings were given larger insects and in 83 feeding visits that van Someren watched there were 33 butterflies (mainly *Belenois*; also *Mylothris, Papilio, Pyrameis* and *Precis*). After the birds fledged he recovered over 4,400 insect heads or wings from one nest, all being honeybees excepting 10 other hymenopterans, 3 moths, 6 pierine butterflies, 6 beetles, and 12 *Phytomyia* flies (his analysis was evidently not microscopic). I collected adult pellets at the same place and they held nearly 700 worker honeybees and a single drone, 13 doryline ants, 9 other hymenopterans (*Larpelites, Liris, Ropalidia, Halictus, Nomia*), 2 lepidopterans, 2 odonates and a beetle. Pellets from a roost in Bahati forest, Nakuru, Kenya also consisted overwhelmingly of honeybees, and the birds had probably been feeding around gardens where bees abound. Elsewhere they are likely to take a smaller proportion.

VOICE

A long *tzee-ip* or a treble *tee-si sip* uttered when a bird alights by its mate[577]. This is the homologue of the *s'lip* of Little Bee-eaters. Their song is much like that species and may be rendered the same way: *siddle-iddle-ip-d'jeee.*

BREEDING

Sites, see above. Tunnels are always drilled into vertical cliff faces. Pairs seldom if ever nest solitarily. Usually from two to five pairs (once ten) nest together in loose association; the ten pairs occupied all of a road-cutting 50 m long[577]. At some nests a helper occurs (G.R. Cunningham-van Someren pc). On arrival at the start of the nesting season each bird of a pair digs its own hole or holes; three years after bee-eaters invaded a quarry to nest there were 50 tunnels, although never more than three pairs of birds[577]. Both members of a pair soon concentrate their efforts at one burrow, the clutch being laid after two weeks. Tunnels incline slightly upward and are 60–70 cm long, ending in an offset brood chamber 20 cm long, 15 cm wide and 7 cm high, with the floor 4 cm below level of tunnel. In central Kenya there are a few clutch records for February and March and one for April, but the large majority are for October–January, in and just after the short rains; in other climatic regions of East Africa breeding is in December–February (once March), in the dry season[92]. The clutch is always two eggs in Kenya[316,577] and often three in Tanzania[379]. V.G.L. van Someren asserted that two broods may be raised, which G.R. Cunningham-van Someren (pc) has recently confirmed in the grounds of Nairobi Museum without, however, marking birds individually. It is unique in the family (replacement clutches excepted). Incubation by both sexes, mainly ♀, by day in half-hour spells with five-minute breaks. Nestling period 25+ days[577].

ADDITIONAL DESCRIPTION

Monotypic. ADULT ♂, ♀ Black gorget has a 1 mm wide dark blue band running across front edge and in some individuals there is distinct purple wash over whole patch. Tertials fade blueish. Green in remiges brighter and more extensive than in Little Bee-eaters; secondaries have 2 mm white tip and 14 mm wide black subterminal zone—otherwise wing like those of two preceding species. Rectrices green, with ochre basal halves of inner webs of 2nd-4th feathers only. The same four feathers have 4 mm white tip, 2 mm green subterminal band and then a 20 mm wide black zone. Outer feather the same but with only 10 mm of black in outer web, towards its tip; and median rectrix is all green but for whitish tip and dusky subterminal area. JUVENILE Distinguishable from juvenile Blue-breasted Bee-eater (qv) only by size. BARE PARTS Same as Little Bee-eater. WEIGHT ♂ 27.2 (25–29, n = 5[78]). MEASUREMENTS *Beak* to skull ♂ 45.2 (43–48, n = 5), ♀ 44.2 (42–46, n = 5), depth ♂ 5.8 (5.3–6.4, n = 5), ♀ 5.6 (5.3–5.9, n = 5). *Wing* 102 (98–106, n = 10). *Tail* 87 (82–92, n = 10). *Egg* averages 19 × 23 mm. STRUCTURE Primaries extend 2–13 mm beyond tertials in folded wing. P7 longest, p10 37–42 long and 35–37 shorter than p7, p9 4–6, p8 0–2, p6 2–4, p5 12–15, p4 17–21, p3 21–26, p2 24–27, p1 25–30 and s1 25–30 shorter.

Swallow-tailed Bee-eater   *Merops hirundineus*   (Plate 3)

Merops hirundineus Lichtenstein 1793, Cat. Rer. Nat. Rar. Hamburg, p. 21 (Orange River, *vide* Levaillant).

Merops furcatus Anon. = Stanley 1814, in Salt's Voyage to Abyssinia, App. IV, p. 57 (Adowa, Ethiopia, in error for Mossuril, Mozambique, *vide* Wagstaffe, Type Spec. Birds Mersey Co. Mus., 1978, p. 13). (*Merops hirundineus strenuus* Clancey 1962, Durban Mus. Novit., 6, 13, p. 150[126], is a synonym.)

Merops chrysolaimus Jardine and Selby 1830, Illustrat. Orn., 2, pl. 99 and text (Sierra Leone).

Dicrocercus hirundineus heuglini Neumann 1906, Bull. Brit. Orn. Cl., 16, p. 113 (*Dicrocercus* Cabanis and Heine 1860, Mus. Hein., Th. 2, 1859–60, p. 136).

FIELD CHARACTERS

Easily distinguished from its closest relatives (the three preceding bee-eaters) by its long blueish, white-tipped forked tail. Length (including outer-tail streamers) 20–22 cm (8–8½ in). Rather long-beaked. In savanna woodlands in pairs and small parties, feeding at tree-top level and thereby quite conspicuous. Vocal, but voice very subdued. Upperparts and breast bronzy green, rump caerulean blue, mask black, chin and throat bright chrome yellow, narrow blue gorget and blue belly. Secondaries rufous; wing with black trailing edge band. Outer edge of tail almost straight (not as curved as in Plate 3) and the forked tips curve slightly inward. Juveniles, lacking yellow throat and blue gorget, resemble juvenile Little Bee-eaters but have pale blue belly and blue or green tail lacking rufous.

HABITAT

Tall savanna woodland. North of Equator mature *Isoberlinia* woods, drier woods and bushed grassland; likes burnt bush. Similarly in southern Africa: tall *Baikiaea* woodland on Kalahari sand, mopane (*Colophospermum*), *Brachystegia*, *Combretum* woods, riverine thickets, *Eucalyptus* windbreaks, bushy river plains, parkland and semi-desert with scattered *Acacias*. Feed mainly at canopy level. Essentially a lowland species; much of its southern African range west of 30°E is over 1,000 m, but it commonly exceeds 1,500 m only in Namibia.

DISTRIBUTION AND STATUS

See map. Sedentary or vagrant, and partly migratory. Nearly everywhere uncommon and its movements are poorly understood. There are different northern tropical and southern African populations, each consisting of two subspecies. In northern tropics, ranges through moist woodland belt from Gambia, coastal Senegal, Sierra Leone and Mali south of 14°30'N (where it is sparse and probably sedentary[202,267,363]) to Nigeria and thence in the acacia belt as well to southern Chad and northern Central African Republic. In Nigeria it occurs sparsely in little-disturbed woodland between 6½° and 10½°N and may move south for the dry season[186]; in Ivory Coast it is frequent and regular as a migrant to coastal savannas about 6°N, present for the dry season, from November to April[556]. Not yet recorded in Cameroun[378]. In between Cameroun and Sudan very few records exist and here racial intergradation occurs: six localities in southern Tchad and northwestern Central African Republic between 05°N, 15°E and Miltou, Am Timan and Ndélé, and two on Boro river (08°25'N, 24°55' and 25°10'E) in western Bahr el Ghazal Province, Sudan. But in Bahr el Ghazal east of 28° E the bird is widespread, resident and locally common in well-wooded savannas[114] (G. Nikolaus pc). The eastern race ranges into Akobo river salient of Ethiopia and Omo river valley (with one old record far to the north, between Taccazze and Gash rivers[418]), suggesting that it may occur locally along the Ethiopia-Sudan border, like Red-throated Bee-eaters, and through Equatoria into Kidepo

Valley National Park and the Moroto area of Uganda and to upper Uele
(Zaire) and northeast shores of Lake Mobutu. A scarce and local
inhabitant of dry country, and April passage along Nile suggests some dry
season incursion into Uganda[79].

South of the Equator a lowland sandveld race ranges from Lake
Victoria and Shimba Hills in Tanzania to Katanga (Zaire), Western
Province of Zambia, Luangwa and lower Zambezi valleys and down the
Mozambique plain nearly to Natal[253]. Not uncommon in Malaŵi, at least
in low-lying savannas; extends into lowveld of Zimbabwe along Sabi and
Lundi valleys. Migratory, at least in Katanga, where present only from
May to November[147]. Confluently to the west a poorly differentiated
upland race ranges to Benguela coast and Malanje highlands of northern
Angola, through Botswana (where locally common in the northeast[317])
and Namibia to borders of Namib Desert, and Orange river in South
Africa[604]. Its distribution is complicated by seasonal movements[288,551]. On
the Zimbabwean highveld 85% of records of Swallow-tailed Bee-eaters
fall in April-September; in the other half of the year the western race is
thought to move westward to breed toward the periphery of Kalahari
sandveld in Namibia, Botswana, Angola, Barotseland and Matabeleland, and the eastern race southeastward to breed in lowland sandveld in
Mozambique[579,288]. The Western bird just enters Transvaal and is uncommon and local in the northwest, not yet proven to breed[330]. Further south
there are records of vagrants at Schmidsdrif on Harts river, Gumtree,
Vosburg, Oudtshoorn, Stutterheim and Uitenhage[68,468,521,604], and a
breeding record from Kimberley[288].

FOOD AND FORAGING

Feeds by 'flycatching' in same way as other smaller bee-eaters, but
perches high (2–20 m, often on bare limb or telegraph wire) and associated with trees rather than with shrubs or grasses. I doubt whether they
take insects "freely from flowers"[382], except in the sense that they readily
perch in a flowering tree like *Kigelia* close to its blossoms, to prey *in flight*
on *flying* insects attracted to the flowers. Like all bee-eaters, can be a pest
at hives[68]. A food sample from Harare, Zimbabwe, of 380 insects was 83%
honeybees, 13% other hymenopterans and 4% flies, beetles, butterflies,
odonates, bugs and grasshoppers. Prey also includes cicadas (G.L.
Maclean pc).

VOICE

Call is quiet but given often, particularly by small flocks. Expressions
seem to be the same as Little Bee-eater, but there is a rolling quality, the
voice drier and less sibilant than Little or Blue-breasted Bee-eaters.
High-intensity greeting behaviour, with erect posture and excited tail-

quivering and chasing is accompanied by *dreee-dreee*. Low-intensity contact call indistinguishable from Little Bee-eater's.

BREEDING

Nests solitarily or sometimes two or three pairs in fairly close proximity[267], in flat or shelving ground with bare patches of sandy soil or in sandy roadside banks. In Gambia breeds in May-July, immediately before the rains[267,427]. In East Africa the only record was in April, early in the rains, but they may also lay a few weeks earlier at the end of the dry season[92]. In 18 South West African nests with eggs or young (for details of which I am indebted to the SAOS nest-record scheme), inferred laying dates were all from early October until early or mid January; other southern African records suggest early nesting at low latitudes (July-August, central Angola, northern Zambia)[288]. In Malaŵi and on Matabeleland highveld it breeds in October–November[56] and at 20°S in Mozambique in September–November[288]. The South West African nests were 0.8–1.0 m long and were sited 0.15–1.5 m high (average 0.75 m) in sand mounds, sides of ditches, or near the top of perpendicular sand cliffs, and once in the side of an Aardvark tunnel (R.A.C. Jensen pc). The clutch is 2–4 eggs.

BEHAVIOUR

R. Jensen filmed three adults visiting one nest, so there are evidently helpers; otherwise it is probably monogamous. Solitary when breeding; thereafter in family parties which combine into a flock often of 8–10 and rarely of 20–32 birds[288]. Such flocks roost in tight-packed ranks within the foliage of a leafy tree, but it is uncertain that they roost on one anothers' backs as formerly claimed[382].

SUBSPECIES

(1) *M. h. chrysolaimus* Senegal to Chad (Chari river drainage). Blue forehead and eyebrow; tail (except median rectrices) green.

(2) *M. h. heuglini* Southern Sudan (Bahr el Ghazal, Upper Nile and Equatoria Provinces) and adjacent districts of Ethiopia, Uganda and Zaire (Uele). Possibly parapatric with *chrysolaimus*, from which it differs only in having darker blue gorget and uppertail coverts.

(3) *M. h. furcatus* From northern Tanzania through Malaŵi to southern Mozambique with adjacent lowveld in Zaire, Zambia and Zimbabwe. Forehead and eyebrow green; tail all blue.

(4) *M. h. hirundineus* Parapatric with *furcatus* but on highveld, west to Angola and Namibia and south to Orange river. Forehead and eyebrow green; greens are bronzier than in *furcatus*, yellow and blue in underparts paler, and gorget narrower[313].

ADDITIONAL DESCRIPTION

(Nominate race) ADULT ♂ Forehead broadly pale azure blue, extending backward at sides to form a short blue eyebrow. Crown, nape, mantle and closed wings bronzy green, the back a little paler and merging to bright caerulean blue on rump and uppertail coverts. Edges of secondaries and inner primaries show as rusty wedge in closed wing. Outer webs of outer primaries olive green. All primaries dark grey or blackish distally; secondaries have narrow pale grey tips and broad blackish subterminal band. Exposed parts of tertials bleach same shade of greyish blue as tail. Wing lining pale rufous. Tail has middle pair of feathers greyish blue and remainder greenish blue, all but the median and elongated outer pair broadly grey-white tipped on inner web and with subterminal dusky zone on both webs; underside dark grey. Chin and throat chrome yellow and gorget ultramarine with 1 mm pale green front edge and at sides shading to white (some individuals having cheeks almost as white as in Blue-breasted Bee-eater, and yellow throat bordered pale green or pale blue next to black mask). Breast green, belly and flanks pale caerulean blue darkening to undertail coverts. ADULT ♀ Like ♂ but paler, less strongly coloured underparts, and less markedly forked tail. JUVENILE Like juvenile Little Bee-eater but breast not washed with brown, belly and rump pale azure blue, median rectrix dull blue and rest of tail lacking rufous. BARE PARTS Beak black, iris orange-red to crimson (dark brown in juvenile), legs and feet dull mauve-black with pale soles, nails black. MOULT In Zimbabwe postnuptial and also post-juvenile moults begin in late December and continue until April[288]. WEIGHT 23.1 (19.5–29.0, n = 18, SD ± 2.6[288]). MEASUREMENTS *Beak M. h. heuglini* to skull, ♂ 35.6 (33–39, n = 10), ♀ 34.0 (32–37, n = 10), *M. h. hirundineus* ♂ to feathers 29.2 (26–31), to skull (unsexed) 33.3 (29–38, n = 74[288]). *Wing* 95.1 (89–102, n = 76[288]). *Tail* to central rectrices 66–70, to outer rectrix ♂ 102.5 (100–106, n = 10), ♀ 101.6 (96–111, n = 10), with fork in adult 38 (31–46, n = 20) deep. *Egg* 18–19 × 20–21.3. STRUCTURE Unworn, each median rectrix is markedly attenuated toward its tip and 5 mm longer than next feather; with wear, it has a rounded tip and is same length. Succeeding rectrices have slightly elongated or hooked tips to outer webs, and inner web tips are angled so that (in outermost feather) greatest width is 35 mm from its tip. In folded wing primaries project 6–11 mm beyond secondaries. P8 longest; p10 29–31 long and 40–44 shorter than p8, p9 1–3, p7 1–4, p6 8–13, p5 17–18, p4 22–23, p3 26–27, p2 29–30, p1 31–33 and s1 31–32 shorter.

Stretching

Red-throated Bee-eater   *Merops bullocki*   (Plate 4)

Merops Bulocki Vieillot 1817, Nouv. Dict. Hist. Nat., 14, p. 13 (Senegal).
Merops frenatus Hartlaub 1854, J. Orn., 2, p. 257 (Sennar).
Merops Boleslavskii, Pelzeln, Sitzungsb. Akad. Wiss. Wien, Math.-Naturwiss. Cl.,
   31, 1858, p. 320.
Melittophagus bulocki, Peters, Check-List Birds World, V, 1945, p. 231. (The
   specific epithet is generally spelled *bulocki*, perpetuating Vieillot's inadvertent
   error. Orthographically it is *bullocki*, an amendment permissable under the
   International Code of Zoological Nomenclature. *Merops Boleslavskii* was the
   name given to yellow-throated birds, which are now realized to be a variant; see
   below.)

FIELD CHARACTERS

A gregarious and approachable medium-sized bee-eater, vocal with a
characteristic *wip* call. Length 20–22 cm (8–8½ in). Fly-catches from edge
of leafy small trees and flies high only when moving to destinations 1 km
distant. Sedentary. Nests in aggregated colonies of about 50 birds, the
burrows bored into a cliff. Sexes identical; unmistakable—the only
savanna species with a scarlet throat except for the allopatric White-
fronted, qv. Glossy grass green upperparts, warm buff nape and breast,
conspicuously ultramarine undertail coverts, spread tail ochreous. In
flight, wings green with black trailing edge band. Eye brown. 2–10 birds
per thousand have golden yellow throats; in low evening sunshine
red-throated individuals can also look yellow-throated.

HABITAT

Bushy savannas dissected by wooded small rivers and seasonal streams.
Lateritic or hard sand cliffs 2–5 m high are a requirement for nesting and
at no season are birds found much further than 2 km from such places,
which are provided equally by streams and by gullying erosion in
overgrazed areas. Well timbered gardens and farmland, edges of woods
around fields and marshes, edges of gallery forest in the northern tropical

moist woodland zone, parkland, sometimes scrub like *Combretum* in the dry woodland zone but only when a minimum of evergreen bushes along nearby watercourses.

DISTRIBUTION AND STATUS

Map opposite Plate 4. Entirely sedentary over most of its range, with some evidence for local migration at the periphery. From Senegal and Gambia rivers throughout the moist woodland zone east to Chari river drainage area and, beyond the Darfur gap between 20° and 25°E, a different race from upper Mbomu, Uele and Dungu rivers in northeasternmost Zaire through Bahr el Ghazal and Equatoria (Sudan, where common), to northwestern Uganda (common, if local, at Masindi, Gulu, Kitgum[79]), Ilubabor lowlands of western Ethiopia, the Blue Nile north to 14°N and drainage of Atbara river north to the same latitude. A year-round resident on Uele river and its tributary the Garamba[580]. A single bird was seen recently with White-fronted Bee-eaters in Virunga Park, Zaire[112]. From Ivory Coast to Nigeria the western race is plentiful between 9° and 12°N. It breeds to nearly 13°N in Nigeria and to 14°30'N on River Niger in Mali[363], and in westernmost Africa ranges from northern Sierra Leone (one record) to Senegal river, where it is common from above its delta to its source[425]. Exceeds 1,000 m in altitude only on Jos Plateau in central Nigeria[184].

Throughout, the distribution of Red-throated Bee-eaters is almost exactly coincident with that of northern tropical races of Swallow-tailed Bee-eaters.

Extended studies in Nigeria show that the species is highly sedentary in the north. But the only record in the southeast was of 20 birds flying north at Enugu (latitude 6°25'N) in late July which were thought to be migrating[512]. It has once been reported at the Nigerian coast, in savanna near Lagos in January[257]. In The Gambia it occurs upriver from 15°W appearing commonly during the rains (July to October inclusive) with the majority having departed for the upper reaches of Gambia river in Senegal by February–March. A few remain until April, perhaps nesting. Upstream there is a large colony or colonies in Niokolo Koba National Park where laying seems to be in late February and fledging in late April[267] (M.E.J. Gore pc).

POPULATION

At the start of the breeding season there were nine colonies comprising 520 birds in an acute-triangular area of 25 km^2 in Zaria Province, Nigeria (including feeding territories each of 1–2 km^2), ie a density of 21 birds/ km^2 [176]. The density there is high, doubtless owing to the abundance of suitable cliffs along streams with gullied banks; other equally good areas are beyond the watersheds, about 5 km away. On the basis of 25 km² high-density areas regularly spaced 5 km apart, I calculate a mean density over the terrain as a whole of one colony (average 58 birds) per 98 km². Extrapolation to the 2,930,000 km² range of the species (see map) gives a total population of 1,730,000 birds at the beginning of the breeding season or twice that number immediately after breeding. Such precision is of course spurious but the true population probably lies between the limits of that value divided and multiplied by $\sqrt{10}$, ie 547,000 and 5,470,000.

FOOD AND FORAGING

Feeds at stations intermediate in height above the ground between levels preferred by Little and Swallow-tailed Bee-eaters; foraging perches are generally between 2 and 5 m high. Otherwise no differences in hunting technique have yet been discerned between this and other small or medium species. On clear warm days active feeding begins about an hour after leaving roost and continues at about 30 sorties per hour (of which one-third are successful, but bird always returns to its perch whether successful or not) until departure for roost at dusk, diminishing in rate with wind, early-afternoon heat, rain and severe haze, and increasing when a large brood has to be fed. Very rarely it feeds in continuous flight aloft, probably catching easily-consumed soft insects like flying ants and termites; and fly-catches when sitting on the ground, returning to beat the capture against hard earth (H.Q.P. Crick pc).

Four thousand insects have been identified from pellets collected around the year in Nigeria. Numerically, worker honeybees comprise one quarter of the adult diet (24.6%, varying from <5% in July–August to >45% in March–June). Drone honeybees are rarely taken. By weight and calorific content honeybees will comprise a greater proportion of the food eaten, since they are amongst the heaviest prey: I estimate about 50% by weight. A further 16% of the diet, numerically, are four or more species of the tiny stingless sweat-bees, *Trigona*, taken abundantly from January to March. Flying ants predominate in the diet in July–August, when they are commonly on the wing after rain. A huge variety of other hymenopterous insects is consumed, ichneumon-flies, chalcidoids, ruby-tailed wasps, velvet-ants, true wasps, spider-hunting wasps, digger and potter wasps and all manner of bees (see Appendix 6), and Hymenoptera comprise four-fifths (79%) of the total prey. The remaining one-fifth is beetles (14%, again in huge variety), bugs and flies (5%), dragonflies and damselflies, moths and butterflies, termites, and grasshoppers (together <2%). All main components vary seasonally in incidence accordingly to their availability, dry-season and wet-season diets being in marked contrast[231].

The average weight of freshly-regurgitated pellets is 0.31 g (maximum

0.60 g) and of faeces 0.14 g[141A], but I do not know the rate of production of these wastes.

A brood is fed 2–18 times per hour (depending on its number, age, and the presence of a helper[176]) with insects substantially larger than those being eaten by adults at the time. In Nigeria the cicada *Platypleura truncaticeps* features importantly in nestling diets; also odonates, long- and short-horned grasshoppers and crickets, hawk-moths, whites and yellows (Pieridae), browns (Satyridae) and brush-footed butterflies (Nymphalidae), and some large wasps and bees. Food-delivery is so rapid that of nearly 500 deliveries watched at one colony on one day I could only identify 19 grasshoppers, 16 cicadas, 7 moths, 2 odonates, one fly, one honeybee and one hornet. Insects fed to nestlings weigh 0.1–0.6 g each and on average 0.3 g[141A].

VOICE

Not yet investigated rigorously; but because of its frequency and variety vocal communication is clearly important among Red-throated Bee-eaters. (1) Commonest call by perched bird is a low intensity *wip*, frequently uttered as a *contact call* during all day-time activities. It seems to have a variety of tones and inflections and is given (2) with a slight terminal inflection as a low-intensity *flight call*. High intensity flight call is a loud *weep, wit*; (3) general *excitement call*, flight intention, or low intensity alarm is a chattering *tic-ic-ic-ic-ic-ic*, at higher intensity a chur with a slight cadence; (4) *alarm* about a nearby danger (hawk, man, elephant), *tic-tic-tic*; (5) *alarm* about a distant high-flying hawk, *prrrrr'ng*—short, fast, treble and falling (H.Q.P. Crick pc); (6) *greeting*, an excited cadenced trilling *trrrr-trrr-trrr-trr-trr-trr-tr-teu*, falling in <1 sec to the quiet final syllable; sometimes rather more varied and I have written it *tee-tee-peu-peu-pirri-pirri-prrrrrp-teu-teu*; (7) *roosting-intention*, a single plaintive low-pitched *pee-ouw* or *prre-ow*; (8) during *copulation* a muffled sound difficult to represent phonetically. It is also given inside nest-holes and may then accompany copulation; which sex responsible, not determined; (9) on arrival at perch with item of food for delivery to mate, a *courtship-feeding chuf . . . chuf . . . chuf*; (10) on arrival at nest burrow entrance with food for young, a *food-delivery-intention prrrp* or *chrrup* delivered six or seven times in 3 sec as a bird approaches from 30 m; (11) on *departure after food-delivery*, a soft *you* or *oop*, then the flight call *wip*; (12) *fledging call*, by adult encouraging nestling to fledge, like (10) above, less loud, sometimes followed by *teu* (H.Q.P. Crick pc); (13) *begging* by young nestling a sibilant chirruping with an insistent, regular beat—*sirri-sirri-sirri-sirrip-schirrup-schirri-schirri-schirri-schirrup*; (14) advanced nestling or *juvenile soliciting food*, a persistently reiterated begging *weep* or *wirrp*; and (15) a *nestling contact-call* (?), *djewy* (with a very soft *dj*).

SOCIAL ORGANIZATION

Gregarious in and out of the breeding season; society complex, with interacting tiers of relationships. Monogamous, and basic social unit is the pair. After fledging, and a 'weaning' period of about six weeks during which juveniles perfect the art of bee predation while closely attended by adults, young birds remain with their parents while foraging and roosting, and in the following breeding season one, occasionally two or three, of them may remain bonded to their parents and become helper(s) at their nest, sharing parental tasks if less sedulously. An experienced bird may also become a helper when its nest fails, or after breeding in a previous year. About a third of nests in a colony have helpers, with single helpers at six times as many nests as have multiple helpers. The breeding pair and helper are selectively territorial at the burrow entrance, defending it against intrusion by some, but not all, other members of the colony: members of some other breeding units are evidently tolerated as occasional visitors to the nest burrow entrance, as in White-fronted Bee-eaters[289]. Adults and juveniles commute daily in groups between a roosting station and a foraging territory 1–2 km distant. The feeding territory is weakly defended against conspecifics, although incursions by other members of the colony seem neither common nor persistent (H.Q.P. Crick pc).

SOCIOSEXUAL BEHAVIOUR

Antagonistic behaviour is rare on feeding grounds but commonplace at roosts and nesting colonies. Mostly it takes the form of harmless bickering between a perched bird and another perched or intending to perch nearby: threat with wide-opened beak directed at newcomer, head lowered and stretched forward, forecrown feathers flattened, mantle feathers fluffed, wings held slightly away from body, and a vehement version of the greeting call (6), qv. Transient beak-grappling may occur at perch, and rarely aerial pursuit and fighting for up to a minute, two birds in the air grappling beaks and falling interlocked to the ground where they struggle by lunging and beak sparring. Battling birds can be interlocked on the ground for five minutes or so, an impasse with each gripping the other's wing, getting quite soiled as they struggle around (H.Q.P. Crick pc).

A greeting display is commonplace, indeed the rule (except in nestling period) whenever a bird flies in to sit near others already perched (A). It is chiefly vocal, accompanied by upstretched head, opened beak, raised crown feathers and fanned and vibrated tail, and may involve several birds at once. A rarely-seen courtship can develop out of this greeting display when two birds, still with upright stance and vibrating tail, bob the head four or five times a second through a few mm, with the tips of their beaks nearly touching (B). Apart from sexual chasing and greeting

A   B

the only obvious element in courtship is feeding, always of a female by a male (including male helpers). Courtship feeding is frequent, usually without immediate consequence but often followed by copulation, after or before the female has had time to swallow the food morsel. Copulation occurs at a defended perch close to the nest and sometimes the female emerges from the burrow for the purpose, and retires there afterward (copulation *may* also sometimes occur within the nest). During coitus the male seems to peck at the insect held by the female, or if she has swallowed it he jabs at, holds, or presses down upon her forehead feathers. Rarely, he mounts without surrendering the courtship feed and after coitus eats the insect himself. A male helper may copulate with the same female immediately afterward.

Individual distance with bonded birds is zero, for they sit touching and roost hard up against each other. Non-bonded birds tolerate strangers sitting at 10–15 cm.

A bird clinging to the cliff at its nest hole often momentarily dips its head into the entrance, then flutters up about 20 cm and returns to the tunnel entrance; the 'head-dip and flutter' display lasts for only 1–2 sec and probably serves to emphasize ownership[141A].

BODY CARE

Because of their gregarious hole-nesting habits, Red-throated Bee-eaters carry a heavy ectoparasitic load, and they have a diversity of behaviour evidently directed at cleansing themselves. When nesting, most birds are infested with microscopic harvest mites *Neoschogastia* causing swelling around the cloacal feather papillae, and 5% are infected with a cheyletid mite *Neocheyletiella*, which causes skin lesions 25 mm² in extent on the skin of the belly[249]. Neither is debilitating. The feather-mite *Meromenopon meropis* is abundant and there are probably at least two other genera of Mallophaga[394]. The hippoboscid fly *Ornithophila metallica* is quite common beneath the plumage.

At rest, the bee-eater commonly sits with its back to the sun and the mantle feathers raised and splayed. Less common is the 'broken-necked' sunning posture with the head turned acutely aside, sunward eye closed and neck feathers on the sunny side fluffed. These postures are followed by vigorous preening, and scratching of neck and head by the foot, over-wing. Sometimes a bird suns itself by spread-eagling on sloping soil, the outstretched wings resting on the ground, or closed with the body tilted to one side exposing breast and flanks to the sun. It may also spread-eagle on a vertical cliff near its nest entrance, clinging by its claws, the head hanging down over the back, fluffed throat to the sun, looking totally bemused. Dust-bathing occurs with the body held close against the ground, the head stretched forward with throat feathers touching the ground and shaken rapidly (like a dog shaking off water), wings are half open and beaten, and tail fanned and depressed against the ground. Further body-care activities are bathing, beak-wiping and in a sense 'gritting' (see pp. 138 and 219).

BREEDING

Obligate cliff-burrowers, in more-or-less vertical sandy, clayey or lateritic streamside and erosion-gully cliffs usually about 2 m high, rarely over 5 m, and exceptionally under 20 cm[142]. Quarries, borrow-pits and road-cuttings are also used. The cliff is plane or sometimes irregular, convex or concave. Often in same cliffs as Carmine Bee-eaters. There are seldom fewer than five or much more than 50 occupied nests in a colony. Tunnels, including numerous 'false starts', are spatially concentrated on the cliff, the entrances often 10 cm apart and occupying an area of about 1 m radius or (large colonies in low cliffs) arranged horizontally. With use the entrance becomes A-shaped with the feet wearing two channels. Mean tunnel-length varies between colonies from 79 to 84 cm; individual extremes are 56 and 139 cm. Burrows are 6 cm in diameter and incline at 20° for two-thirds of their length, expanding, after a shallow hump or lip in the floor, into an egg-chamber about 10 cm high, 20 cm long and 15 cm wide.

Nest-hole excavation starts about September, towards the end of the rains before the ground has begun to harden as it dries. New holes may be dug at a previous year's colony site, or a new site may be chosen. There is little activity or even presence at sites in November and December, and in January birds recommence digging and refurbishing and some roost at the colony. Occasionally a female lays in a burrow other than the one she dug (H.Q.P. Crick pc). In Nigeria egg-laying is mainly from the last days of January through to the first week of March and it seems to be the same in the rest of the northern tropics. The earliest record is of young in most nests in a colony at Assob, about 1,000 m altitude near Jos, on 21 January with breeding finished by the end of February[532]. The latest record, by far, is of nestlings in late May (one born about 15–20 May) in a colony near

Matam on Senegal river (G.J. Morel pc[427]).

The clutch is 1–5 with a mode of 3 and a mean varying annually from 2.9 ± 0.1 (n = 78) to 3.1 ± 0.1 (n = 54)[176]. The second egg is laid about 24 hrs after the first, and the third egg a day or sometimes two days after the second (H.Q.P. Crick pc); incubation begins with the first or second egg. If the clutch is accidentally destroyed a replacement clutch is laid in some cases, a few days later. Within a colony all eggs are normally laid within 12 days, but adjacent colonies may vary in mean laying dates by a fortnight.

Both parents (and helpers?) incubate, and roost in the egg-chamber, which is unlined but soon acquires a bed of trodden pellets. The incubation period is 19–21 days (mode 20). A 2-egg clutch takes 17 hours to hatch, a 3-egg clutch 43 hours and a 4-egg clutch 72 hours[176]. Nestling period about 28 days.

SUBSPECIES

(1) *M. b. bullocki* Senegal to Chari river drainage.

(2) *M. b. frenatus* Sudan southeast of 15° N and 25° E and adjacent parts of Zaire, Uganda and Ethiopia. Differs from nominate race in having forehead, broad eyebrow and cheek streak azure blue, not green. Whole forecrown often washed azure.

ADDITIONAL DESCRIPTION

(Nominate race). ADULT ♂, ♀ Upperparts bronzed or golden green and moderately glossy, except that nape is warm buff and 2nd–5th rectrices are strongly ochreous but for tips and edges. Crown and tertials bleach dull blue. Primaries are narrowly dusky-tipped and secondaries broadly (about 14 mm) black-tipped, bordered proximally by a small caerulean blue patch on outer web. Mask black; chin (ie small feathers between rami of mandibles) black and throat scarlet; many individuals have green cheek streak between the black and scarlet, which may be age-related (green in younger birds?). Red throat merges quite sharply into buff breast and belly, which are often green-washed. Flanks and undertail coverts glossy ultramarine blue. Wing lining pale buff; underside of tail (closed) slaty, (open) cinnamon with slaty tips. JUVENILE Like adult but hue of red throat and blue flanks and undertail coverts much less intense. A broad green cheek stripe. BARE PARTS Beak black, inside mouth flesh pink, iris dark brown, legs and feet dark grey, or blackish frosted white, nails dark brown. MOULT[229] Post-juvenile and also post-nuptial moult begin 4–6 weeks after fledging and breeding are over, with centrifugal replacement of primaries and of most secondaries, the outer three or four secondaries being shed centripetally. Inner four primaries moult nearly synchronously, and thereafter outer six ones are replaced one by one, descendently, over a period of two months, so that the aerodynamically important wing tip is never without a good complement of feathers. Outermost rectrix replaced in an otherwise serial centrifugal sequence about same time as second or third innermost feather. WEIGHT Nestlings grow fastest about days 8–12, then rate of weight increase slows to a peak about days 19–23, when some can achieve 34 g. Their weight has fallen somewhat by the time they fledge a week later. Adults average heaviest in February (♂ 26 g, n = 56, unhelped ♀ with oviducal egg 26.5 and helped ♀ with oviducal egg 27.5) and again in wet season, June to September; they become light during incubation (♂ 23, ♀ 22.5) and are lightest in April, at end of breeding season (♂ 23, ♀ 21) (n > 45 for all values). Fresh egg weight 3.8 g[178]. MEASUREMENTS *Beak* to feathers ♂ 30–34, ♀ 28–31[29], to skull ♂ 38.1 (35–41, n = 15), ♀ 36.0 (33–37, n = 10), depth 6.1 (5.8–6.3, n = 10). *Wing* 100 (96–104, n = 20[29]). *Tail* 84–92 (n = 20[29]). *Egg* 17.3 × 20.8 (16.1–18.4 × 19.4–23.5, n = 60[508]). STRUCTURE Plumulaceous part of throat feathers grey; only pennaceous part scarlet, barbs stiff, radiating, open and practically devoid of barbules. Primaries project 3–13 mm beyond tertials in folded wing. P8 longest, p10 40–41 long and 34–35 shorter than p8, p9 2–3, p7 0–1, p6 2–4, p5 12–14, p4 18–20, p3 20–23, p2 23–25, p1 25–26 and s1 26 shorter.

White-fronted Bee-eater   *Merops bullockoides*   (Plate 4)

Merops Bullockoides A. Smith 1834, S. Afr. Quart. Journ. (2), p. 320 (Marico river).
Melittophagus bullockoides, Peters, Check-List Birds World, V, 1945, p. 231.
Merops bulocki bullockoides, White, Revised Check-List Afr. Non-Pass. Birds, 1965,
  p. 234.
Merops bullockoides randorum, Clancey, Durban Mus. Novit., 4, IV, 1953, p. 57.

NOTE White-fronted Bee-eaters are closely related with Red-throated Bee-eaters,
and some authorities have treated them as belonging to the same species (their
ranges do not overlap). I treat them as separate species, because their differences—voice, facial appearance, size—are sufficient to prevent significant inter-
breeding, I predict, were the two populations ever to meet in nature. The natural
history of the White-front is much like that of the Red-throat and the following
account is abbreviated accordingly.

FIELD CHARACTERS
Middle-sized, gregarious, sedentary; in East and southern African
savannas. Length 21.5–23.5 cm (8½–9½ in). Noisy; commonest voices a
not-very-pleasant muffled *gaaa* and a shriller *kwannk*. Forehead dirty
white, crown mealy, nape, breast and belly buff, mask black, chin and
cheeks white, throat silky scarlet, back, wings and tail green (often blued),
vent, under- and uppertail coverts midnight blue. Tail quite long, square,
not streamered. Differs from Red-throat in facial features (Plate 4) and
blue uppertail coverts, also markedly in voice; but only in Uganda where
their ranges approach might there be any problem with identification.
Elsewhere unmistakable. A very rare morph has a yellow, not scarlet,
throat[193].

HABITAT
Dry water-courses, eroded gullies, scrub-covered stony hillsides, bushy
pastures, woodland along seasonal and perennial rivers.

DISTRIBUTION AND STATUS

Map opposite Plate 4. Sedentary or locally migratory, wandering widely outside breeding season. In central Africa birds vacate rivers after nesting and reappear in early winter when annual floods are subsiding[86]. Regionally abundant, but sometimes absent where habitat looks suitable, hence distribution is patchy. Prone to vagrancy. Overall, probably occurs at about the same density as Red-throated Bee-eaters (qv) or perhaps rather less densely. It ranges on Atlantic coast locally from Libreville[256] and Gabon savannas to Cuanza river and is widespread in the interior between Cuanza and lower Cunene river, Angola[565], and across south-central Africa, north to Kasai savannas at Lusambo and south to Okavango river. East of longitude 25° E it has a greater latitudinal range, north in western Rift to Semliki river below Lake Edward and in eastern Rift to Turkwell river, and south as far as Durban (where vagrant). It is absent from plains and savannas around Lake Victoria and from Tanzania (see map) except at mid elevations around Mts Meru and Kilimanjaro (breeding on Ngarenanyuki river[44]) in the northeast and highlands and lowlands in the south of that country (Lake Rukwa, Ruaha National Park, Kilosa, Bagamoyo, Dar-es-Salaam)[79]. In Kenya it is much commoner in Rift Valley highlands at 1,400–2,000 m than elsewhere, and below 1,400 m breeds only on Kerio and Turkwell rivers just southwest of Lake Turkana[79]. In point of fact this eastern Rift population seems to be quite isolated from the main range of the species.

By the western Rift the White-fronted Bee-eater is rare on plateaux of Kivu and Katanga[118] and resident at low elevations in Ruzizi plain in Burundi and extreme southwest Rwanda (J.P. Vande weghe pc). It is local rather than uncommon in southern Tanzania, throughout Zambia, Malaŵi (where it breeds as low as 100 m), Zimbabwe, Botswana south to Lake Ngami and Botletle river[534], southern Mozambique, Transvaal south to 26° (rarely to 27°)[330], and northeastern Natal[127,148]; and on many rivers it is very common (eg Luangwa, Zambezi and Kafue in Zambia[58]).

It is said to emigrate northward after breeding in Zimbabwe, Malaŵi and Zambia and to be a passage migrant in central Katanga, in March (direction?)[147]. Status in northern Mozambique poorly known. More southerly records (Swakopmund[401], Fish river[521], Modder river[141], Durban[235] and Fish Hoek[519A]) and East African coastal ones (Malindi, Bagamoyo, Dar-es-Salaam[79] and Ruvuma river mouth[235]) refer to dispersed, non-breeding birds.

FOOD AND FORAGING

I have examined a large pellet sample from Zimbabwe and smaller samples from Zimbabwe, Zambia and Tanzania (all from adult birds) with 1,200 insects altogether, and the overall proportions of insects in

them were Hymenoptera 87.3%, beetles 6%, bugs and flies 5%, dragon-flies, damselflies, moths, butterflies and grasshoppers <2%. Of Hymen-optera, honeybees comprised more than half and other bees (small sweat-bees and large carpenter-bees) a quarter, the remainder being ichneumon-flies, wasps, scoliids, ants, etc. Cicadas featured in every sample, and odonates included tiny damselflies and large dragonflies. The similarity of food of White-fronted and Red-throated Bee-eaters extends even to the genera of insects they catch (despite geographical separation of the places where I have studied their respective diets): for instance, of six genera of bugs in *M. bullockoides* pellets in southern Africa five were also found in *M. bullocki* pellets in Nigeria (*Acanthomyia, Cletus, Sphaerocoris, Cydnus, Nerthra*).

Foraging behaviour is like the Red-throated Bee-eater, in stable group-defended territories quite distant from nesting and roosting sites, and has been studied intensively in Kenya[290]. Members of the commune or clan (see below) space themselves out within their foraging territory and hunt solitarily, mainly from the lower levels of trees and tall shrubs in bushy grassland and light woods. A bird makes about 300 sallies or feeding-attempts in an 8-hour day, dropping to the ground or momentari-ly hovering close to it <10% of the time and for the remainder hawking and sally-gleaning in equal proportions—hawking is a rapid dash some-times with a convoluted chase, and sally-gleaning is a slower, gliding flight downward towards grass and low herbage with the insect snapped up in a brief hover close to the vegetation[289]. Nearly all sallies are within 15 m radius of the perch and there is a good correlation of increasing prey size (and success rate) with increasing distance of the sally. The overall success rate varies with temperature between 50% in bushy habitats and 70% over grass[289].

During their 32 days in the nest, nestlings reared successfully in an Austrian aviary each consumed in total 625–645 insects (of 275 g fresh weight, 88 g dry weight and 667 kcal)[347]. During the whole nestling period each produced about 54 pellets (in sum 15 g fresh weight, 5.8 g dry weight and 37 kcal). Food consumption declined slightly from a peak about day 17.

VOICE AND BEHAVIOUR

Voice mainly a nasal, muffled *gaaa* or *gaauu* and variants, sometimes faintly rolled or disyllabic—*krrrt, kwani, waaru, karará* etc[403]. Alarm a sharp *waark*. No studies of the voices have been made, but these rather ugly bass calls are each clearly homologous with one of the many Red-throated Bee-eater calls, although the latter species with its treble *wip* sounds so different.

Both have a high-pitched avian-predator alarm. On average a White-fronted Bee-eater sights a potential bird predator (including shrikes and perhaps drongos[189]) at least twice a day; if surprised by an overhead hawk it may flatten itself horizontally on its perch and remain silent until the hawk moves away[289].

SOCIAL ORGANIZATION

Breeding colonies commonly contain 10–20 active nests and, at least in Kenya, sometimes as many as 150[292,577], with up to 450 birds[291]. Sixty percent of breeding pairs have helpers numbering from 1 to 5 in decreasing abundance[190] and recent studies in Kenya have shown that within a colony three or four pairs with their helpers comprise a social commune or clan, quite freely visiting each others' nests but excluding visits by other bee-eaters not belonging to the clan. The species is essentially monogamous and most pairs stay together for life, from time to time having a helper (as opposed to a casual visitor) which is usually either their own previous offspring, or a failed breeder of either sex belonging to the clan. Dissolution of the pair bond sometimes occurs, however, either permanently or just for the one nesting attempt with another mate[190,289].

Every day the clan members leave their nesting cliffs and fly together up

Above and facing page,
starting to dig tunnels

to 7 km to their feeding territory, where the constituent pairs and helpers all have different but largely overlapping foraging ranges. The communal territory is vigorously defended against incursion by all other conspecifics[291].

Helping is not merely a transitory phase in a young bird's life, a stepping-stone to subsequent breeding; but a high proportion of helpers have previously been breeders and most of them own a nest hole and a feeding territory. During its average lifetime of 5–6 years, an individual can change roles between breeding and helping several times[291].

BREEDING

Nests only in perpendicular cliffs (never in flat or sloping ground), often near a Carmine Bee-eater colony. Breeds in the dry season, as Red-throats do, laying in September and early October in South Africa[401] and August–September in Zimbabwe and Zambia[58,377]. Following heavy unseasonal rain in 1982, nestings in Zimbabwe were found, exceptionally, in March and May[377]. In Kenya, with two rather unpredictable rainy

seasons, breeding has been recorded in all months, with a peak in October–February, in the short rains and the following dry season. There is a lesser peak in April–June, in the long rains and into the cool dry season[92]. The typical pattern is that each bird breeds only once a year, either in the short rains or in the long rains (S.T. Emlen pc), but several instances have been documented of a pair nesting again seven months after successful breeding and within two months of unsuccessful breeding[190]. In Zimbabwe the clutch is 2–5 eggs, averaging 3.23 eggs[210], but in Kenya it is smaller and averages 3.06 in helped and 2.54 in unhelped nests[292].

ADDITIONAL DESCRIPTION
Monotypic. (Southern Tanzanian birds were described as racially distinct from South African birds on the basis of four specimens which were slightly darker and larger[125]; three Zaire skins are dark and smaller[125]; to me the differences seem too small to warrant nomenclatural separation.) ADULT ♂, ♀ Forehead white, merging through grey forecrown to warm buff hindcrown and nape; but grey-brown bases show through the white feathers with result that head-top nearly always looks scruffy. Mealy appearance accentuated by forehead and forecrown feathers becoming pointed with wear (as in Somali Bee-eater). Vestiges of a supercilium, whitish above eye and blueish behind it. Cheeks snowy white, sharply defined from black mask and scarlet throat. Chin white, merging into scarlet of throat. Uppertail coverts same deep purplish or midnight blue as vent and undertail coverts. Back, wings and tail a bluer shade of green than in Red-throated Bee-eater, where the green has olive or golden hue. Spread tail uniform green above (central rectrices often blued) and blackish below (*cf* Red-throated Bee-eater, where it is green and ochreous or cinnamon). WEIGHT[78] Non-breeding ♂ 35.8 (34–38, n = 5), significantly heavier than non-breeding ♀ which averages 33.6 (31–35, n = 8); breeding ♀ 34.8 (34–36, n = 3) (Kenya). Unsexed Zambezi birds lighter: 28.8 (25–32, n = 5). MEASUREMENTS *Beak* to skull 40.3 (36–44, n = 15), depth 6.7 (6.1–7.2, n = 10). *Wing* 112.6 (108–117, n = 15). *Tail* 93.0 (86–97, n = 15). *Egg* 18.8 × 22.7 (17.3–20.5 × 20.2–25.0, n = 44[401]). STRUCTURE P8 = p7 longest, p10 43–44 long and 40–46 shorter than p8–7, p9 2–5, p6 1–3, p5 12–14, p4 17–20, p3 20–24, p2 22–27, p1 25–30 and s1 28–32 shorter.

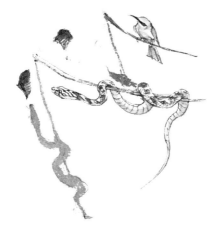

Somali Bee-eater   *Merops revoilii*   (Plate 4)

Merops revoilii Oustalet 1882, in Révoil, Faune et Flore des Pays Çomalis, Oiseaux, p. 5, pl. 1 (Somaliland).

FIELD CHARACTERS

A small bleached-looking bee-eater of desert country in the Horn of Africa. Length 16–17 cm (6½ in) ie barely larger than the Little Bee-eater. Tail not streamered. Crown and back mealy greenish, glossy, nape and mantle buffy, rump kingfisher blue, quills dull blue-green, mask black, throat white, breast and belly fawn and undertail coverts pale blue. Even in freshly moulted plumage this bee-eater never manages to look smart; forehead and crown feathers are sharp-pointed and appear dishevelled and the throat feathers are thin and fluffy; moreover in its harsh thorny desert habitat the plumage quickly bleaches and abrades. Moulting may be more protracted than usual. In the field it often looks leggy, with an attenuated, heat-shedding stance seeming to belie its small size: sits with body high above perch, exposing leg nearly to the knee joint, neck stretched, crown feathers raised and wings held slightly away from the body. Beak rather stout. Wings fulvous in flight. Quiet. In solitary pairs. "Oblivious of the presence of man and utterly confiding"[17].

HABITAT

Open thorn scrub, arid steppe, grassland with scattered bushes and trees, thorn fences around cultivation, the neighbourhood of desert wells, coastal dunes, irrigated terraces, palmeries. Occasionally dense bush, with clearings.

DISTRIBUTION AND STATUS

See map facing Plate 4. Sedentary; evidently extending its range southwards in the early 1970s[371]. The Somali region, from Cape Guardafui (not Socotra) southwest inland of Golis range to lower Omo river and Lake Turkana, avoiding Gulf of Aden coastal plain and staying south and east of Ethiopian highlands above 1,500 m. In Ethiopia common around Hargeisa (1,500 m) and in Webbe Shebeli and Ganale Dorya valleys east of about 41° E, and widespread in eastern part of Ogaden and Haud. Common on eastern plateau of Kenya up to 1,000 m, ranging from Lake Turkana, North Uaso Nyiro river and Wajir District to Tana river (Meru National Park, Garissa) and south to Tsavo East and West National Parks to Galana and Voi river. Occasional even further south, to Dar-es-Salaam, Tanzania (once)[387]. A bird sighted by J.J. Pujals near Biljourshi, Al Baha, in late June 1983, sounds more likely to have been a Somali Bee-eater than the only other possibility, a very young White-throated. If so, it is the first Saudi Arabian record.

Commoner than the Little Bee-eater in the more arid parts of its range, and very numerous in northwestern Somalia[17].

FORAGING

From what I have seen it forages by flycatching like other small bee-eaters, perching at 2–5 m and mainly below 3 m. Feeding situations are like the Little Bee-eater's except that the Somali Bee-eater avoids reed beds[17]. Diet has not been investigated. Feeds actively through hottest part of the day on a variety of small insects; I have not seen it bee-rubbing.

FIELD NOTES

An approachable bird which normally utilizes low perches and behaves more like Little Bee-eaters than any other species[17] (J.S. Ash pc). Voice not recorded. Spends much time scratching (overwing) and preening; also sunbathing with raised mantle feathers. ♂ courtship feeds ♀.

BREEDING

Two pairs nested "in company" in holes dug into the perpendicular sides of a deep well, 1 m below ground level, near Burao, and had nestlings in early June[17]. A nest at Iskushuban, Somalia, was a straight declining burrow 60 cm long in a steep earth mound formed around the roots of a fallen date palm; in late April it contained at least one large nestling (J.S. Ash pc). Adults have been seen collecting food for unseen young at Badweyn in late May, and feeding fledglings near Fanweyn in early October (J.S. Ash pc). In Kenya a nest with young was found at El Wak, 02°49′N 40°56′E, in June 1975 and another in a low bank cut by a road grader in Shaba National Park, 00°20′N 37°45′E, in June 1982 (G.R. Cunningham-van Someren pc).

ADDITIONAL DESCRIPTION

Monotypic. ADULT ♂, ♀ Bases of forehead and crown feathers grey with dark shafts; narrowed tips green-yellow in centre of crown and turquoise to the sides; narrow eyebrow bright blue; mantle buffy green; rump pale azure passing to bright cobalt blue on uppertail coverts. Remiges and rectrices dull green when fresh becoming dull blue or greenish blue with time; grey below. Lacks black trailing edge band of wing of several other bee-eaters, although remiges are obscurely and narrowly dusky-tipped. Upperwing coverts olive, edged blueish. Wing lining very pale buff. White chin and throat have pale blue sheen when viewed carefully in the hand. JUVENILE Not known. BARE PARTS Beak black, iris dark red-brown, legs and feet dark grey or blackish. WEIGHT 13.1 (one bird, J.S. Ash pc). MEASUREMENTS *Beak* to feathers 27.7 (24–31) and to skull 31.8 (28–34, n = 8); depth 4.8 (3.8–5.7, n = 7). *Wing* 76.5 (74–79, n = 8). *Tail* 65.4 (63–72, n = 8). STRUCTURE The pointed forehead and crown feathers are unique among bee-eaters but recall similar ones in the White-fronted Bee-eater; the mutual affinity of those two will be considered in Chapter 3. Primaries extend beyond tertials in folded wing. P8 = p7 longest; p10 25–31 long and 25–30 shorter than p8–7, p9 2–6, p6 1, p5 6–9, p4 11–14, p3 12–15, p2 14–17, p1 16–19 and s1 16–19 shorter.

White-throated Bee-eater   *Merops albicollis*   (Plate 4)

Merops albicollis Vieillot 1817, Nouv. Dict. Hist. Nat., 14, p. 15 (Senegal).
Aerops albicollis maior, Parrot, Orn. Monatsb., 18, 1910, p. 12.

FIELD CHARACTERS

   The boldly pied head makes this species quite unmistakable. The only bee-eater with a black crown, even in the juvenile; made even more conspicuous by the feathers often being raised. Length 20 cm ($7\frac{3}{4}$ in), and streamers that may exceed 12 cm (nearly 5 in)—the longest in the Family. Gregarious and vocal, the voice a melodious trilling like European Bee-eater's. A very conspicuous daytime intratropical migrant in many parts of Africa, between desert-edge breeding grounds and rainforest-zone 'winter' quarters. Creamy throat offset by very broad, oblong gorget; breast apple green, belly white, nape and wings ochreous, back green, tertials, rump and tail blue; wings with black trailing edges.

   This bee-eater is an oddity in several respects; not only the black crown and pied head and sizes of pectoral patch and streamers, but also in some of its feeding habits and its butterfly-flight courtship (qv). The genus *Aerops* was raised for this and Boehm's Bee-eaters on account of their long outer primaries. But the two birds are not closely related, and although the White-throated Bee-eater is atypical in some ways, in others it is not and for the most part, in the field, it typifies the genus *Merops* and I see no compelling reason to remove it therefrom[578].

HABITAT

   In the breeding season sparsely-wooded sub-desert steppe, sandy wastes, wadis and laghs but not associated with flowing water as several other bee-eaters are; arid thorn scrub on Somali maritime plain. On its wintering grounds, large clearings in equatorial and West African forests and a wide variety of habitats at borders of the main forest blocks. Hawks from tops of the largest emergent trees in primary forest; inhabits cut-about forest being opened up by logging, middle-height secondary growth, plantations, gardens and suburbs with large trees as well as grassy open spaces, the edges and perhaps the canopy of narrow gallery-forests in savanna, moist savanna woodland, orchard bush, etc. Migratory flocks pass over and forage in practically all habitats between the desert and forest extremes, most commonly in fairly well bushed and treed places. Typically below 1,400 m altitude and only occasionally as high as 3,000 m[79].

BREEDING DISTRIBUTION AND STATUS

See map facing Plate 4. Highly migratory, and seasonally common throughout most of the breeding and wintering ranges shown on the map. Only 20 years ago White-throated Bee-eater nests were virtually unknown; in the interim they have been reported at some 25 localities— still few in view of the obvious abundance of the species, but the former element of mystery has now disappeared and it is clear that the bird nests abundantly in such uncompromising terrain that few ornithologists come across them. Breeding is in a narrow band of sub-desert steppe along the southern edge of the Sahara, from Senegal to Eritrea, and it is a common breeding bird in the southwest corner of the Arabian peninsula, on the Tihama from about Al Lith (20°10′N 40°17′E) south to Lahej, Aden (M.C. Jennings pc). Nearby in Africa nests have been found near Djibouti and in the Ethiopian Rift, commonly on the west shore of Lake Turkana, and near Olorgesailie and Lake Magadi, Kenya.

MIGRATION AND NON-BREEDING RANGE

At Lake Magadi it has been recorded in all months[79], but north of the Equator it visits its breeding grounds only for the rainy season: Lake Turkana from late February to early September (J. Hopson pc), Eritrea from April to about September[525], central Chad from late May to late September[439], and in northeasternmost Nigeria from late April to October. It migrates with much regularity; for instance at Arada in Chad arrival dates are in the period 11–26 May[439], at Kaduna in Nigeria 'autumn' passage is from 8–27 October to 13–22 November and at other latitudes wintering and spring passage sojourns are equally predictable[186].

Migration appears to be leisurely, but two evidences suggest otherwise. Just before departure from wintering grounds migratory fat is laid down, increasing a bird's weight up to 15%[223]; and on arrival in the north sand-storms kill large numbers—hundreds of corpses were found at Dire

and Goundam in Mali in April (B. Lamarche pc).

The bird spends the non-breeding season in the equatorial and west African rainforest zone, throughout, from Guinea east and south to Congo and Ituri rivers, around and above but not inside the forest. Wintering grounds include forest-savanna mosaic of the 'derived savanna' belt immediately north of the forest, as well as the belt of 'southern Guinea' moist savanna woodlands north of that, so that in Nigeria the northern wintering limit is about 9–10° N[186 (Fig. 48)]. It occurs east to Cape Guardafui but in northeastern Somalia is probably only a passage migrant to and from Yemen. South of the equatorial forest block the bird winters commonly only in the savannas of middle and lower River Congo. It is absent from Kasai and Manyema, south of River Congo in Zaire, and is a rare vagrant in Angola[565]. Birds wintering in Cabinda and at mouth of River Congo are 2,200 km from the nearest breeding region (Lake Chad) and might have to migrate as much as 3,000 km if they nest, say, in Sudan. In East Africa the position is not so clear, because some birds stay to nest in what are otherwise wintering areas. It is found mainly between September and April, in west Kenya principally as a passage migrant from September to November and in February–March. It winters west and east of Lake Victoria, southwest to lower Rusizi plain (and south in Burundi to Giofo, 4° S) and the north end of Lake Tanganyika and southeast to Rufiji river and Kilwa. An old record from Zambia is unacceptable[57]. In southwest Arabia it has been reported in all months from April to September inclusive, and also December and February, so a few probably winter at elevation there.

FOOD AND FORAGING

Feeds by 'flycatching' from perches in general more elevated than those of the foregoing bee-eaters, and prone to make longer sorties. Occasionally takes grounded prey (see below); on its breeding grounds feeds of necessity mainly from low perches, but on its winter grounds forages often very high, from perches at 10–20 to 50–70 m. Members of migrating flocks sometimes appear to be feeding in continuous flight, not bringing their evident prey to a perch for treatment. They gather, sometimes in hundreds, to exploit hatches of flying ants and termites[555]. Sometimes hawks from the ground[135A].

In addition to these typical foraging methods, White-throated Bee-eaters will follow cattle or a vehicle in long grass to feed on flushed insects[145], and they have an extraordinary feeding association with squirrels. In and near the rain-forest a variety of animals feed avidly on the oily, high nutritious outer layers of ripe nuts of oil palms, *Elaeis guineensis*. Tree squirrels like *Funisciurus anerythrus* eat them where they grow in the crown of the palm, tearing off and discarding the orange outer fibrous layer to get at the more succulent mesocarp. As strips of skin fall to the ground they are intercepted by the bee-eaters, which gather excitedly in groups of up to ten, perching on the hanging-down tips of the fronds and flying to snap up a falling strip in the open airspace below, in the manner in which they would catch a bee or dragonfly. This surprising habit was first discovered when I came across orange strips up to 16 mm long in the birds' gizzards[221,223]; only later was it revealed how they got there and shown that when a squirrel feeds in an oil palm the birds quickly gather to exploit the situation, practically to the exclusion of feeding on insects[462].

The 'typical' diet of airborne insects is largely flying ants, in winter quarters in southern Nigeria as well as on passage at the beginning of the rainy season in central Nigeria. In large food samples I found from 35% to 91% ants (overall 56%), and in Ivory Coast flying ants (with some termites) constituted 55% of the 1,400 insects in 50 gizzards[558]—one of which contained over 200 *Crematogaster* ants[555]. Termites are not common-ly eaten, which is surprising because they tend to fly at the same times as ants do, and also because the bee-eaters have an evident predilection for oil-rich foods (and termites are fatty). On nesting grounds on the Nigerian shore of Lake Chad ants still feature importantly but amount to only 17% of insects eaten by the adults; hardly any are fed to the nestlings, which thrive instead mainly on grasshoppers (half of their diet), butterflies and wasps. The rest of the adults' diet, at all seasons, is chiefly hymenopterans and beetles. Of 2,500 prey items which I examined altogether, honeybees formed only 3% and sixty other sorts of hymenopterans (excluding ants) 10% and fifty sorts of beetles 17% (Appendix 7), but in Ivory Coast[558] there were 24% 'other' hymenopterans and 12% beetles. The remainder of the diet is mostly bugs and flies, with a few dragonflies, damselflies, shorthorned grasshoppers, termites, butterflies[216] and ant-lions and—

uniquely among the bee-eaters—small lizards.

Closely watching birds arriving at their nest entrances with food for the young, I have seen lizards about 40 mm long, probably young *Mabuya* skinks, brought on four occasions, although I have never seen one being caught. White-throated Bee-eaters take other prey from the sand surface too—the flightless black tenebrionid beetle *Pimelia*, common on the sand dunes at Lake Chad, and once an ant-lion larva. Rarely, small caterpillars are eaten by adults and also fed to nestlings—but whether taken from the ground, vegetation or the air (suspended on silk threads) I cannot say. Nestlings are fed remarkably large prey items: about half of their diet is short-horned grasshoppers, and they can also engulf an adult ant-lion *Palpares* 70 mm long, a 22 mm carpenter bee *Xylocopa*, or a 36 mm sphecid wasp *Chlorion*, as well as small skinks.

VOICE

Like the voice of European Bee-eater but more treble, and the flight call *prrp, pruik* is reiterated more often and in bouts of longer duration. The effect from a feeding or migrating flock is a pleasant medley of far-carrying sound in which individual calls are lost in an excited babble, starting and ceasing rather abruptly and prolonged for 5–10 sec.

SOCIAL ORGANIZATION

Strongly gregarious out of the breeding season. Breeds in loose colonies, nests tens or even hundreds of metres apart, but in their rather featureless, sandy nesting habitat nearly all birds are in sight and sound contact with their neighbours. Eight nests were clustered at least 30 m apart in an area of 4 hectares[179]. Up to three or perhaps five helpers at a nest, and about 90% of breeding pairs have helpers attached to them: of eleven Nigerian nests one had no helpers, seven had 1, one 2 and two 3 helpers[179]. Thus the co-operative breeding phenomenon is developed to a greater degree than in any other bee-eater. Essentially monogamous; but helpers, which are all or mostly male and probably participate (as Red-throated Bee-eater helpers do) in all breeding functions, also copulate with the female. One bird was noted to be feeding two broods at once[179]. Territoriality and roosting behaviour hardly studied.

SOCIOSEXUAL BEHAVIOUR

Antagonistic behaviours (threats, fighting, appeasement, individual distance) seem much like those of congeners. A greeting, or recognition, ceremony is commonplace and like those of Red-throated or European Bee-eaters: excited trilling calls by both birds when one flies in to perch next to another, accompanied by upright stance, elevated black crown feathers and fanned and vibrated tail, the display subsiding after 2–3 secs.

Mainly in the evening, during the 20 mins when birds are gathering before departure to roost, there are more elaborate displays significantly different from any in other bee-eaters. An aptly-termed 'butterflying' display is a high-winged glide alternating with shallow wing beats, accompanied by vociferous calling. A butterflying bird has a deep-chested appearance. After butterflying it perches next to another with the wings raised, whereupon the already-perched bird usually raises its wings also; both raise the forehead feathers fully, giving a peaked profile (Figure A) and call loudly and excitedly while facing each other; then the wings are folded and with the crest raised even higher an extreme upright stance is adopted with the whole body bobbing up and down from rapid flexing and extending of the legs (Figure B), the birds continuing to call. It sometimes leads into a final phase of courtship which is the direct prelude to coitus, when vertical bobbing alternates with bouts of rubbing the beak against the perch on the partner's near side (Figure C) with a motion very like bee-rubbing. This behaviour starts before bee-eaters have left their wintering grounds, when courtship-feeding is also frequent, and it continues during nesting, latterly without copulation.

A

C   B

BREEDING

Nesting is during the rains, or embraces the rainy season at latitudes where it is ephemeral. Courtship having begun before the pre-breeding migration, nest-excavation starts as soon as the birds arrive on their breeding grounds, ie in May about latitude 15°N or June towards 18°N[363]. Nest holes are always in flat or shelving sand, often in the lee of an isolated tussock, stick, or large-mammal dropping; nests are solitary, or in loose aggregates of up to 250 in the same area year after year (B. Lamarche pc). They are prone to be occluded by blown sand and probably always have to be dug anew each season. Burrows are straight, declining at 20–24° (average of 11 burrows, 23°[179]), with the terminal nest chamber angled horizontally to one side with its floor 38–58 cm below flat ground. Nests are 1–2 m long (mean of six 160 cm, and another six 125 cm, M. Dyer and H. Crick pc). Near the Nigerian shore of Lake Chad the commonest clutch size is six, and 11 half-grown broods numbered from 4 to 7 (average 5.4 young)[179]. In Mali 2 clutches of seven, 17 of six and 17 incomplete clutches of five or four eggs have been found (B. Lamarche pc), and in Sudan clutches of 5 and 6[300]. At Lake Magadi in Kenya usually only two birds fledge[481]. Laying frequency and incubation and nestling periods unknown. After fledging, the young return to the nest on occasion, at least in the next day or two[481].

ADDITIONAL DESCRIPTION

Monotypic. Northeast African and Arabian birds are a little longer-winged (102.7 mm) than West African ones (97.7 mm), a clinal difference with Congo-Uganda-Sudan birds at 100.0 mm[118,506]. Eastern birds are also longer-beaked[215]; they have been separated as *maior*, but it seems best not to recognize any subspecies. ADULT ♂, ♀ Forehead and eyebrow white, yellowish by beak, feathers sometimes tipped blue; crown sooty dark brown, almost black, sometimes faintly scalloped with pale blue tips to rounded feathers. Mask black, cheeks snowy white, chin and throat cream-white or pale yellow. Crown sharply delineated from ochreous nape which blends into gold-green or blue-green mantle and back, and wing-coverts, grading into greyish blue tertials, rump, uppertail coverts and tail. Rectrix shafts dark brown above, streamers black. Black gorget 10–15 mm deep, very narrowly edged pale blue in front and broadly fringed pale blue behind. Breast very pale green, of a shade rare in birds, and flanks ochreous pale green, shading into silky white or off-white belly and white or very pale blue undertail coverts. Remiges strongly ochreous or buff with yellow-brown shafts, and outer webs strongly suffused green. Primary tips dusky, secondary tips black-tipped on both webs, giving a 14 mm black trailing edge band. Wing linings warm buff or pale rufous. Undertail grey, shafts ivory. JUVENILE Like adult but green parts more olive; breast and tertials olive green. Central pair of rectrices dull green-blue, with 15 mm oval patch near ends (which will elongate into the black streamers). Chin and throat pale yellow. All dark contour feathers (ie black, olive-green and blue) narrowly pale-tipped, giving plumage scalloped appearance. BARE PARTS Beak black, iris dull crimson to bright red in adult, brownish red in juvenile, legs and feet light brown. MOULT Post-nuptial moult seems to be deferred, in West African birds, until arrival in the winter quarters. Moult of primaries begins in November but replacement is very slow—half of birds are still replacing outer primaries and body feathers in April and a few in May (such birds may be juveniles, whose complete annual moult is synchronous with adults but starts a little later[558,567]). WEIGHT Ivory Coast[558]: November–February 22.9 (n = 14, all lean) and March–April 24.4 (n = 38, several with migratory fat); Nigeria, July, ♂ 25.9 (24–28, n = 7), and unsexed 22.9 (20.6–25.0, n = 14) (H. Crick and M. Dyer pc); Ethiopia, pre-breeding 24.5 (21.4–31.7, n = 34) (J.S. Ash pc). MEASUREMENTS (all West African) *Beak* to feathers ♂ 26–30, ♀ 25–28, to skull ♂ 33.0 (31–36, n = 15), ♀ 31.3 (30.5–33.7, n = 10). *Wing* ♂ 96–104 (n = 15[29]), ♀ 91–97 (n = 12[29]). *Tail* ♂ 73.6 (65–82, n = 15), ♀ 68.9 (64–74, n = 15), with ♂ streamers up to 122 and ♀ up to 85 longer (n = 200). *Egg* 15 × 21[17]. STRUCTURE Tertials long, primaries project 4 (♂) to 8 mm (♀) beyond them in folded wing; p8 longest, p10 25–29 long and 41.5 (♂) and 39.5 (♀) shorter than p8, p9 1–3, p7 2–4, p6 9–11, p5 16–18 (♂) and 14–17 (♀), p4 19–22, p3 26–28, p2 29–33, p1 31–34 and s1 31–34 shorter.

Butterflying

Little Green Bee-eater   *Merops orientalis*   (Plate 5)

Merops orientalis Latham 1801, Index Orn., Suppl., p. 33 (India = Mahratta).

Merops viridissimus Swainson 1837, Birds West Africa, 2, p. 82 (Senegal).

Philothrus cyanophrys Cabanis and Heine 1860, Mus. Hein., Th. 2, 1859–60, p. 137 (mountains of Qonfudah = Kunfuda = Al Qunfidha).

Merops muscatensis, Sharpe, Ibis, 1886, p. 15 and 165.

Merops ferrugeiceps J. Anderson 1878, Anat. Zool. Res., p. 582 (Upper Burma and Sanda).

Merops viridis birmanus, Neumann, Orn. Monatsb., 18, 1910, p. 80.

Merops viridis cleopatra Nicoll 1910, Bull. Brit. Orn. Cl., 27, p. 11 (Mazghouna, Egypt).

Merops viridis beludschicus Neumann 1910, Orn. Monatsb., 18, p. 80 (Sarbac, Baluchistan).

Merops orientalis najdanus Bates 1935, Bull. Brit. Orn. Cl., 56, p. 9 (Riyadh).

Merops orientalis, Peters, Check-List Birds World, Vol. V, 1945, p. 236: sub-species *viridissimus, cleopatra, cyanophrys, muscatensis, najdanus, beludschicus, orientalis* and *birmanus*.

Merops orientalis ceylonicus, Whistler, Spolia zeylanica, 23, 1944, p. 223.

Merops orientalis flavoviridis Niethammer 1955, Bonn. Zool. Beitr., 6, p. 53 (Archei, Ennedi, Sudan).

(See the NOTE on p. 110 about the confusing former use of the name *Merops viridis* for this species.)

FIELD CHARACTERS

Throughout its vast range from Senegal to Vietnam, much the smallest of the streamer-tailed bee-eaters: <15 g; length 16–18 cm (6–7 in), plus streamers varying geographically up to 10 cm. Bronzed or golden green, the races varying greatly in colour of throat (green, yellow, azure, caerulean) and crown and nape (grass, golden or olive green, or rufous) (Plate 5). A black gorget, wide in some races but a narrow band in others; black trailing edge band in wing.

A tame and confiding, solitary or quite gregarious 'flycatching' bee-eater of arid habitats in Africa and the Middle East, and pasture and bushy countryside in Sri Lanka and Burma. Voice a quiet buzzing trill. Juvenile separable from juvenile Little Bee-eater by plainer, pallid green underside and absence of rufous in tail; but best distinguished by accompanying adults. Boehm's Bee-eater is similar to the Little Green but is southern tropical.

HABITAT

In northern tropics of Africa sub-desert woodland far from water, with scattered trees or small shrubs, where soil is mainly bare, often sand; commonly in wadis. Ranges into less xeric vegetation in Sahel zone: quite dense woods of *Acacia*, *Commiphora* and *Leptadenia* with open spaces and a nearly continuous ground cover of grasses like *Cenchrus*, *Chrysopogon* and *Aristida* up to 1 m tall; around date palm groves; sandy vales with scattered doum palms; thickets and thorn hedges around crops; lakeside sedge sward; land grazed bare but for islands of green *Salvadora* and *Lantana* shrubs; and spacious gardens around townships where the dominant vegetation may be exotic (exotic trees such as *Azadirachta* and *Eucalyptus* are used for roosting). Uses similar habitats in Middle East: open country interspersed with light forest and cultivation, up to 1,500 m in Himalayas and 2,000 m in Nilgiris, and at the coast shows a marked preference for sandy zone above high tide mark[6]. In India and Burma widespread and common in open cultivated country, nesting in banks by roads, canals and ravines; shelving sandy river banks, and in sand hillocks in desert lands[26].

DISTRIBUTION AND STATUS

See map facing Plate 5. Mainly sedentary. In Africa, the dry woodland zone from Senegal to Darfur mainly between 12° and 16° N and only exceptionally south of 10° N (except in Cameroun, where it occurs south to $8\frac{1}{2}$° N[378]) or north of 18° N. In Mali it has occurred south of 12° N (at Kangaba—and there are dry-season records south in Ivory Coast nearly to 9° N[93]) and a few nest south of 14° N (Markala, Ké Macina), but main breeding latitudes are 15°–17° N; post-breeding dispersal takes a few birds into Adrar des Ifoghas region, north to 20°10′N (B. Lamarche pc). East of longitude of Darfur, it occurs from northernmost Uganda and Kenya, where it is a scarce non-breeding winter visitor[79,146,187], through Sudan and Eritrea (north of 15°N confined to oases, Nile valley, and Red Sea coastal plain) to Egypt, where found discontinuously along Nile but not in more distant oases[419]. Common over most of African range. Breeds commonly on the Nile between Luxor and Helwan and at Cairo but not certainly north of Benha in central delta. Common on Suez Canal, lower Nile, and in Faiyum in winter, occurring south to Lake Nasser, where small flocks roam widely[405,515]. Absent from Sinai. In Israel it is a common breeding resident in *Acacia tortilis* woodland in the length of the Rift Valley from Gulf of Aqaba nearly to Dead Sea (eg common at Yotvata, 29°52′N and Hazeva, 30°46′N; D.H. Thomas pc); formerly it was rare, and its increase may be a consequence of agricultural development in the region (A. Zahavi, pc). Recorded from Wadi Sawawin (27°22′N 36°15′E) in Saudi Arabia in November, December and January[323] (M.C. Jennings pc), and perhaps they are winter visitors rather than breeders there. Elsewhere in Arabia, resident from about Medina south to Yemen and Aden; near south coast sporadically from Mukalla to Muscat and Oman; in United Arab Emirates a fairly common resident in and around the mountains and also near Dubai[97]; and in the desertic interior around Riyadh. It is common within 100 km of Riyadh and in acacia country east of it to Tuwaiq escarpment, and is sedentary or partially migratory[323] (M.C. Jennings pc). Around the north of Persian Gulf, probably southeast Iraq[561], and in Khuzestan north to 32°N; lower elevations of Zagros Mts east to Kerman, and in coastal plain from Persian Gulf[307] to Makran coast and Quetta valley (Baluchistan) and the whole of the Indian peninsula from Punjab and lower elevations in Nepal, Sikkim, Bhutan and Assam to Sri Lanka, Bangladesh, and plains and lowlands of Burma[6,536]. Also Yunnan, the Shan States and the whole of Indochina, except Tonkin and the Malay Peninsula south of Koh Lak.

Markedly seasonal in the Indian subregion, withdrawing from northern areas in winter and from wet areas during the monsoon. Subject also to altitudinal movements.

FOOD AND FORAGING

Some 400 insects from pellets which I collected at Lake Chad comprised 75% Hymenoptera of >50 species. Flying ants were most numerous, then halictine bees. They and ichneumon-flies, chalcidid, scolioid, vespid, pompilid and sphecid wasp species were small, but a few honeybees *A. mellifera* and similarly large hymenopterans were taken too. Beetles were 17% of the sample and the remaining 8% were termites, assassin-bugs, squash bugs, shield-bugs, Microlepidoptera, and flies of at least six families ranging in size from tiny fruit-flies (*Drosophila*) to robber-flies and clegs. At Lake Chad the most abundantly eaten beetle was a bruchid, *Spermophagus*, and like its congeners the Little Green Bee-eater doubtless hunts opportunistically, catching whatever suitable insects that pass.

In the Orient dragonflies are commonly taken, like the large *Crocothemis servillea*, and in bee-keeping districts of the Indian subcontinent so are honeybees. Eight-hundred and fifty birds killed in a study by apiculturists in Pakistan in 1950[367] contained up to 31 *Apis cerana* and an average of 3.45 each (I expect that they were killed at apiaries, so these values will be unrepresentative of the year-round diet). In Burma the formidable Rock Honeybee *A. dorsata* is eaten[536]. Of 300 insects recovered from gizzards in a turn-of-the-century Indian study[393] about one-third was *A. cerana* and one-third *A. florea*; in sequence of decreasing abundance the remainder was beetles (*Gymnopleurus, Onthophagus, Myllocerus, Tetragonoderus* and other carabids, *Balaninus* and other weevils, aphodiids, *Coccinella* and other chrysomeloids, etc), other hymenopterans (*Chrotogonus, Chrysis, Tiphia, Camponotus, Sphex lobatus, Polistes hebraeus, Vespa orientalis, Halictus*), flies, noctuid and pyralid moths and the nymphalid butterfly *Melanitis ismene*, crickets, a dragonfly and a spider. In cotton fields a good many Cotton Leaf Roller Moths *Sylepta derogata* are eaten, and their caterpillars plucked from cotton by bee-eaters in flight[309], which must redeem the bird somewhat in agriculturists' eyes.

Usually hunts low down, making sallies from a fence, post, shrub or grass stem; but prey is always snatched in flight, never from the ground. Forages from backs of grazing cattle in India[6]; also from telegraph wires. From the perch it makes a rapid pursuit of a passing insect, either a fast glide or a short flapping flight following twists and turns of the prey. The capture is made with an audible snap of the beak and the bird glides in an arc back to its perch, where small items are swallowed immediately and large ones are immobilized and sometimes dismembered by being beaten against the perch. In short, it feeds like other small bee-eaters and in particular like the Little Bee-eater.

VOICE

A pleasant quiet monotonous trill *trrr trrr trrr trrr* with a buzzing quality; *trrr* is a high frequency roll, repeated 4 times per sec. A staccato *ti-ic* or *ti-ti-ti*, without rolling quality of the *tree* note, is probably the alarm. The *tree* note is uttered perched and flying, throughout the day but mainly in gregarious situations: assembly at roosts is accompanied by much excited trilling as birds bicker and supplant each other at coveted perches[6].

BEHAVIOUR

Lives year-round in pairs or small, loose-knit flocks; more gregarious in the Orient than in Africa. In Africa they breed as solitary pairs evenly distributed along wadis, canal banks and other linear habitats. Localization of nesting sites can lead to aggregation of pairs which are then semi-colonial. In India and Burma breeding colonies are well-defined, with up to 30 pairs or more.

Evidently monogamous; helpers at the nest have not been reported, although little systematic study has been made. A pair has a home range of <5 hectares, weakly defended at all seasons.

What little is known about its courtship and sexual behaviour is like Red-throated Bee-eaters. Roosting at night is in the nest or (at any season) in leafy trees. Birds assemble at communal roost site in pairs or small flocks about sunset, earlier when cloudy, later when fine, and before light fails groups make noisy flights high into the sky, quickly returning to roost where they sleep huddled shoulder to shoulder[35]. Departure from roost is 30 mins before sunrise, in groups of 5–30 birds, which disperse to feed not much further than 2 km away[35]. Congregates in parties up to 20 to dust-bathe on earth roads in evening[530]. Said to enjoy bathing in rain, crouching on a telegraph wire "turning and twisting from side to side"[252A].

BREEDING

Nest burrows are dug into flat or gently sloping bare ground of firm soil, the surface often dusty or sandy. The edges of wadis are a typical African situation; in India they often use vertical surfaces: half-metre high banks of drainage ditches and borrow pits, river banks and earth cliffs of ravines*. The burrow slopes evenly downward at 20°–30° declination, is 5–6 cm wide and 50–100 cm long in hard soil or up to 200 cm long in soft soil. The terminal egg chamber is about 15 cm long, 12 cm wide and 9 cm high. Near the nest are several abandoned, half-excavated 'false-start' tunnels. Usually, new tunnels are dug each breeding season, but sometimes old ones are used again[26]. Often breeds solitarily, sometimes in loose colonies with nests 10–100 m apart and, particularly in Pakistan and in Burma, colonies of 10–30 pairs occur with all nests close together[26]. Both sexes participate in digging and providing for the young, but the female incubates more than the male.

The breeding season in northern tropics of Africa starts in February–April. Incubation and nestling periods are unknown, but nestlings have been recorded from late April to late May, and flying young from May to July. From Senegal to Eritrea laying is therefore in the mid or latter part of the hot dry season, and fledging about the time of the first rains or before them. In Egypt laying is from early April and in Arabia somewhat later[406]. All over India egg-laying is from mid-March to May and occasionally early June[26]; in Sri Lanka early June is the main time, May common, late April and early August exceptional[464]. Single brooded. Clutch (in India) 4–8, mode 6[26].

SUBSPECIES

(1) *M. o. viridissimus* Senegal to Eritrea through Sahel and soudanian savanna zones; north on the Nile to Khartoum and (once) Gebel Elba (Egypt)[405]; south to about 8° N (Upper Nile Province, Sudan). Crown and throat bronze-green, uniform with body; black gorget a band about 5 mm deep; streamers up to 96 mm longer than tail.

(2) *M. o. flavoviridis* Sub-desert steppe, mainly north of *viridissimus*, from

---

* Baker added a picturesque and a dangerous site: "a mud bank about a foot high, made to mark the limits of a badminton court in the Artillery Mess compound" and "the front of a butt of a rifle-range at Allahabad, where the bullets constantly struck the bank close to their burrows"[26].

Ennedi massif (Tchad) to Red Sea coast of Sudan[233]. Throat mustard-yellow. This race requires validation[233,578], and C. S. Roselaar considers that yellow-throated birds are merely *viridissimus* in very fresh plumage.

(3) *M. o. cleopatra* Dead Sea Valley; Nile valley from Lake Nasser (about Wadi Halfa) to Cairo and the delta; south in winter (probably this race) to northern Uganda. Like *viridissimus* but purer green, less bronzed; streamers up to 86 mm.

(4) *M. o. cyanophrys* Arabia, on Red Sea coastal plains and immediate hinterland from about Medina through Asir and Yemen to Aden; at Mukalla and Tarim on Gulf of Aden and in the east at Muscat and sparsely throughout Oman. Forehead and eyebrow azure blue and chin and throat caerulean blue; black gorget wider and less clearly defined than in other races, blending through purple-blue (hue depending on angle of view) with blue of throat; breast and belly washed blue; crown green washed olive and nape slightly more rufescent; remaining upper-parts bluer green, less golden-hued, than *viridissimus*; streamers short (maximum 23 mm). Southern Arabian birds (Yemen to Oman) have been separated as *muscatensis* but that race is not tenable[578].

(5) *M. o. najdanus* The desertic central Arabian plateau (Wadi Rima, Riyadh, Kharj, Rub'ayina, Khafs). Like *cyanophrys* but paler, less blue-washed; streamers up to 27 mm.

(6) *M. o. beludschicus* From north end of Persian Gulf to Baluchistan, the Indus, Sind, Punjab and western Rajasthan. Forehead and eyebrow green, crown and nape golden green, chin and throat pastel blue shading to green in front of gorget which is a transverse streak merely 1–2 mm deep, sides of throat azure blue next to black mask, rest of plumage green or pale green; streamers up to 60 mm.

(7) *M. o. orientalis* East of *beludschicus* from Rann of Kutch[5] and eastward throughout India (intergrading in Assam with the following race), Sri Lanka and Bangladesh, commonest in dry country. Not well differentiated from *beludschicus*, darker, less golden green[392]; streamers up to 71 mm. The Sri Lanka population has been separated as *ceylonicus* but is too poorly differentiated to recognize[578].

(8) *M. o. ferrugeiceps* (the proper name for the race also called *birmanus*[578]) Assam[392] and Burma to Viet Nam[597]. Forehead, crown, nape and mantle rufous with a few green feathers, eyebrow green; azure cheeks or stripe at side of throat bordering mask; chin, throat, belly and undertail coverts pale green, sides of neck and breast green suffused with brown; back, wings and tail grass green; streamers up to 63 mm.

ADDITIONAL DESCRIPTION

(*M. o. viridissimus*) ADULT ♂, ♀ Uniform bronzed or golden green. Usually a few azure blue feathers at sides of throat, next to mask. Throat and upper breast sometimes with yellow wash or a few yellow feathers. Tertials fade blueish. Remiges ochreous, outer webs washed and edged green and tips broadly blackish. ♂ has brighter throat and slightly broader gorget than ♀[252A]. JUVENILE (All races) Late nestlings and fledglings are pallid versions of adults lacking a gorget; all feathers are pale tipped, giving plumage a barely-discernible scalloped appearance; mask dusky rather than black; breast pale green, belly almost white; gorget begins to show during post-juvenile moult and at first appearance may be transitorily blue rather than black. Occasional juveniles of every race have mustard-yellow or yellowish-green throats. BARE PARTS Beak black, mouth pink, iris crimson, legs and feet dark grey or black, frosted white. MOULT Tail feathers moult from two foci as in other bee-eaters, in the sequence 1, 6, 3, 2, 4, 5[392]. WEIGHT Single examples: 14.5 (Lake Chad), 15, 18 (India), 17 (Sri Lanka), 18–20 (n = 4, Sind, plus a female with oviducal egg at 27 g)[6]. MEASUREMENTS (*M. o. orientalis*) *Beak* to skull 28–33 (n = 52) and to nostrils ♂ 23.2 (20–25, n = 25) and ♀ 22.6 (19–26, n = 27). *Wing* ♂ 93.6 (89–97, n = 20), ♀ 91.4 (89–95, n = 22). *Tail* ♂ 71.2 (68–74, n = 19) and ♀ 70.4 (65–74, n = 24)[392], excluding streamers up to 72 mm long in ♂ (probably shorter in ♀). *Egg* 17.3 × 19.3 (15.8–18.0 × 17.6–21.4, n = 100)[26]. STRUCTURE Primaries project 10 mm beyond tertials in folded wing. P9 = p8 longest, p10 13–14 long and 50–58 shorter than p9, p7 4–7, p6 14–15, p5 20–21, p4 25–26, p3 29–30, p2 31–32, p1 34 and s1 34 shorter.

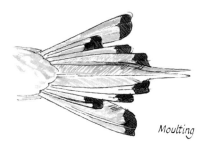

Moulting

Boehm's Bee-eater   *Merops boehmi*   (Plate 5)

Merops (Melittophagus) boehmi Reichenow 1882, Orn. Centralsbl., 7–8, p. 62 (Bumi, Kilosa, Tanzania).
Aerops boehmi, Peters, Check-List Birds World, Vol. V, 1945, p. 233.

FIELD CHARACTERS
A small, unobtrusive green bee-eater, not gregarious, in all plumages with cinnamon forehead, crown and nape and warm ochreous chin, throat and upper breast, separated from the black eye mask by a powder-blue line. Length 15½–17 cm (6–6½ in), excluding tail streamers up to 7 cm long in adult males. Tail, except streamers, broadly black-tipped. Eye red. A sedentary, quiet, thin-voiced 'flycatcher' found in pairs in woods and open undergrowth. Juvenile like streamerless adult.

HABITAT
Glades and open rides in leafy woods. Likes park-like woods with large shade trees separated by patches of short grass sward, often with nearby thorny scrub or thickets with lianes; also riparian forest. Sometimes on burnt-over ground and in small hedged and wooded fields. Nests in flat ground, at side of path or edge of sandy clearing, and feeds from overhanging thin leafless branch.

DISTRIBUTION AND STATUS
Map opposite Plate 5. Sedentary. Probably commonest in low-lying land around Lake Malaŵi and in the even lower Shire valley. From there south to lower Zambezi downstream of about 33° E and south through Manica e Sofala District of Mozambique as far as Revue river (tributary to Buzi river), and from northern Malaŵi eastward across southeastern Tanzania along Ruvuma river north to Uluguru lowlands, Kilosa and lowlands between East and West Usambaras, and near Indian Ocean seaboard from Lindi to Pugu Hills[79]. Occurs up to 900 m altitude in

Malaŵi[312]. To the west, what seems to be a separate population is found between 900 m and 1,400 m from Lake Rukwa and lower Lake Tanganyika (north to near Uvinza, Kigoma on the eastern littoral and to Lake Suse, Marungu on the western) to Lake Mweru and its western hinterland and Lake Retenue in Zaire, in Zambia to East Lunga river at 13°00'S and upper and middle Kafue valley[58]. Has been recorded on upper Zambezi from near Livingstone, but not yet certainly in Zimbabwe[312]. The bird is absent from the Luangwa and its drainage, and the two populations have their nearest approach 400 km apart at Mbesuma[314] (10°02'S 32°04'E) in Zambia and Bana, Nkhotakota (12°24'S on west shore of Lake Malaŵi).

In most of its range Boehm's Bee-eater is uncommon, although perhaps rather less so in southeastern Tanzania. Locally it may be quite common, as at Lake Suse in Zaire at 1,175 m[118], formerly around Ndola, Zambia, and evidently in places in lower Zambezi and Shire valleys[281]. Common in Lengwe National Park, Malaŵi, where there may be hundreds of pairs in a small part of its area of 117 km². Elsewhere it is unaccountably absent from many localities which look quite suitable.

FOOD AND FORAGING

Fifty pellets from adults, collected on Lufupa and Shishamba rivers in Zambia in October, contained nearly 300 insects in the proportions: honeybees *Apis mellifera* 19.6%, 5–9 other bee genera 16.3%, 13 other hymenopteran families 42.8%, flies 17.3%, and beetles, grasshoppers, butterflies, cicadas and other bugs 4.0%. One pellet from Lengwe, Malaŵi, had 12 honeybees and a pteromalid (Hymenoptera). I saw an adult catch a 3-cm stick insect. Noteworthy are the high incidence of flies (Diptera) and the occurrence in one pellet of soldiers of the driver-ant *Dorylus*, which are flightless and do not climb vegetation and so must have been taken from the ground.

Feeds by hawking in short forays, keeping watch typically from a long horizontal twig over clear airspace, 2–3 m above ground in dappled shade. Chases passing insect in 5–12 m sally through the trees or into and around canopy or in swoop very low over the ground. Does not perch on grass stems, and seldom perches higher than 7 m. Bouts of active feeding alternate with long periods of inactivity, the bird perching in dappled shade and either sitting stolidly, or looking alertly at passing insects although not giving chase. Beats and rubs bees in manner of other bee-eaters.

VOICE

Fairly vocal but voice very quiet. Most expressions very like Little Bee-eater's, and since the two often occur near each other their voices have to be distinguished with care by the observer. A common monosyllabic *sip* seems to be a contact call; sometimes more definite and nearly disyllabic. Can be repeated and elaborated into a song of about 1.5 sec duration, a quieter version of the Little Bee-eater's *siddle-iddle-ip, d'jeee*, given eg by male emerging from nest hole after bout of excavation and finding female perched nearby. Usual greeting uttered by perched bird when its mate arrives is a dry, rolling *drreee* given with tail half opened and violently quivered.

BEHAVIOUR

Monogamous; helpers unknown. Pairs nest solitarily although I have found two pairs' nests only 16 m apart; up to five holes have been found clustered along 25 m of a sandy pathway (D.B. Hanmer pc), although that does not necessarily mean as many as five pairs. By day (at least shortly before breeding) the pair stays in a small area of 100–1,000 m² nearly all the time, roosting at night in the nest or in trees a few hundred metres away. Courtship feeding not accompanied by calling and seems rather half-hearted; sometimes male arrives with food item for female but then eats it himself. Copulation is preceded by courtship feeding. Sun-bathes with mantle feathers raised. Rather inactive, spending much time perched in shade doing nothing except irregularly wagging tail up and down through 1 cm arc.

BREEDING

In Zambia lays in September (once August) and in Malaŵi in September and October (two clutch records each) with a further 15 pairs close to laying in mid and late September. Nest burrows are in part-shaded and well-drained sandy soil, usually bare except for dead leaves, the ground perfectly flat or sometimes gently sloping (once in the steep side of a hoed ridge in a cassava patch), the entrance in a barely-perceptible low hump. Adjacent false starts are rather uncommon. Both sexes dig. Fifteen evidently completed holes were from 75 to 103 cm long, more or less straight and gently declining. Clutch 2–4. Incubation and nestling periods unknown.

ADDITIONAL DESCRIPTION

Monotypic. ADULT ♂, ♀ Except for head and breast, green, uniformly on mantle, back, rump, and upper surfaces of wings and tail (tips and edges of these feathers bleach blue with time since previous moult); lower breast golden green and flanks and belly apple green or pale blue-green, with undertail coverts powder blue with green wash. Underside of wings warm buff with grey flight feathers; underside of tail steely grey. Trailing edge of wing with rather indistinct blackish border 3 mm deep; rectrices (except central pair) with 1 mm grey tip and 5–6 mm black subterminal bar; shafts dark brown above and straw below. Tail streamers of ♂ average longer than those of ♀[281]. JUVENILE Yellow ochre throat and breast are suffused with green; otherwise plumage like adult, more so than in any other bee-eater species. BARE PARTS Beak black, iris crimson-red in adult and dark brown in juvenile, legs and feet light brown. WEIGHT 16.6 g overall, monthly means varying from 16.4 to 17.8 g (14.4–19.5, n = 50[281]); males are probably heavier by 1.1 g than females[281]. MEASUREMENTS[281] *Beak* to feathers 29.9 (25–31, n = 48)[281], ♂ 31.0 (28–34, n = 17) and ♀ 30.7 (26–34, n = 14)[314]. *Wing* ♂ 80.8 (78–83, n = 21), ♀ 79.3 (77–82, n = 17)[314]. *Tail* 65.7 (63–69) without streamers and 115–156 (n = 93)[281,314] with them; longest streamer, 70 mm. *Egg* 15.0–15.2 × 18.0–19.0[401]. STRUCTURE Except when very worn, streamer feathers of tail are markedly spatulate-tipped; tip is 0.7 mm wider than rest of pin portion of feather. Primaries project 3–8 mm beyond tertials in folded wing. P8 longest, p10 27–32 long and 26–31 shorter than p8, p9 3–6, p7 0–1, p6 2–3, p5 9–10, p4 14–16, p3 17–18, p2 18–20, p1 19–22 and s1 19–22 shorter.

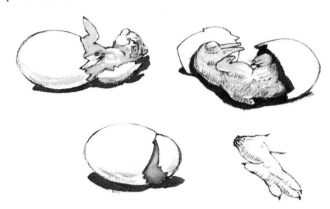

Blue-throated Bee-eater   *Merops viridis*   (Plate 7)

Merops viridis Linnaeus 1758, Syst. Nat., ed. 10, 1, p. 117 (Java).
Merops americanus P. L. S. Müller 1776, Natursyst., Suppl., p. 95 ('Isle de France', error; = Philippine Islands).
(Strictly, Linnaeus' 1758 name *Merops viridis*, for material referred to Java and also to Bengal, is indeterminable. Many early authors applied it to the Little Green Bee-eater (see p. 98) and E. C. S. Baker[26] thought that it may have applied also to the juvenile Bay-headed Bee-eater. Contemporary use restricts it to the Blue-throated Bee-eater.)

NOTE In Philippines called the Chestnut-headed Bee-eater[156]. But if that name is not too entrenched there I would recommend that 'Green-throated Bee-eater' be adopted instead (the Philippines race being green-, not blue-throated), to avoid confusion with *Merops leschenaulti*, qv.

FIELD CHARACTERS
The brilliant pale blue rump serves to distinguish it from all other bee-eaters except the smaller Bay-headed. A middle-sized, dashing, long-winged, gregarious bird with dark chestnut crown and mantle, blue or green throat, no pectoral gorget, green wings and streamered blue tail. Length 20–23 cm (8–9 in) excluding streamers up to 9 cm (3½ in). Readily told from other southeast Asiatic forms, the Bay-headed and Blue-tailed Bee-eaters by throat colour and Little Green by rump colour. Juvenile plumage is distinctive: head-top, mantle and wings are uniform dark green, rump blue-white, tail blue; chin buffy, throat blue or green, breast apple green shading to blue-white belly and undertail coverts. But for its rump, the juvenile might be confused with juvenile and adult Blue-tailed Bee-eater.

Behavioural characters are like Blue-tailed Bee-eater's; colony sites and non-breeding habitats much the same as that species, voice similar, and also dragonflies feature prominently in diet.

HABITAT

In Malaysia breeding birds inhabit beach scrub, pasture, suburban gardens, tin-tailings, sandy clearings and riversides in the lowlands; but wintering birds occur in forest and forest clearings up to 670 m altitude and also in mangroves[402].

DISTRIBUTION AND STATUS

Map opposite Plate 7. Migratory, at least in part. A summer visitor to Yunnan, Kwangsi-Chuang, Kwangtung and Fukien Provinces in southern China, north to about 25° N in Yunnan, 27° N in Kiangsi and 29° N in Chekiang Provinces[197], breeding in Hainan but absent from Taiwan and Hong Kong, where not even a vagrant has been recorded (unexpectedly, since it evidently breeds immediately to the north). Occurs as a breeding species throughout Indochina, but apparently local and not yet recorded from north nor south Laos[335]. In Thailand occurs mainly east of 101° E; absent from northwest and central areas but common in peninsular Thailand[335]. Absent from Burma. Breeds throughout peninsular Malaysia, where colonies exist in Narathiwat, Kelantan, Penang, Perak, Trengganu, Pahang, Selangor, Negri Sembilan and Malacca provinces, also in Singapore, some small, others of several thousand birds[402]. Found throughout Sumatra and Java and has occurred on Nias, Bangka, Beliton, North Natuna and Karimata Islands, although not necessarily breeding there. Occurs widely in Borneo as a breeding bird and winter visitor, with coastal and lowland nesting colonies at Seria, Bangawan, Kimanis and elsewhere[537]. A different form, *americanus*, with a green rather than a blue throat, is resident throughout the Philippine Islands including Palawan, Basilan and Sulu Archipelago (M.D. Bruce pc).

MIGRATION

Presumably Philippine birds, which are taxonomically distinct, are sedentary there, and the same applies to Sumatra and Java residents, which have a lesser claim to taxonomic distinction. Mainland birds are, however, substantially migratory. In Malay peninsula, breeding grounds on the coastal plains are vacated by early September, and southbound flocks can be seen moving over open lowlands of Selangor from late July through August and September exceptionally until late October, crossing Malacca Straits from Cape Rachado to Sumatra mainly in mid August[402]. In spring, landfalls at Cape Rachado have been observed in February and at Port Dickson in mid April, and flocks migrating north over coastal plains from early March to early April[402].

Inland, there is an influx into forest at all elevations in Malay peninsula in September and October, the birds remaining in and over forest until about April, with northbound migrants being seen at considerable elevation at Fraser's Hill and Cameron Highlands in mid April and early May[402] (D.R. Wells pc). Probably most of this wintering population is from Thailand and China; but juveniles in primary forest southeast of Kuala Lumpur in late June (D.R. Wells pc) must have been of Malayan origin. It is not clear where the northern wintering limit lies; some in Sriracha, Thailand, in October, may have been wintering there[483].

FOOD AND FORAGING

Blue-throated Bee-eaters have the dashing pursuit flight of all of the long-winged species. They feed from tall trees, telephone wires and power lines, making a fast sally after a passing, near or distant insect and returning with a larger capture to perch in order to immobilize or devenom it; they also hunt in continuous flight aloft, often in large flocks, hawking for such insects as termites which are evidently swallowed at once. Flocks are said to travel ahead of swift-moving tropical storms[263] and they probably exploit insects which are undoubtedly carried up on turbulent air. They gather at jungle fires to feed on fleeing insects, and congregate at termite and flying ant hatches.

Hunting birds usually perch quite high in vegetation, at 7 m or higher, although a pursuit sally may take them close to the ground. Feeding by hovering at tall grass stems to pick off winged ants and termites crawling up the stems preparatory to flighting[537] must be exceptional. Blue-throated Bee-eaters were also seen "hopping over the lawn picking the same insects (winged termites and ants) from the close turf"[537] which is even more unexpected. If that behaviour were in the evening another, more likely, interpretation would be that they were not feeding but obtaining grit.

Birds with nestlings on the point of fledging which I watched at the large Padang Kemunting colony on Penang Island, Malaysia, fed over and along the edge of swampy gallery forest adjacent to white sand ridges where the colony is situated. Ninety percent of insects brought to the nest were large dragonflies and 10% small beetles and hymenopterans; the adults themselves ate non-odonates, including small bees devenomed by rubbing and beating in typical manner. Ringing recoveries showed that adults foraged up to 24 km away from a nesting colony at Sungei Buloh, Malaysia, apparently on daily flights[398].

A small sample of adult pellets and insect débris collected from Penang nests contained a majority of hymenopterans (*Apis cerana*, *Trigona* sp., *Xylocopa* sp., *Vespa affinis indosinensis*, the large *Chlorion lobatum*, and several species of scoliids) and a minority of odonates, bugs and beetles (scarabs

Glycyphana parvula and *Onitis* sp., chafer *Lepidiota* sp., buprestid *Belionota ?prasina* and weevil *Hypomeces squamosus*). Some hymenopterans were large, but scarabs and chafers, which were numerous, were even larger, about 42 mm long, and probably out-weighed the sum of Hymenoptera.

Another small pellet sample, from Province Wellesley, Malaysia, in May, consisted mainly of dragonflies (58% by weight of material identified), also Hymenoptera (35%) and beetles (7%), and there were traces of flies and vertebrate bones[24] which I presume were of lizards. Fishing by bee-eaters for surface fry at a fish hatchery in Sumatra has been described[109], and the birds concerned would have been Blue-tailed or Blue-throated. The latter has been observed to dive onto water "to pick off small stick-like insects"[537].

VOICE

Vocal, the voice like that of Blue-tailed Bee-eater, and an almost continuous, pleasant trilling emanates from a large foraging or roosting flock. The commonest call is a fast roll of about $\frac{1}{3}$ sec duration, repeated irregularly 1–3 times within 1–2 sec—*ija-ija-ija* (the *j* soft and rolled). High intensity flight call *prrrp* six times in 2 sec; at a distance it sounds more like *yeeg*. The Malay name *běrek-běrek* is onomatopoeic. Alarm, a sharp *chip*.

Adults bringing food to the nest usually perch nearby for a minute or so, calling from time to time, whereupon the nestling immediately responds with *jew-i, jew-i, jew-i* (the *j* very soft), a begging call also made by the fledgling.

BEHAVIOUR

Little is known about Blue-throated Bee-eaters other than the findings of D. M. Bryant and C. J. Hails, who recently studied the species' energetics in Malaysia[94B, pc]. Reproductive, roosting, body care and other behaviours are the same as those of Blue-tailed and Blue-cheeked Bee-eaters. Bryant and Hails (pc) found no evidence of helpers at a colony near Kuala Lumpur, although on Penang Island I was fairly sure, observing unmarked birds, that some nests were being visited each by more than two adults.

At their breeding colony adults spent 11.4 h at night roosting; by day they spent 21% of the time flying, 71% perching, and the remainder at the nest, preening, sunbathing and water-bathing (Bryant and Hails pc).

On one occasion a brood of four fledglings was led by the parents to roost in their nest hole for at least ten successive nights, the parents themselves departing to sleep elsewhere[416]. In hot, still weather flying birds sometimes trail their legs to shed heat[94A].

BREEDING

Occasionally nests are solitary, but large colonies are the norm; the Penang colony used to number some 900 birds. Nests are dug in sandy soil, within 1 m of each other in flat ground, coastal dunes and sloping beaches only 6 m above the tide-line, flat sandbanks on river islets and in dried-out water-courses[383], or closer together in the less common sites of steep slopes and high banks. Burrows are 1–1.5 m long, but at two sites in Borneo ranged from 2.7 m to 4.5 m long[537], the record length for any bee-eater.

Laying is from late February to about late April in Borneo[537] and from the beginning of May until about late June in the Malay peninsula[402]. The clutch is 3–4, rarely 5 and once 6[415]; the mean of 10 clutches was 3.9[94B]. Eggs are laid at intervals of 2–3 days[537] and the clutch takes 3–9 days (average 5.2 days) to hatch[94B]. Breeding success is evidently poor; of 39 eggs only 23 hatched (60%), and at six nests the production of fledglings was merely 1.8 on average—often the youngest, smallest member of a brood succumbing about two weeks after hatching[94B] (as happens among tropical African bee-eaters).

SUBSPECIES

(1) *M. v. viridis* South China, Thailand and Indochina to Sumatra, Java and Borneo and some intervening and adjacent small islands. Head-top, nape and mantle dark chestnut, chin and throat blue. Javan birds have been separated as having bluer underparts[27], but this apparent difference may just be age or wear related.

(2) *M. v. americanus* Philippine Islands. Head-top, nape and mantle rich rufous, chin and throat green.

ADDITIONAL DESCRIPTION

(Nominate race). ADULT ♂, ♀ Mask (lores, ear coverts, narrow line of feathers below eye) black. All plumage above and behind mask rich dark mahogany or chestnut; mantle the same. Back, rump and uppertail coverts pale blue, each feather white grading to light blue distally; the whole in striking contrast with rest of upperparts plumage. Tail blue, more intensely on central than outer rectrices, and outermost being dusky blackish with blue wash mainly over inner web. Wide proximal half of central pair of rectrices blue with dark brown shaft; streamers dusky blue terminally (about 4 mm) and very pale blue with white shaft subterminally (15–20 mm). Wings grass green, tertials and inner greater coverts blueing with time since last moult, to same shade of blue as tail. A black band 5 mm deep across trailing edge of wing. Folded primary tips are black terminally and sometimes blueish subterminally, passing into the green of remainder of feather. Chin and throat bright blue, slightly paler towards cheeks, azure when viewed down-light and almost mauve (due to feathers having grey bases) when viewed up-light. Breast apple green, merging fairly sharply into blue of throat and less perceptibly into very pale blue of belly, flanks, vent and undertail-coverts. These pale blue feathers are subterminally white, making belly look as pale as rump. Underwing pale rufous, shading to grey distally; marginal underwing coverts green. Underside of tail grey. (*M. v. americanus*) ♂, ♀ like nominate race except that head-top, nape and mantle are rufous rather than chestnut; chin and throat are same shade of green as breast, with only the cheeks pale blue in a broad line bordering the mask; streamers are black terminally (7 mm) and blue with black shafts subterminally. JUVENILE Differs from adult in having forehead, crown, nape and mantle uniform dark green and chin straw-coloured. In some specimens the cheeks are also straw-coloured rather than pale blue. BARE PARTS Beak black, iris red-brown, legs and feet frosted dark grey, nails black. MOULT[402] A small proportion of adults begin to replace inner primaries while finishing breeding, in mid-June to mid-July, but most birds emigrate before moulting. The single annual moult appears to be protracted, neither adults nor first-year birds finishing until March. WEIGHT 34.1 (28.4–39.5, n = 35, Penang, Malaysia, March (Lord Cranbrook pc); 35.1 (28.9–45.0, n = 124, Selangor, Malaysia, in breeding season (D.R. Wells pc). MEASUREMENTS *Beak* to feathers ♂ 34.4 (33–36), ♀ 32.9 (32–34), to skull ♂ 40.6 (39–43, n = 10), ♀ 38.8 (38–41, n = 10), depth 7.6 (7.2–8.1). *Wing* ♂ 113 (111–115, n = 5), ♀ 113 (110–117, n = 5). *Tail* ♂ 76 (67–78, n = 5), ♀ 77 (73–79, n = 5), excluding streamers up to 89 mm in ♂ and 50 in ♀ (and 71 in ♂ *M. v. americanus*). *Egg* 19 × 23 (n = 7[537]). STRUCTURE Outer two rectrices moderately hooked and all remiges hooked except for the longest two primaries. Primaries extend 21–29 mm beyond tertials in folded wing. P9 longest, p10 10–13 mm long and 71–74 shorter than p9, p8 0–5, p7 10–13, p6 18–22, p5 25–30, p4 31–35, p3 35–40, p2 39–44, p1 41–47 and s1 44–46 shorter.

Blue-cheeked Bee-eater   *Merops persicus*   (Plate 6)

Merops persica Pallas 1773, Reise Versch. Prov. Russ. Reichs, 2, p. 708 (Caspian
    Sea).
Merops superciliosus, Shelley, Ibis, 1890, p. 167 (Yambuya).
Merops persicus, Sharpe, Cat. Birds Brit. Mus., 17, 1892, p. 66.
Merops persicus persicus, Hartert Vog. Pal. Fauna, 2, 1912, p. 860, Fig. 114.
Merops chrysocercus Cabanis and Heine 1860, Mus. Hein., Th. 2, p. 139 (Senegal).
Merops superciliosus persicus and *M. s. chrysocercus*, Peters, Check-List Birds World,
    V, 1945, p. 234, 235.

NOMENCLATURAL NOTE This and the following Madagascar and Blue-tailed
Bee-eaters are closely allied and have often been treated as comprising a single
species, *Merops superciliosus*. But D. Marien has shown that in the Punjab
Blue-cheeked and Blue-tailed nest sympatrically without hybridizing and are thus
specifically distinct[392]. How the Madagascar Bee-eater is then treated (as conspecific with the Blue-cheeked or with the Blue-tailed or as a distinct, third species) is
academic. I prefer not to multiply species without good reason and in this
complex—a clear example of a single intercontinental superspecies—I regard the
Madagascar as conspecific with the Blue-tailed Bee-eater[235].

FIELD CHARACTERS
Very like Madagascar Bee-eater, with which easily confounded where
both occur (East Africa, northwest India, northern Pakistan). An elegant,
long-winged, long-streamered species, quite large but slim and slightly
built, all burnished green save for pale blue forehead, eyebrow and cheeks,
black mask, yellow chin and rufous throat. Length 24–26 cm (9½–10 in)
excluding streamers. Beak long and thin; eye red. Usually in small flocks,
in desert steppe in summer and tropical African bush in winter, making
long pursuit flights from telegraph wires. Nests solitarily or in loose or
dense colonies; on the whole more gregarious than European Bee-eaters.
Voice like European, with which overhead migrants can be confused:
coppery underwing of Blue-cheeked is a useful criterion, also its green (not
gold) scapulars.

HABITAT
On Asiatic breeding grounds, steppes, deserts and semideserts with low

hills, dunes, ravines in arid dissected country, and river valleys with banks and cliffs[157]; similarly around the Sahara, ergs, wadis, oases, and steppe carrying a bare minimum of vegetation. In such desert land they often nest near tracks, roads and railways, using associated fences and tele-graph lines as observation posts[391, 561]. Some more southerly breeding localities in West Africa are wooded green valleys like the winter habitat. Migrants occur "almost throughout" Arabia[406] and cross the Red Sea and Sahara, foraging in steppe and desert and perching on low vegetation, rocks and buildings; in eastern Sahara they shun the worst desert and are common along the Nile[17]. In northwest India migrants occur on sandy sea-shores and at tanks (reservoirs) and canals. On wintering grounds flocks range widely over open bushed grassland and cultivated light woodland, seldom very far from open water or above 1,500 m[79], but the main habitats are riparian: wooded swamps, open lake-shores with *Papyrus*, reedmace and reeds in the shallows, and mangroves. Favours places with scattered trees, and tends to perch fairly high, 10–15 m, on dead limbs; also fond of perching on wires and cables. Roosts in leafy trees and often in reed-beds.

DISTRIBUTION

Breeding Range A breeding visitor to northwest Africa, discontinuously south of Atlas Mts in Morocco and northern Algeria from about Wadi Dra (06°30′W)[488] to Beni Abbès (where abundant[174]), Tafilalet (31°40′N 04°00′E) and Figuig (32°05′N 01°11′E) to Wadi Msab (= Oued N'Ça, 32°05′N 04°40′E) and Biskra[293]. No certain evidence of breeding in Tunisia[196,559], and does not breed in Libya[95] (G. Bundy and S. Cramp, pc). South of western Sahara the same race (*M. p. chrysocercus*) breeds commonly near Mauritanian coast between 18° and 17° parallels and near Senegal river (Mederdra, and 16°36′N 15°55′W and about 16°36′N 15°50′W) (P. Browne pc), and discontinuously across Sahel savanna zone from Dakar, Lake R'Kiz and Khouma near Richard-Toll in Senegal[426], also probably Basse river (13°13′N 14°15′W) in Gambia[116,425], to the inland delta of Niger river[363], near Fafa (15°20′N 00°35′E) south of Ansongo in Mali[342], the west side of Lake Chad in Nigeria (ie New Marte, 12°30′N 13°55′E, M. Dyer and H.Q.P. Crick pc, and probably also near Nigerian/Niger border) and eastern shores of Lake Chad[581]. Two breed-ing colonies on River Niger at 09°55′N in Nigeria were exceptionally far south[585], the birds present each year only from April to July[590].

M. p. persicus breeds in the Nile delta where there are a few colonies north of Delta Barrage[405], also along Sweetwater Canal between Cairo and Ismailia[310]. In Israel there have been only a few breeding records in the last 40 years (A. Zahavi pc). Absent as a breeding bird from Sinai and Arabian Peninsula except on its eastern seaboard, where it breeds on

Sooty Falcon chasing Blue-cheeked Bee-eater

north Batinah coast, Oman[250]. (There are also recent unconfirmed reports of breeding 40 km southwest of Riyadh and at Buraydah, 26°20'N 43°59'E, M.C. Jennings pc). 'Green' bee-eaters nesting on Maskan Island off Kuwait in 1942[162] may have been this species[97] or more likely, I think, Little Green Bee-eaters. Breeds widely in southern Turkey east of Taurus Mts, on the Mediterranean Gulf of Iskenderun and in adjacent Ceyhan river delta[360], and in Syrian grasslands in immediate vicinity of Euphrates (but not south of it) where it has been described as the commonest bird present[359]; through northern Iraq and Mesopotamia (where there are colonies of thousands at Museyib and near Baghdad and Basra[561]) and throughout lowland Iran, all Pakistan except Peshawar, Rawalpindi and Lahore Provinces in the north, and in India in western Gujarat[333] and Rajasthan and southwestern Delhi and Punjab Provinces[6]. Some may in fact breed in northeastern Pakistan, where T.J. Roberts (pc) has noticed a few present in Blue-tailed Bee-eater colonies. It is widespread in the Indus lowlands south of about 30°N, and particularly common as a breeding bird and a migrant throughout Sind, on the lower Indus from Kashmor to Keti Bandar[183,302]. Easternmost localities are Bhavnagar (21°45'N 72°10'E), Jagatpur and Sultanpur near Delhi[252A], Sultanapur (50 km south of Amritsar), and Bannu (33°00'N 70°18'E)[392].

In USSR[157] it breeds in Armenia only casually but is common and widespread in Lenkoran Plain and along adjacent shores of the Caspian from Iran border north to Baku (Azerbaijan). It has nested north of the Caucasus at Stavropol and on lower Volga river at Ganyushkino (46°35'N 49°20'E). In Kazakhstan[164] it breeds in places on northern shore of the Caspian and in lower Ural and Embe river valleys up to Kokdzhida, and sparsely on eastern Caspian shore at Fort Shevchenko, Taushik and Shulder gorge, also probably at Cape Dzhiland and Eraliev lakes. Some may nest on northwest and southwest shores of Aral Sea, where a few breed on Kuland Archipelago and many on eastern shore south to

Kuvan-Dariy and adjacent islands. They nest commonly all along the Syr Darya from its mouth to Golodnyi steppe, on Keles river close to Tashkent, probably on the Arys', and on Talda and other small rivers rising in western Kara Tau range, as well as on lower Sarysu river where it dies out in Segiz lakes and along Chu River below 500 m (Akzhaykyn lakes, Tasty, and Chu). To the north of Chu they are very common birds on the Ili distributaries and its delta on Lake Balkhash and they probably breed between Myn-Aral and Burubaytal on the lake's southwest shore.

In Kyzylkum Desert southeast of Aral Sea Blue-cheeked Bee-eaters nest at wells and oases, and in Tokhtatau Mts. Unlike European Bee-eaters they do not occur in foothills of the great Tien Shan and Kirghiziya ranges; but there is an outlying breeding population on south shore of Kapchagayskoye Reservoir west of Chilik river mouth, on lower Charyn river and between Ili river and Panfilov very close to the Chinese border[164]. South of Kazakhstan, they breed throughout Turkmenia from Gasan Kuli (37°40'N 54°20'E) and Kopek-Dag Mts to Amu Darya River, and the lowlands of Uzbekistan and Tadzhikistan[157].

Winter Range M. p. chrysocercus vacates north Africa and winters in West Africa, probably entirely south of 15°N. The southern Saharan population probably also moves south in autumn, into West African savannas. Winters commonly in Gambia on the coast and the lower river[324], and in Sierra Leone common on coast and in adjacent swamps and valleys (G. Field pc), but in both countries much less common further inland. Uncommon in southern and rare in northern Ivory Coast[556], but north of there found in the winter/dry season around Bamako and Ségou in southern Mali[363]. In Ghana reported from only one locality, near Upper Volta border (six dates from November to May)[545]; and rare in Nigeria except on her Lake Chad shore. Widespread in Cameroun[378]. Status in Republic of Chad uncertain; the species (this race?) was reported to be common and widespread in the south[385] but more recent observers have not seen it at all[439,501], except near Lake Chad.

M. p. persicus winters throughout eastern tropical Africa, west to Congo basin. It does not winter in upper Egypt[405], but is a fairly common visitor from October to May in northern Sudan (less common in the south), found mainly in the Nile valley[114]; in Ethiopia a common to abundant bird from August to May in Rift Valley and to the east in arid lowland savannas[573]; in Somalia the picture is confused owing to presence of breeding Madagascar Bee-eaters, but December to February records indicate overwintering at least in the south (J.S. Ash pc). A widespread visitor to Uganda, Kenya and Tanzania from late October to early April, commonly in the Nile and Rift Valleys and Lake Victoria basin and locally in swamps elsewhere[79]. West of the Rift common from Lake Edward to eastern Katanga and also in western Zaire on lower River

Congo down to Kinshasa and in region of Lake Leopold II, although sparse in Kasai[118]. In Angola known in coastal plains from Cabinda to Luanda with the odd record inland[565]. In Zambia, Malaŵi and Mozambique widespread and locally quite common mainly from late November to mid April, along marshes, rivers and flood-plains[56,58]. Widespread but less common in Zimbabwe[312] and scarce in Transvaal, November to April, and occurs sparsely along Zululand and Natal coasts and in northern Namibia. A few have been seen in northern Botswana, southwest to Lake Ngami[534].

MIGRATIONS

Migrates mainly by day, small and large flocks passing on a broad front often at great height. On occasion they have been heard moving at night[310], and they have struck light-houses[405]. Over nine years T.J. Roberts (pc) noticed 25 night arrivals of spring migrant flocks on the Pakistan coast near Karachi, between 22.30 and 03.30 h, and only 3 arrivals before dusk or after dawn. Most west Saharan birds probably cross the desert directly (although there is southbound autumn coasting in Mauritania—P.W.P. Browne pc) and in spring small numbers occur regularly near Moroccan/Algerian border at Defilia and Beni Abbès in April[531,533]; they arrive on breeding grounds from late March but mainly in April. Then, and again when they disperse after breeding from July to September, some wander north to Atlantic and Mediterranean coast[293]. (Vagrants in Europe, however, are mainly of the eastern race. The bird often visits Cyprus; there are at least 6 records from Greece, 11 from Malta, 8 from Sicily and Italy, 5 from France, 2 from England—the Scilly Isles in 1921 and 1951[454]—one from Holland and one from Sweden[264].)

In the plains immediately south of Lake Chad Blue-cheeked Bee-eaters—presumably *M. p. chrysocercus*—occur on north- or northeast-bound passage from mid December to mid February[228,301]. Two hundred km away to the north, well beyond New Marte (see above), they occur all winter and commonly in March–April, and are still present around reed islands far out in Lake Chad in mid July[168]. If not New Marte or other locally breeding birds[21] these spring migrants might be of Lybian and lower Egyptian origin.

I cannot find grounds for a recent assertion[147, p. 322] that *M. p. chrysocercus* migrates eastward in autumn from northwest Africa to Egypt.

Emigration of *M. p. persicus* from Africa is by way of the Rift Valley in Ethiopia, and western and northern Somalia. From mid January to mid May very large numbers move northeast through this region and cross Gulf of Aden coast in April–May all along from Hargeisa to Cape Guardafui (J.S. Ash pc). Probably they continue northeast, coasting along Hadhramaut to Oman and crossing Gulf of Oman onto Makran coast to head for Indus valley and beyond. At any rate migrants are common in Oman from March (mainly) to May[96] and there is substantial northward movement through Delhi from late May through the first three weeks of June[310]. Mesopotamian breeding birds may arrive by way of the Persian Gulf rather than from the southwest[310], although there are quite large northward movements on the Nile near Cairo and along the Egyptian eastern desert littoral with some eastern exodus into Sinai[310]. It is probably the Nile route which leads migrants to Cyprus almost every year in spring[264]. Passage through the Nile delta and Sinai is in late March, three weeks earlier than European Bee-eater migration over Cairo; they arrive at breeding grounds in Mesopotamia a fortnight before European Bee-eaters[561]; in Lenkoran Plain and the Caucasus, however, arrival and passage are a little later than those of European Bee-eaters[157]. Spring passage flights have been seen at many places east of the Caspian and are sometimes impressive, eg "flew over Makhachkala in unbroken flocks on 3–4 May"[157].

In Asia, autumn passage is not well documented and migrants probably are less concentrated temporally and geographically. Indian and Pakistani breeding grounds are not deserted until October or early November—much later than by European Bee-eaters[264]. Many must cross or coast down the Red Sea, since Blue-cheeked Bee-eaters are by far the commonest prey of Sooty Falcons in the Dahlac Archipelago[131]. There is conspicuous movement along the Nile, large flocks arriving at its source in September–October, traversing Uele district of Zaire to head towards Congo, or moving along Rift Valley into southern Africa. Westward coasting has been seen on Aden coast in October[424], when some birds fly further south, crossing Arabian Sea direct to Kenya (a distance of at least 3,000 km)[420].

FOOD AND FORAGING

Eats dragonflies and damselflies (Odonata) and to a much lesser extent Hymenoptera (ichneumon-flies, scoliids, chalcids, ants, spider-hunting wasps, true wasps, sand wasps, honeybees and others) and other flying insects (cicadas, assassin bugs, pond skaters, lygaeid ground bugs, squash bugs, pentatomid and cydnid shield bugs, leafhoppers, toad bugs, water scorpions; flies; butterflies, moths; dung beetles, weevils, bostrychid beetles; short-horned grasshoppers and mantises). Analysis of 100 pellets from four West African sites shows that two-thirds of the diet (65.5% numerically) are odonates, that hymenoptera amount to only one-fifth of the odonates, and bugs and flies together equal the Hymenoptera[239]. Odonates also predominated in the diet of nestlings near Tashkent, USSR[500].

That it is evidently a dragonfly specialist is at odds with field

observations that it takes mainly butterflies[301], wasps and bees[341]; although of course there is no doubt that it will do that as opportune. Some Zaire birds were eating termites[118]; in Algeria they took sand wasps *Bembex*, *Ammophila*, *Psammophila* and *Philanthus* (the last itself a bee eater) and large beetles (*Sphenoptera*, *Gymnopleurus*, weevils)[341]. When honeybees are plentiful they are eaten to the exclusion of all else: a bird shot in Zimbabwean farmland contained two drones and over 40 workers of *Apis mellifera*[72], and in Russia they can inflict serious losses at bee-hives[157]. Desert locusts *Schistocerca gregaria* and other large grasshoppers are also on record[264], although this bee-eater may ignore them even when plentiful[40].

Feeding is by sallying from telegraph wires, tree-tops, fences and rarely from the ground; the bird makes height with fast even wing beats, glides for some distance on outstretched wings and then twists abruptly after its prey. Insects are caught from below and taken in the tips of the bird's mandibles, sometimes with the head momentarily thrown back, as depicted in the heading to this species account. Usually the bee-eater returns directly to its perch to beat the insect and rub a venomous one, and on the way it may be passed back and forth between the tips of the mandibles or even tossed into the air and recaptured[177]. On occasion small insects are eaten in flight, including some venomous ones, the bird remaining aloft for three or four successive captures; sometimes birds look as though they are feeding successfully like that when at considerable height, hunting in swift, graceful and acrobatic flight. They may also fly behind vehicles for several hundred metres to feed on insects disturbed from the ground and herbage[73].

Rarely they may take insects and small fish near the surface of water as do other bee-eater species, although the evidence for it in this species is equivocal.

VOICE

Very like the voice of European Bee-eater, the various expressions clearly homologous. Although the two species remain separate when migrating, they mix together when stopping to feed, at roost, and also when nesting[310], so it is surprising that they seem not to respond to each other's voices (in captivity[341]). The Blue-cheeked Bee-eaters' voice is higher in pitch (sometimes lower), harder in tone, shorter, more definitely disyllabic, and less attractive than the European's (qv), contralto compared with the European's soprano[11]. A call frequently uttered on the wing is a mellow rolling whistle or chirp[592], a repeated musical interrogative *tetew?* which is a migratory contact call[6]; *kri-kri-kri* repeated several times[157]; *diripp, driüüü;* alarm, *dick-dick-dick,* sharper than European's[264]; roosting call given with fanned and vibrated tail, *dirippdirippdiripp*[341].

BEHAVIOUR

Gregarious, keeping mainly in small loose foraging flocks with individuals in sight and sound of each other. Forms loose-knit but large flocks on migration. Loosely colonial when nesting, with a dozen nests scattered over an area up to 25 ha; often colonies are more compact, with 60 nests in a quarter-hectare of flat ground[391] or 2–3 nests per linear metre of canal bank[500]. Colonies rarely exceed about a hundred pairs, but in Syria they sometimes number hundreds[414] and in Iraq thousands of birds "swarming over the nest holes like bees"[561]. They seem to be monogamous; there are no reports yet of helpers at the nest.

Adults roost in the nest burrow at night and also take refuge there during sand-storms[341], but males may roost elsewhere[285]. There is an old report which needs verifying, that up to the time of hatching nest openings in flat ground are frequently closed with soil by the birds at nightfall or on leaving the burrow as a defence against predators[157]. Outside the breeding season they roost in leafy trees, tamarisks, date-palms, *Papyrus* and reed-beds[147], sleeping shoulder-to-shoulder. By day they sometimes rest on open sand, and are said also to sleep on ground clear of vegetation[264].

Courtship feeding occurs, and pair formation is accompanied by "wrestlings with locked beaks and display of the brilliant under-surfaces of the wings. . . . The vertical raising of the wings is usually an aggressive gesture; so is a lunge towards the opponent with the pale feathers of the face expanded. In displays of amity the wings are raised at the carpus, with primaries horizontal; the feathers of the nape may be ruffled; and there is a strained "leaning away" from the mate which exactly reverses the bearing of the lunge of enmity . . ."[285].

BREEDING

Nest holes are dug in flat or shelving sandy ground or in a low vertical bank, in loose colonies (see above). Tunnels are at least a metre long in hard soil and up to 2.5 or even 3.0 m long in soft soil, nearly straight and horizontal in banks or declining at about 20° in flat ground. Entrances are

65–85 mm wide and 52–75 mm high and the terminal egg chamber 15–20 cm long, 9 cm wide and 12 cm high[500]. Typical sites are banks of canals and irrigation ditches; sloping calcareous sand of seashores, above the tide line (southwest Caspian, northwest India); low cliffs of compacted, wind-scoured sand dunes around the Sahara; and hard-baked sandy mud in plains with spaced dried-out tussocks of grass. In Iran holes are commonly dug in earthen shoulders of metalled roads, the burrow extending beneath the tarmac (S. Howe pc). In Uzbekistan rollers, owls, doves and sparrows may share bee-eaters' colonies[500].

Eggs are laid in the first half of May in northwest Africa and the Nile Delta, in March in Mesopotamia and from April to the end of June in Iran[26]. In Sind (southern Pakistan) laying is in the second half of June immediately after nests are dug, the young hatching in second and third weeks of July and some not fledging until well into August[183]. At the north of the species' range, on Syr Darya river east of Aral Sea, laying is in late May to early July and fledging from early July onward[157,500]. In West Africa eggs are laid in the early-wet-season months of May and June in more southerly latitudes, but further north in Sahel zone and southern Sahara breeding is much later and also more protracted, with laying from late April until early October[240]. There is a single clutch, usually of 4–6 eggs, commonly 6 in Iraq, Iran and India and occasionally 7 or 8 in Iraq, Afghanistan, India and USSR.

Eggs are laid at intervals probably of at least 24 hours and incubation begins with the first egg. By day both sexes incubate, the male up to 30 min and the female up to 3 hr at a time. An incubating female is often fed by the male, accepting an insect at the nest entrance or flying away to be fed distantly. At night only the female incubates, for up to $12\frac{1}{2}$ hr[285]. In flat-ground colonies eggs can sometimes be found on the bare ground, but whether they are "laid by birds whose holes are not fully excavated"[562] is perhaps open to question.

Incubation can last as much as 24–26 days; the nestling period has been given as only 23 days[500] but is probably about four weeks; aviary-reared nestlings fledged at 30 days[341]. Nestling growth[500] is much like that of European Bee-eater.

SUBSPECIES

(1) *M. p. chrysocercus* Edges of western Sahara from Morocco to Lybia and from Senegal to Lake Chad. Golden green above; ♂ streamers 70–104 mm longer than tail.

(2) *M. p. persicus** Lower Egypt, and from Euphrates and Persian Gulf

---

* A specimen in the Museo Civico, Milan, collected in Eritrea in 1906, was described by E. Moltoni as *M. p. erythraeus*[417] and later treated by him[418] as a colour mutant of *persicus*; it is blue or blue-green in place of typical grass-green and its forehand and cheeks are white to northern shores of Caspian and Aral Seas, southern Lake Balkhash, lowlands north and south of Hindu Kush, Delhi and Gujarat; winters in eastern tropical Africa. Very like *chrysocercus*; less golden a green above, and ♂ streamers only 45–67 mm longer than tail.

ADDITIONAL DESCRIPTION

ADULT ♂, ♀ (sexes similar except that ♀ tail streamers average shorter than ♂). Some inter-population variation in shade and density of green in plumage, and in facial colours. Upperparts grass green in fresh plumage, wings and tail more golden green and sometimes all except rump quite strongly olive. Worn plumage looks blueish owing to faded edges of feathers, particularly tertials and rump. Wings have vestigial narrow, dusky, trailing edge band. Underparts a paler green, washed golden or blueish, and usually paling towards vent and undertail coverts. Typically, forehead narrowly white by beak shading backwards to powder blue; superciliary stripe and cheeks powder blue (cheeks often with some white feathers); black mask narrower than in European Bee-eater; chin pale yellow with white feather bases, shading to russet or brick-red throat which is separated from blue cheeks by green moustache. Often (first-year birds?) forehead is very narrowly yellowish, without white, and blue eyebrow poorly developed; cheeks may also be narrowly white rather than broadly blue; and chin dull not bright yellow. Axillaries and entire underwing except distal halves of flight feathers russet, dull except for axillaries, and more ochreous in greater under primary coverts. Underside of tail feathers silvery grey. As with all bee-eaters except European, there is no distinct *winter plumage*. But by late summer green tertials and flight feather edges have bleached blue and with wear whole plumage becomes less fresh green, more olivaceous, chin whiter, throat paler rufous[264].

JUVENILE Upperparts olive green except for blue-green rump and ochre tinge on nape; markedly scaly due to contour feathers having very narrow whitish fringes. Forehead narrowly buffy and supercilium narrowly yellowish-buff. Chin pale buff washed yellow; throat warm buff, yellower or whiter towards cheeks. Breast very pale green, scaly and with grey feather bases showing through; belly and undertail coverts palest green. Juvenile plumage soon becomes like adult, and four or five weeks after fledging juveniles can be distinguished only by having forehead, superciliary and cheek stripes less demarcated and greener than in adult.

BARE PARTS Iris claret in ♂, orange-red in ♀, and dark brown in juvenile; beak black; legs and feet frosted blackish in adult and flesh or yellow-brown in juvenile; nails black in adult and dark brown in juvenile. MOULT

without any trace of yellow. The British Museum has a specimen of identical appearance, taken in Kashmir in 1918, and marked "sent in spirit by Mr Gordon", and I am sure that both birds owe their yellowless plumage to prolonged spirit immersion.

Post-nuptial moult begins before migrating in autumn with the replacement of scapulars and outermost three or four primaries. Moult is then suspended[501A] until arrival on wintering grounds when it is completed by adults and juveniles from November to January (exceptionally October–March). Thereafter adults and first-year birds said to be indistinguishable[392]. WEIGHT 45.9 g (41.7–57.0, n = 18, pre-breeding, Lake Chad), 43.1 (38.1–50.3, n = 8, wintering and migrating Ethiopia (J.S. Ash pc) and Algeria[533]). Spring migrants in Chokpak Pass, Kazakhstan were 50.3 (46.0–53.7, n = 10) and autumn migrants were (adults) 49.3 (41.3–57.0, n = 37) and (juveniles) 44.7 (35.0–54.7, n = 59) (E.I. Gavrilov pc). In Kazakhstan birds are significantly heavier in the second than in the first ten days of September: 49.9 ± 1.1 g (n = 140) *versus* 46.8 ± 1.3 g (n = 11)[501A]. MEASUREMENTS *Beak* to feathers $\circlearrowright$ 39–45, $\circa$ 38–40 (n 20[29]), to skull $\circlearrowright$ 46.2 (43.5–49.0, n = 13), $\circa$ 45.7 (43.6–49.0, n = 11)[264]. *Wing* $\circlearrowright$ 145–164, $\circa$ 143–153 (n = 20[29]), mean 154.6 (n = 9) and 148.1 (n = 11) respectively[264]. *Tail* $\circlearrowright$ 88.2 (83–91), $\circa$ 86.5 (82–90), excluding streamers up to 67 mm in $\circlearrowright$ and 45 in $\circa$. *M. p. chrysocercus* slightly smaller in all measurements, eg wing $\circlearrowright$ 139–151 and $\circa$ 136–149 (n = 10), except for streamers which are up to 104 mm long in $\circlearrowright$ and 75 in $\circa$. *Egg* 20.9 × 26.2 (20.0–22.6 × 24.1–27.1, n = 100[26]) and 21.9 × 25.5 (n = 64)[500]; weight of fresh egg 6.37 g[500] and of shell 0.36 g[264]. STRUCTURE Folded wings reach within 15 mm of end of tail (excluding streamers) and are 48–52 longer than tertials which are themselves long. P9 longest; p10 minute, sharp-pointed, 12–14 longer than its under covert and 103 shorter than p9; p8 9–13, p7 19–27, p6 33–40, p5 40–50, p4 52–60, p3 60–67, p2 69–74, p1 76–80 and s1 84 shorter. Adult tail streamers acutely triangular, tapering rather evenly from 10 mm width (level with tip of tail proper) to 1 mm at tip (less when worn).

Shedding heat

Madagascar and Blue-tailed Bee-eaters *Merops superciliosus*
(Plate 6)

Merops superciliosus Linnaeus 1766, Syst. Nat., ed. 12, 1, p. 183 (Madagascar).
Merops philippinus Linnaeus 1766, Syst, Nat., ed. 12, 1, errata at end (omitted from p. 183) (Philippine Islands).
Merops Javanicus, Horsfield, Trans. Linn. Soc. Lond., 13, (1), 1821, p. 171.
Merops philippinus celebensis, Blasius, Zeitschr. Ges. Orn., 2, (3), 1885, p. 239.
Merops Salvadorii, A.B. Meyer, Ibis, (6), 3, (10), 1891, p. 294.
Merops persicus superciliosus, Sassi, Ann. Naturh. Hofmus. Wicn, 26, 1912, p. 372.
Merops superciliosus alternans Clancey 1971, Durban Mus. Novit., 9 (5), p. 42 (Carunjamba, Lucira, Moçamedes, Angola).
Merops philippinus philippinus, Marien, J. Bombay Nat. Hist. Soc., 49, 1950, p. 156 (cf *Merops superciliosus persicus*, ibid., p. 156).

(see NOMENCLATURAL NOTE about *M. superciliosus* superspecies under Blue-cheeked Bee-eater. These species are so similar that I have trimmed the following account in some respects which would be merely repetitious.)

FIELD CHARACTERS
The Madagascar Bee-eater is green tailed and in Africa distinguishable in the field from the Blue-cheeked Bee-eater only by its duller plumage (olive green rather than grass green) and dark olive brown cap (not bright green). Forehead and supercilium are white (greenish where they border the dark cap, and supercilium sometimes pale blue) and cheeks white (most Blue-cheeked Bee-eaters are conspicuously pale blue in those parts but some are nearly white). Axillaries and underwing coverts paler than in Blue-cheeked, ochreous rather than cinnamon.

In northwest India adult Blue-tailed Bee-eater can be told from Blue-cheeked by having its forehead and supercilium green, concolorous with cap. The difference in tail colour (green in Blue-cheeked Bee-eater) is too dependent on incident light to be of much value in the field, where it often does not show at all[310]. Young birds safely distinguishable only by tail colour when clearly seen.

HABITAT
In Africa mangroves, coastal plains, rivers, lakeshores and swamp

edges, open light woodland not necessarily near water, and bushy savannas; in Madagascar and Comoro Islands open, dissected country, farmland, forest edges abutting farmland, plantations, paddies. In Asia it inhabits less arid country than Blue-cheeked Bee-eater but, like it, usually near open water: wooded lake-shores and river valleys, beach scrub, creeks, mangroves, jheels, tanks, pasture, paddies, immature or open oil palm plantations, coconut groves, tin tailings, large suburban gardens, and secondary forest borders where there is plenty of open ground.

DISTRIBUTION

See maps facing Plate 6. In southwest Africa abundant along lower Cunene river, breeding there[606] and on desert littoral north of its mouth, near Lucira (Angola) and north to lower Cuanza river. Ranges south to Ondagua, Ovamboland, east to Okavango river valley and north to about Luanda. A separate population occurs on the African coast of Mozambique Channel, breeding at Masambeti near Beira and probably breeding regularly and numerously thence south to Bazaruto and Santa Carolina Islands (22° and 23° S). Inland it has nested on the Zambezi in Zimbabwe at Mana Pools in 1961 and 50 km downstream from Victoria Falls in 1981 (C. Pollard per P. Lorber pc) and probably at Wedza, Fort Victoria and recently near Bulawayo[241]. Breeds on Mayotte and probably also other main Comoro Islands; widespread as a breeding bird in Madagascar from Sambavu in northeast to Tuléar in southwest, from lowlands up to at least 1,500 m, but probably absent from east coastal plains. Breeds on East African coast on Pemba Island, probably Lamu and adjacent Kenya coast[453] and around Mogadishu, Somalia (J.S. Ash pc); also at Malindi, on Galana river, near Dar-es-Salaam, Mafia Island, and sporadically inland near Kisumu, on upper Tana river, perhaps Athi river; also near Omo river and Mogadishu hinterland[241]. Common and widespread in Guban area of northern Somalia, breeding in at least three coastal and three inland localities; also in Awash river valley, Ethiopia (J.S. Ash pc)[241].

Blue-tailed Bee-eaters have a vast range, from Pakistan to New Britain. In northwest India and northern Pakistan they are more-or-less parapatric with the Blue-cheeked Bee-eater; breeding at Bannu and Delhi (as does Blue-cheeked), also Peshawar, Lahore, Ferozepore and Gujarat. T.J. Roberts (pc) has found colonies of Blue-tailed Bee-eaters in northern Punjab containing a few Blue-cheeked, and 500 km to the south colonies of Blue-cheeked containing a few Blue-tailed Bee-eaters; but in no instances was he able to determine whether the minority birds were themselves nesting. Further east it formerly nested near Delhi[252A] and breeds to-day from southern part of Gangetic plain (lower Chambal and lower Yamuna rivers) in Uttar Pradesh south to Godavari river delta (Madras), Waltair near Vishakhapatnam and Rajahmundry (Andhra Pradesh)[437], Cauvery river[437] and Coorg (Kerala)[392] and in easternmost coastal Sri Lanka (Pottuvil, Akkaraipattu and Kumana)[464]. In northeast of Subcontinent breeds in Bihar, Bengal, Assam, lowland Nepal, and Bangladesh[6]. Nests throughout southeast Asia in lower-lying country, in north from northern Burma and southern China (Yunnan, Kwangsi-Chuang and western Kwangtung Provinces but neither Hong Kong nor Hainan[197]), south through Thailand and Indochina (except north Annam?) to northern Malaysia where it nests certainly only at Padang Kemunting, Penang[402].

Populations barely differentiable from the mainland form[154] occur in Sulawesi, where the bird is common in open habitats in all parts (R. Watling pc) except perhaps the southeast (P. Holmes pc), and throughout the Philippine Islands including Basilan and Sulu Archipelago (M.D. Bruce pc). Breeding colonies are known in Sulawesi at Malino-Lombasang (05°13'S 119°50'E)[542], Palu (01°00'S 119°59'E) and Kalawara (01°20'S, 119°00'E) (R. Watling pc). Possibly it breeds adjacently in Borneo, in the extreme southeast[537]. Nests yet to be found in the Philippines[398]. The species occurs in New Guinea and locally in New Britain. In Papua New Guinea*, Blue-tailed Bee-eaters occur in all extensive areas of natural and anthropogenic open country except for high grassland and for the savanna around Port Moresby. In the northeast they are found in grasslands near Sentani[485], Sepik river plains[262] although not in cleared land on coast nearby, Ramu river valley, Madang and Saidor[61], Lae, Popondetta[203,204] and Tufi[507]. Absent from Karkar and Umboi Islands but common all year on Long Island in between, nesting in sea cliffs of volcanic tuff[139]. In New Britain they have been recorded recently at Cape Gloucester in the west[133], but not on the south coast[262] because of a lack of cleared ground. In trans-Fly region of southern New Guinea, there are specimens from Princess Marianne Straits in the west and Lake Daviumbu in the north, and breeding records from Bensbach and Morhead rivers in the southeast[206,372] (H.L. Bell pc), and the species probably ranges throughout.

MIGRATIONS AND WINTER RANGES

In eastern Africa Madagascar Bee-eaters range west to Rift Valley lakes, Lake Upemba and savannas of eastern Katanga, from late April to early September; they just enter Sudan†, south of 5°N[442]. Passage migrants in Zambia and Malawi, common in September, less so in April–May, occurring south to Zambezi valley (west to Victoria Falls). The complex movements remain mysterious but do not necessarily

* Information on Papua New Guinea was kindly researched and provided by Dr Harry Bell.
† A sun-bleached, moulting bird from Khartoum, May 1912, is of this species and not (as marked) *M. p. persicus* (Brit. Mus. reg. 1915.12.24.2178).

involve passage between Africa and Madagascar as formerly supposed[241].

Indian Blue-tailed Bee-eaters move southeast in autumn into southern India and Sri Lanka. Southeast Asian birds withdraw totally only from most-northern parts of breeding range and some remain during winter as far north as central Burmese plains (rare), lower Irrawaddy and its delta (sparse, local) and northern Tenasserim (common)[536]. But most migrate southeast to Andaman and Nicobar Islands and to occupy the whole of peninsular Malaysia, large and small Indonesian islands east to Timor, and Borneo (common in southern lowlands, sparse elsewhere[537]). It is not clear whether Philippine and Sulawesi birds include wintering visitors or whether all are residents.

FOOD AND FORAGING

Little studied in Africa; specimens shot in Comoro Islands contained flies, beetles, bugs (Homoptera), grasshoppers and a butterfly[54], and in Madagascar three contained grasshoppers, wasps and a cicada[473]. In India diet is mainly dragonflies, wasps and bees; also butterflies[212] including the noxious *Danaus chrysippus* (T.J. Roberts pc), moths, beetles, bugs and bluebottle flies[3]. Odonates from gizzards included *Crocothemis servillea*, *Platygomphus dolobratus* and *Trithemis pallidinervis*; Hymenoptera included honey-bees *Apis cerana* and *A. florea* (together more than half of the insects in 13 gizzards), *Chrysis*, *Camponotus*, *Oecophylla*, wasps *Polistes hebraeus*, *Vespa orientalis*, *Rhynchium benghalense*, leaf-cutter bee *Megachile carbonaria* and carpenter bee *Xylocopa dissimilis*[393]. T.J. Roberts (pc) found that dragonflies were the prey most commonly fed to nestlings in the Punjab—at least six species. In Malaysia the identified content of winter pellets showed dragonflies (Anisoptera), hymenopterans (Vespidae, Apidae, Sphecidae), beetles, and others in proportions *by weight* of 68%, 24%, 3% and 5% respectively (the 'others' being bugs, termites, damselflies, grasshoppers and flies)[24]. I obtained rather different results from a comparable number of winter pellets: honeybees greatly predominated with 82% *numerically* of *Apis indica* and 7% of the large *A. dorsata*, 7% of other Hymenoptera (wasps, ants, ichneumon-flies, scoliids, etc), and remaining 4% of odonates, flies, grasshoppers, bugs, beetles and butterflies. The difference is doubtless because the first pellet sample was collected on paddy-fields and the second, mine, on a suburban campus unsuitable for odonates. Pellets from a winter roost in Singapore mangroves also consisted mainly of wasps and bees[402]. Of course, like other bee-eaters it will feed upon one insect species, where abundant, almost exclusively; that has been noted in respect of the large dragonfly *Crocothemis servillea*, and with the fearsome wasp *Vespa orientalis*[393]. A flock of birds hawking over a large wood-stack seemed to be feeding entirely on two sorts of wood-boring beetles, *Dinoderus minutus* and *Sinoxylon anale*[393].

Claims that Madagascar Bee-eaters may occasionally dive into water to catch insects and fish[480,563] are vindicated by discovery of the small surface-feeding mosquito fish *Gambusia affinis* in Blue-tailed Bee-eater pellets in Malaysia[239].

Hunting techniques are like those of Blue-cheeked Bee-eaters, loose flocks hawking insects from power lines, telephone wires and trees. Birds can see even a small hymenopteran 80–95 m away[239], and fly fast to intercept it from below, returning to treat it at perch or remaining aloft to feed like a swallow, sometimes above water quite far from land[6]. Some prey species, like the hornet *Vespa tropica*, are caught by the bird rising below it and reaching straight up to seize it in the beak tip, momentarily holding the curious sky-pointing attitude while making several wing beats as it returns to the perch[239]. The posture is portrayed in the Blue-cheeked Bee-eater heading illustration, p. 116.

BREEDING

As gregarious as the Blue-cheeked Bee-eater, nearly always nesting colonially, from a dozen nests to a hundred or more. At Forozepore they arrive in thousands in May and "great numbers" nest in crumbling mud walls of the old forts there, while in banks of bigger Burmese rivers "vast" colonies are often to be found[26]. Dry sandy or loamy banks of waterways are favoured; they also nest in coastal dunes and quite flat grassy sand as at Padang Kemunting, Malaysia, and in Papua New Guinea in perpendicular sea cliffs of volcanic tuff, in road cuttings and—the commonest site—flat grassy plains or claypans which may be rock-hard (H.L. Bell pc).

North of the Equator they breed in March–April (Malaysia), February–May (Burma) and April–May (Sri Lanka, India). In the Afrotropics laying times vary irregularly from March in the north to December in the south as follows: March Dar-es-Salaam; April north Somalia coast; April–May Awash and Omo valleys (Ethiopia), near Kisumu (Kenya) and near Mogadishu (Somalia); May hinterland of north Somalia coast at 1,400 m, and Galana River (Kenya); June–August Pemba Island; August upper Tana river (Kenya); September Momela Crater Lake and Mafia Island (Tanzania) and Mana Pools (Zimbabwe); October Masambeti (Mozambique) and Mayotte (Comoro Islands); September–November Madagascar; October–November Wedza (Zimbabwe); and November–December Malindi, Lamu (Kenya), Fort Victoria (Zimbabwe) and Cunene River (Angola). In Sulawesi they breed about February–May on the Equator (at Palu, the driest location in Indonesia—R. Watling pc) and about September at 5° S[542]; and in Papua New Guinea they nest in September–November, ie the dry season and austral spring (H.L. Bell pc).

SUBSPECIES

(1) *M. s. superciliosus* Madagascar Bee-eater. Eastern Africa, mainly coasts, between about 11°N and 23°S, Comoro Islands and Madagascar. Forehead white, crown dark raw umber, rump and tail green.

(2) *M. s. alternans* Madagascar Bee-eater. Lower Cunene and Cuanza rivers and intervening Angolan desert littoral. Paler and brighter and less olive than nominate race, chin and cheeks whiter, crown not so dark brown, washed green and in 30% of birds wholly green[129].

(3) *M. s. philippinus* Blue-tailed Bee-eater. North Pakistan to Sri Lanka, Burma, western Kwangtung (China), Indochina and south to Penang Island, Malaysia; Philippine Islands, Sulawesi, Flores[404], eastern Papua New Guinea and New Britain. Forehead and crown green, cheeks blue, rump and tail blue.

H.G. Deignan recognized four races of Blue-tailed Bee-eaters on the basis of trifling differences in green hue and brown suffusion in the mantle, namely mainland *javanicus*, *philippinus* on Philippines, *celebensis* on Sulawesi and *salvadorii* in New Guinea[154]. Stuart Keith and Murray Bruce have re-examined part of his material in New York and Chicago museums and they confirm that in mantle colour New Guinea and Philippine populations do differ, but barely, from Sulawesi and mainland ones. All the same I think it expedient not to recognize these races until their breeding distribution and migrations are better understood and further morphological distinctions can be looked for in larger series of birds.

ADDITIONAL DESCRIPTION

Mantles and breasts of all races are alike, and separable in shade from those of Blue-cheeked Bee-eater. Green upperparts and particularly crowns are always suffused with olive, so much so in *M. s. superciliosus* that its crown is dark brown rather than green. Chins paler yellow than in Blue-cheeked. Afrotropical races (1–2) have broad white cheek stripes and the Oriental race (3) narrow pale blue cheek stripes. (1–2) have white or greenish-white forehead and supercilium, (3) has those parts olive green with blueish tinge in very narrow line above beak, lores and eye; (3) has rufous throat patch larger and darker than in (1–2); (3) has rump, uppertail coverts and tail bright caerulean blue, and tertials and exposed fringes of greater coverts and tips of primaries often bleach bluer than in nominate race. Belly and undertail coverts in (1–2) pale apple green; belly in (3) pale green tinged powder blue, and undertail coverts pure pale blue. MOULT *Bare Parts* Beak black, mouth pale pink, iris claret or crimson, legs and feet pinkish-brown, nails black-brown[3]. Indian birds begin post-nuptial and post-juvenile moult in July and it proceeds without suspense (cf Blue-cheeked Bee-eater) until completion in late September and October, juveniles then having adult dress[392]. In Malaysia adults and first-year birds have suspended moult in late October after replacing p5–p3 (D.R. Wells pc) and many do not replace their outermost primary or inner secondaries before February[402]. WEIGHT 38.5 (32–45, n = 31, winter Singapore, D.R. Wells pc), 35.5 (32.5–39.3, Penang, April and Kuala Selangor, October). MEASUREMENTS (*M. s. superciliosus*) *Beak* to feathers ♂ 40 (37–42, n = 10), ♀ 38.5 (35–42.5, n = 10), to skull ♂ 47.1 (43–49, n = 10), ♀ 45.2 (40.5–50, n = 10). *Wing* ♂ 135 (130–140, n = 10), ♀ 130 (127–135, n = 10). *Tail* ♂ 82 (79–86, n = 10), ♀ 80.5 (78–83, n = 10) excluding streamers up to 60 mm in ♂ and 53 in ♀. (*M. s. philippinus*) *Beak* to feathers ♂ 39, ♀ 37, to skull ♂ 45.6 (43–48, n = 10), ♀ 43.2 (40–46, n = 5), depth 7.3 (6.8–7.6, n = 10). *Wing* ♂ 132.8 (127–139), n = 10), ♀ 126.0 (123–131, n = 10). *Tail* ♂ and ♀ 85.6 (80–89, n = 10, 82–89, n = 10) excluding streamers up to 71 mm in ♂ and 50 in ♀. *Egg* 20.1 × 23.2 (18.2–21.3 × 22.0–25.1, n = 100[26]). STRUCTURE Primaries extend 27–32 mm beyond tertials in folded wing. P9 longest, p10 13–17 mm long and 79–87 shorter than p9, p8 3–5, p7 13–17, p6 22–27, p5 30–36, p4 39–45, p3 44–50, p2 48–55, p1 50–59 and s1 52–60 shorter.

Rainbowbird *Merops ornatus*   (Plate 6)

Merops ornatus Latham 1801, Index Orn., Suppl., p. xxxv (New South Wales).

FIELD CHARACTERS

Adult unmistakable, the more so since no other bee-eaters occur in nearly all of its breeding range. Green with the usual black mask, a broad black gorget merging through chestnut to pale straw-coloured throat, burnished crown and nape, rufous primaries, brilliant azure scapulars and rump, and black streamered tail. Juveniles lack the black gorget and in Papua New Guinea could be mistaken for juvenile Blue-tailed Bee-eaters; but tails are black and blue respectively. Length 19–21 cm (7½–8 in), excluding streamers about 2 cm long in females and up to 7 cm in males. A gregarious bird of open habitats throughout Australia, hawking conspicuously from a perch or on the wing for insects. Migratory, wintering in north Australia, New Guinea and Sulawesi, flocks flying high by day and audible from afar.

HABITAT

In summer, flat or undulating sandy pasture, arable land and lightly-wooded savannas, environs of creeks and rivers (although often lives far from permanent water); avoids dense woodland, and extensive treeless grasslands[110]. Nests in flat sandy plains, earth-workings, gravel-heaps, hoed ridges, roadside and river banks. Often near human habitations, roosting in clump of leafy garden trees in otherwise deforested countryside. Favours roadsides, tracks and sugarcane railway lines, using fences and telephone wires as look-out perches. Widespread in open habitats in northern Australia, breeding usually near water, but in the south generally found only in areas of alluvial soil and sandy banks[522].

In New Guinea and New Britain, wintering birds inhabit open suburbs (often foraging from telegraph wires), native gardens, recently logged forest, various stages of secondary growth, forest edge and waterways in undisturbed lowland rainforest (K.D. Bishop pc). They abound in former lowland rainforest areas cleared for oil palm seedlings but shun mature oil palm and coconut plantations. They do not occur within dense forest, but from the ground can often be heard over the canopy as they feed from the tops of 40 m emergent trees (K.D. Bishop pc). New Guinea roost sites include a giant bamboo clump by cattle paddocks, with 600 birds, a 7 m *Acacia auriculaeformis* tree by sewage ponds, and a stand of *Eucalyptus alba* (H.L. Bell and K.D. Bishop pc).

DISTRIBUTION AND STATUS

See map facing Plate 6. Highly migratory. Common in most parts of its breeding range, probably more so than aboriginally despite predation by introduced foxes[523], because of man's creation of favourable habitat by deforestation (H.L. Bell pc). Breeds throughout Australia excepting forested areas of the southwest and southeast, ie between Perth, Pt d'Entrecasteaux and Doubtful Bay. Slater[522] marked it as absent from the 200 km wide coastal belt between Spencer Gulf and Sydney, but in fact it breeds in numerous places on and near the coast there[110]. Absent from Tasmania; but nests on a number of inshore Australian islands such as Southwestern Islands in Torres Straight (D.E. Peters pc) and probably the Pellew Group in Gulf of Carpentaria[110]. Also breeds in region of Port Moresby in Papua New Guinea[46].

Wintering populations occur in northern Australia south to about 18° S in Cape York Peninsula and south at least to Innisfail (H.B. Gill pc), Mount Isa, East Alligator river[110] and the Kimberleys[435], and in Pacific coastal lowlands south to 27°S[541]. Large numbers winter in northern Queensland and a few in the central and southern interior of that State[541]; but the principal wintering grounds are in New Guinea. There they occur throughout, and also in Lesser Sunda Islands (Timor, Flores, Sumba, Lombok; possibly also in Bali and Java), Sulawesi, and Moluccan and Bismarck Archipelagos. To the north of Australia wintering birds occur from March to October, except in Southwest Islands where they are evidently resident. (Southwest Islands are the small group from Wetar to Sermatta, just northeast of Timor, and are not to be confused with the Southwest*ern* Islands in Torres Strait—Banks or Moa Island and others— mentioned above.) There are records in Southwest Islands in August, October, December and from February to June inclusive; but breeding there has not been proven[404]. They are rare visitors between March and October to Solomon Islands[396], while vagrants have occurred as far afield as Saipan, Caroline Islands and Ryukyu Islands (H.L. Bell pc).

MIGRATION

Migrants are prone to occur practically anywhere in continental Australia and New Guinea, including those parts of Australia where the species does not breed. First arrivals in southern Australia are in late September with the main immigration in October[18,430] and departure during March. Emigrants from Australia concentrate at the shortest crossing to New Guinea, ie Torres Straits: "between Warrier Reef and Dungeness Islands (there pass) great flights of bee-eaters, large flocks of them following each other without intermission"[149]. A passage of over 850 birds an hour has been reported[169]. They occur on all of the larger islands in Torres Straits, particularly in the western group and few if any make the long flight across Coral Sea[541]. Migrants arrive at Port Moresby in the second week of March (but 1–2 weeks earlier in west New Britain, K.D. Bishop pc) and flocks of up to 300 remain until mid October, huge numbers spreading in the meantime throughout all of the open lowlands of New Guinea and its satellite islands and occurring in mountain clearings as high as 2,100 m[46,48,49]. Northbound passage over New Guinea remains strong until the second half of April[45], the birds evidently crossing the central spine of mountains by way of passes as high as 3,000 m[47] and 4,000 m[13]. They travel by day, but also sometimes on moonlit nights[595].

R. Draffan has reported huge mortality on spring passage over Torres Straits[169], when little or no fresh water is available and head winds can be severe. On several waterless islands he found dehydrated corpses still perched in macabre rows, or carpeting with green the ground beneath roosting bushes. A light-house keeper describes what happens; of many hundreds which arrived on Booby Island one evening "some were dead by the next day but many survived for two or three days. Late each afternoon the survivors would fly around aimlessly, taking off and landing many times . . . the following morning most were dead, dozens huddled side by side, and when the branch was moved the corpses fell off or simply spun to hang upside down by their clinging toes" (R. Hindmarsh pc). The mystery is that Rainbowbirds should die at all, for the shortest Torres Straights crossing is only 150 km between Papua New Guinea and Australia. The birds' condition suggests that they have flown 1,000 km or so non-stop; thus perhaps they come not from New Guinea at all, but east-south-eastwards from lands in and around Banda Sea.

FOOD AND FORAGING

Seventy pellets which I collected at a roost and near pre-egg nests at Sandy Pocket, Innisfail, Queensland, contained over 1,000 insects: 94.5% Hymenoptera, 3.1% Coleoptera, 2.0% Hemiptera and 0.4 Diptera, Orthoptera and Odonata. The non-hymenopteran prey were all small or minute. Half of the Hymenoptera were honeybees and one-third the small wasp *Ropalidia romandi*. The remaining one-sixth were sweat-bees, carpenter-bees, colletid bees (*Palaeorhiza*), ants, ichneumon-flies and six families of wasps (Scoliidae, Bethylidae, Tiphiidae, Vespidae, Sphecidae, Pompilidae). Because of the varying sizes of prey it is probably true to say that by weight honeybees and *Ropalidia* comprised over 90% of the diet in this instance and that non-Hymenoptera were quite insignificant. In another study[370] honeybees were found in six out of 11 gizzards examined, wasps (*Polistes variabilis*, *Sphex* sp., a mutillid) in four, ants and beetles (including *Onthophagus granulatus*) each in three, moths in two, and blowflies, dragonflies and a spider in one each. Forty birds killed raiding a Darwin bee-keeper's hives not unexpectedly contained mainly bees, drones and workers, with up to 21 per gizzard[400]. A bird collected in New Guinea contained 12 bees, 10 flies (Pipunculidae, Mydaidae) and a brenthid beetle[364]. An old record of earthworms, probably an error, was cited by Lea & Gray[370]. Diving onto water has been described, supposedly for crustaceans or tadpoles[274,591], but the evidence is inconclusive and I suspect that the birds were actually bathing. Moths, large flies, dragonflies and damselflies are commonly brought to nestlings, as shown photographically[319], and in parts of Victoria odonates are the principal food of the young (K. Hough pc) which are also fed butterflies, grasshoppers and beetles (K.D. Bishop pc). Autumn migrants over Torres Straits fatten on the butterfly *Eurema herabe*, which migrates at the same time[169].

Pairs or small flocks hunt by spacing themselves along a wire or around a stand of leafless trees, and scanning attentively for flying insects. A bird

gives chase to an insect passing from 5 to 50 m away, launching itself from
its perch with swift and purposeful flight and snapping up the insect
directly or after rapid twists and turns (the quarry seldom escapes), then
sailing in an arc back to the perch or else rising in the air to carry the food
to a distant nest. Flight is then rather undulating, fast even beats
alternating with effortless glides. Flocks sometimes wheel and swoop at
some height and are then almost certainly feeding on such insects as small
termites, evidently eaten without returning to perch. Most prey items,
however, are energetically beaten at perch, and venomous Hymenoptera
are 'bee-rubbed'[440].

VOICE

Flight call a rolled *drrrt*, rather less melodious and of drier quality than
homologous *prrüik* etc of some other large *Merops* species. Variations in
pitch, duration and intensity seem to me comparable to those of the
vocally better-known European Bee-eater. An urgent, loud *peer peer* in
territorial defence; predator alarm, fast loud *clip-lip-lip-lip*; a soft *tookie
tookie* before entering nest containing young; a loud *cleep cleep* when calling
young birds[430].

BEHAVIOUR

Gregarious. Breeds in loose colonies with individual nests well separated, sufficiently sometimes to be considered solitary ('false start' holes
are commonly made within a metre or two, however). Migrates in flocks
of tens to hundreds. Roosts in flocks of similar size (usually in dense leafy
trees like avocados) up to time of laying; thereafter pairs are more or less
solitary, in weakly-defended nest/feeding territories, often roosting in
nest*. Wintering flocks in New Guinea can roost in the same tree in
successive years[48]. Ringing controls suggest pairing for life[365]. Some pairs
have a helper[136,205] and at one nest 6–8 birds brought food throughout[429].
Of 35 nests in Perth, four had a single helper and one had two
helpers—males in all cases (M. Dyer pc).

Pair-formation involves no complex courtship. Each sex greets its mate
arriving at perch with upright posture, excited trilling call, crown feathers
a little raised, and tail lowered and strongly vibrated. The ♂ adopts a
bolder stance than the ♀, and repeatedly flies in to perch very close to her,
sometimes buffeting her back or side with his wing in the process. She
immediately adopts a submissive, hunched posture, without surrendering
any perch space. Copulation is preceded by the ♂ presenting the ♀ with a

* M.H. Waterman and L.C. Llewellyn, studying Rainbowbirds and White-backed Swallows
in South Australia, once found a nest burrow containing, at night, two adult and four small
nestling bee-eaters and 18 fully-fledged swallows! In another visit three nights later only
bee-eaters were in residence, and another burrow a metre away contained 27 roosting
swallows including a few from the bee-eater's nest[588].

small insect, which she may not have time to swallow before being mounted.

Highly territorial when nesting. Territories are polygons with trees at the corners, and the focal point is a favoured twig perch—the 'observation twig'[429,430]—near the nest, used for several purposes.

In King's Park, Perth, an area of 250 ha, there were 34 nests in summer 1982–1983, mostly well separated. But some were only 50 m apart (closest two: 2.5 m) and in those cases territory-holding pairs were quite tolerant of their neighbours (M. Dyer pc).

Sun-bathes with mantle feathers raised, usually sitting back-to-sun. Bee-devenoming behaviour, which I described for other bee-eater species in 1969, had already been described in Rainbow-birds[440] and it is exactly the same; they also discriminate blow-flies from bees[440].

They have been said to use a small piece of wood held in the beak to assist nest excavation[136], but that was an observational or interpretational error. Similarly, although small pieces of white bone, mussel-shell and even a pearl shirt-button may be found in nests, they do not function "as illuminants"[523] but are simply regurgitated gastroliths eaten probably by lime-deficient laying females. Seeking gastroliths on the ground is often a social activity, as in other bee-eaters. Large pieces of grit may be picked up and eaten without ado (probably what 100 Rainbowbirds "feeding" on tilled ground in New Guinea[12] were actually doing); at other times—particularly in late afternoons in the breeding season—pieces of mineral, insect shard or dry vegetation may be mandibulated and tossed a few cm into the air. It can certainly look like "playful behaviour"[123,336] but equally may be a test of its suitability as a limey gastrolith.

BREEDING

Nests are dug into flat ground (entrance commonly by a tussock), sloping screes, gravel heaps etc, or into side of ruts, ridges or low banks. Higher perpendicular cliffs are less often used, but include 2 m sand cliffs facing an exposed beach with heavy surf (H.L. Bell pc). Of 55 nests, 45 were in flat ground, 6 on slopes and 4 in vertical banks (M. Dyer pc). Digging is by both sexes, mainly the ♀, and tail streamers are often much abraded or broken off during nest excavation (D.E. Peters pc). Nest tunnels in cliffs are horizontal and straight or curving to one side; in flat ground they slope gradually to a depth of about 40 cm (chamber floor averages 42 cm below surface) and their contents are at the mercy of snakes and foxes[523]. Other predators of eggs and nestlings are skinks, goannas *Varanus gouldii* and feral dogs (M. Dyer pc). Tunnels are 1–2 m long (mean of 55, 149 cm; exceptionally up to 3.3 m[587]) in yielding earth or 0.5 m long in hard clay, including an egg chamber about 38 cm long (×20 cm wide × 8 cm high[429]). Excavation rate, c 7.5 cm per day. Migrants return to last year's area[110] and sometimes re-use original nest[430].

Nesting in Port Moresby savannas, Papua New Guinea, is in August and September[48]; and in northern Queensland nests are excavated in August and in southeastern Queensland during September. In southern Australia laying is from mid November to mid December but in the north there is said to be a dual season, unique amongst bee-eaters, with breeding just before and just after the wet season, in September–October and May–July (K.A. Muller[435] and pc). At Mount Isa, 21°S in northeast Queensland, R.K. Carruthers found breeding from August to April[110]. In the late dry season from August to December birds nested in bare, hard-clay flats around dams, seepages and backwaters; and in the rains from January to April they were scattered widely along creeks and rivers, nesting in loamy and sandy soils in creek banks and steeper slopes of river levees. As usual, flat ground nest burrows declined at about 30° but cliff face ones were level or declined only slightly[110]. Evidently young birds left the area as soon as fledged; if so, some adults would also leave (since the young depend upon them for several weeks), so that the wet season population would be largely of different individuals from earlier, dry season nesters.

Clutch 3–7, usually 5 or 4. In Perth, 43 clutches ranged from 4 to 6 eggs, mode 5, mean 5.0 (M. Dyer pc). A clutch of 5 takes at least six days to lay. Incubation starts after the 2nd, or 3rd, egg is laid and lasts for 24 ± 1 days (M. Dyer pc). Other periods on record are, from the last egg, in one case 24 (or 25) days 13 hrs $\pm$ 16 hrs and in another 22 (or 21) days 7 hrs $\pm$ 24 hrs[140]. In his recent research Michael Dyer found that, in eight unhelped pairs, the female incubated for twice as long as the male (69% : 31% of incubation time) but that, in two pairs each with a male helper, the female incubated for only 19% of the time and the males for 81%. Nest relief occurs every two hours, or less.

Eggs hatch nearly synchronously—in one instance all 4 in a clutch hatched on the same day. At 3.5 g the hatchling is relatively heavy, and it grows quickly to achieve its greatest weight (max. 37.3 g) between days 22 and 26, thereafter declining in weight until it fledges on average at 30 days $\pm$ 1 day. Depending on number and age of the young, 3–43 (mean 20) food items are brought to the nest per hour, and there is not much difference between growth rates of the oldest and youngest member of a brood (M. Dyer pc). Nestlings on point of fledging evoke much interest among adults—five or six gave a special call and 'encouraged' them to leave nest and also to return there to roost on 2–3 evenings after fledging[429,430].

ADDITIONAL DESCRIPTION

Monotypic. ADULT ♂ Forehead, forecrown and supercilium green;

hindcrown and sides of forecrown above supercilium russet or rufous, very glossy, in some examples washed green and in others extending into green of forecrown. Nape rufous-washed green. Mantle and upperwing coverts grass green, grading sharply into bright azure scapulars, tertials, back and rump. Uppertail coverts azure, but show deeper blue because backed by black rectrices. Tail black except for outer vane of outer feather, which is blue. Central pair of rectrices may be narrowly edged blue distally, or washed blueish throughout. Shafts and streamers black; each streamer <1 mm wide with a spatulate tip 1.5 mm wide. Mask black; cheeks with narrow line of powder blue; chin very pale yellow merging to yellow upper throat and, via a 1–2 mm bar of chestnut, into black gorget on lower throat and upper breast. Gorget about 20 mm wide and more or less triangular, 10–12 mm deep in midline tapering to points surrounded by chestnut on sides of neck. One third of adult males have hint of blue in posterior edge of gorget (R. Schodde pc). Breast light green with olive wash, merging gradually to pale azure belly and bright azure vent and undertail coverts. Underside of tail black or slaty. Remiges rufous, edged and washed green and with dusky tips forming a 5 mm trailing edge band. Underwing coverts pale buff. ADULT ♀ Like ♂ but hindcrown less bronzy and streamers much shorter, also thicker—each up to 2.0 mm wide and less obviously spatulate-tipped. In a very few males, but over one third of adult females, rear half of gorget is blue not black; in extreme cases blue part is larger than black and conspicuous in field. JUVENILE Forehead and crown feathers olive brown narrowly fringed green, narrow nuchal collar russet brown, and mantle and upperwing coverts olive rather than clear green. Scapulars and tertials pale green, not azure. Central rectrices not streamered. Black gorget absent or very indistinct, replaced by dull rufous brown surrounding pale yellow upper throat and chin and merging into obscurely streaked light olivaceous breast. Belly, vent and undertail coverts paler blue than in adult. BARE PARTS Beak black, iris red in adult ♂, red-brown in adult ♀ and brown in juvenile, legs and feet frosted black in adult and horn-coloured in juvenile. MOULT One complete moult a year, starting in December–January and taking about nine months[161]. WEIGHT Adults southern Australia October–March 29.6 (25–33, n = 42), adults migrating Booby Island, Torres Straits, March and August 22.9 (21–25, n = 12), and juveniles migrating Booby Island March and August 21.7 (18–25, n = 18) (D. Purchase pc); adult males wintering on Karkar Island, New Guinea, 28.7 (28–30, n = 3) and females 28.0 (25–32, n = 6)[161]. MEASUREMENTS *Beak* to feathers ♂ 33.8 (32–36), ♀ 31.7 (30–33), to skull ♂ 40.1 (39–43, n = 10), ♀ 37.7 (37–39, n = 10), depth 6.0 (5.6–6.3, n = 10). *Wing* ♂ 109.2 (108–111, n = 10), ♀ 105.0 (104–106, n = 5). *Tail* ♂ 76.8 (73–80, n = 10), ♀ 76.4 (73–79, n = 5), excluding streamers up to 71 mm in ♂ and 24 in ♀. *Egg* 21.7 × 18.6 (20.5–24.1 × 17.0–20.0).

STRUCTURE Primaries project 17–21 mm beyond tertials in folded wing. P8 longest, p10 9–14 long and 65–72 shorter than p8, p9 0–3, p7 8–10, p6 16–21, p5 23–28, p4 29–31, p3 33–35, p2 36–39, p1 38–42 and s1 39–43 shorter.

Bay-headed Bee-eater *Merops leschenaulti*

Merops Leschenaulti Vieillot 1817, Nouv. Dict. Hist. Nat., 14, p. 17 (Java, in error for Sri Lanka).
Merops quinticolor Vieillot 1817, Nouv. Dict. Hist. Nat., 14, p. 21 (Sri Lanka, in error for Java).
Merops erythrocephalus, Gmelin, Syst. Nat., 1, 1788, p. 463.
Melittophagus erythrocephalus, Stuart Baker, Fauna Brit. India, Birds, 2nd ed., 1927, iv, p. 240.
Merops leschenaulti andamanensis Marien 1950, J. Bombay Nat. Hist. Soc., 49, p. 155 (Port Blair, South Andaman Island).

NOTE Also called Chestnut-headed Bee-eater, which name has been applied in addition to *Merops viridis* (eg in Philippines[156,173]) and is therefore best dispensed with.

FIELD CHARACTERS

In all plumages it uniquely combines yellow throat and azure rump. A little like a miniature European Bee-eater, but unmistakable with rufous forehead, crown and mantle, green wings and tail and belly (tail blue in Java), bright azure rump, yellow throat, and upper breast with narrow chestnut-and-black gorget. Mask black, or rufous. Length 18–20 cm

(7–8 in); there are no tail streamers and instead the bird is markedly fish-tailed. Occurs in pairs and parties of 5–8, collecting into larger foraging flocks before converging onto large communal roost in favoured leafy trees. Breeds in small or large but loose colonies. Hawks insects exclusively from a perch—not known to feed in sustained flight.

HABITAT
Clearings and open spaces in forested country; well-wooded open countryside. Glades in teak forest, plantations, vicinity of rivers, along country roads and railways and mule paths in hills, freely using telegraph wires; large gardens, beach scrub; breeding mainly in banks of large rivers and hill streams.

DISTRIBUTION AND STATUS
Map opposite Plate 7. Over most of its range present year-round, but in places strongly migratory and after nesting disappears from areas of heavy rainfall during monsoon months, about June to September[6]. Tends to occur unexpectedly in forested areas far from known breeding areas. Widely distributed, either plentiful or sparse and localized, in four distinct populations. (1) Sri Lanka and southwestern India. Locally throughout lowland Sri Lanka and up to 1,500 m, more commonly on eastern than other slopes of the central massif, and generally more plentiful in Dry and intermediate than in Wet Zones[464]; numerous in Travancore and locally so in Western Ghats (Kerala, western Tamil Nadu and Mysore) up to 1,200–1,500 m, north to Goa and Belgaum and again in the former Bombay Presidency (Jagalbed, Castle Rock[392]). (2) Very common in submontane zones of Himalayas, the terai, duar, bhabar and dun, from about 78° E. in Uttar Pradesh through Nepal[211,212], Sikkim, Bhutan and across Assam east to Nmai valley (northernmost Burma); less common, and range poorly documented, in Bangladesh and locally southwest through Orissa to about Jagdalpur—not breeding south of Godavari river; from Bangladesh, Nagaland and Manipur throughout Burma (where in south and north a common breeding visitor with evidently rather few remaining to winter[536]), Thailand and Indochina. But absent from lowlands around Gulf of Tonkin and found only in the west of North Vietnam (Lai Chau, Ba Nam Nhung, Muong Mo[28]) and absent from Yunnan[197]. Breeds in Malayan Peninsula and many offshore islands south to Besut (5°50′N, Trengganu) on east coast and Chemor (4°43′N, Perak) on west[402]. (3) Andaman, Great and Little Cocos and Strait Islands. (4) Java and Bali.

FOOD AND FORAGING
Feeds by flycatching from a bush, fence, telegraph wire or bare branch

near top of forest tree. The only published pellet study was of a single pellet which contained mainly social wasps *Polybioides raphigastra* and other Hymenoptera, including honey-bees *Apis indica* and *A. dorsata*[449]. Eats winged insects—bees, ants, termites, dragonflies[6], butterflies including *Papilio crino*[295], grasshoppers etc[464]. Butterflies' wings are not eaten: "you see one of them sweep on to a butterfly close at hand; then you hear a little click of the bill, and as the bird flies off the wings come slowly fluttering to the ground"[308]. "Baillie saw some birds plunging into the water like a kingfisher, but what they were catching was not observed"[536]—probably they were merely plunge-bathing[295].

VOICE
A melodious trill, said to be almost indistinguishable from voices of Blue-cheeked and Blue-tailed Bee-eaters. A sweet, rapid *chewy-chewy-chewy-chewy* of light timbre, and when airborne a more leisurely *churit-churit-churit*[105].

BEHAVIOUR
Variably gregarious at all seasons. Helpers at the nest have not been observed. Large flocks assemble to roost in trees in open forest. Bathes (and drinks?) on the wing, by splashing onto surface of water from low, gliding flight, or dipping down to it from an overhanging perch, returning to shuffle plumage and preen[6]. Comes down to forest paths, probably to pick up grit.

BREEDING[26,464]
Nest burrows are dug in flat, sandy ground with sparse herbaceous growth, flat or shelving sandbanks beside large rivers, or in vertical banks of road cuttings, ravines and streams; rarely a borrow-pit or side of a field-drain. In high cliffs they are sited 3–6 m above ground- or water-level and within 1–2 m of the top. In sandy soil tunnels reach 2–2.5 m, exceptionally 3 m long but in hard earth may be only 45 cm long. Flat-ground burrows decline fairly steeply then level off to run about 25 cm below the surface; in cliffs they slope gently upward for 50 cm or more and then become horizontal.

Nests are scattered singly every few hundred metres along a roadside or river bank, or more often are grouped with up to ten holes (maybe fewer than ten pairs of birds) a metre apart from each other. Colonies of hundreds of birds occur in Malaysia[105,121,402]. Rarely, a previous year's nest-tunnel may be used again, but almost always a fresh one is excavated. Eighty percent of breeding adults in Penang survive to the following year[402].

In Dry Zone of Sri Lanka and Uva Hills, pairs return to breeding grounds in the second half of February and start to dig burrows after a few days. Both birds excavate, alternating in short spells. Both sexes incubate and often are in the nest together. An incubating bird sits very close and is hard to dislodge. During the breeding season adults roost in their burrow at night[402]. In Malaysia holes are dug from early January to mid April and laying is from mid or late February[402]. It is about late March in Sri Lankan Wet Zone and hills, and first half of April in Dry Zone; in India laying is from late March to early May, with replacement clutches in May–June. The clutch in Sri Lanka is 4 or 5 eggs (equally often); in Assam 6 (in nine nests out of ten) and in northern India 4–8, usually 6.

SUBSPECIES

(1) *M. l. leschenaulti* Sri Lanka and southwest India; Himalayan foothills from Uttar Pradesh to northeastern Assam; lowlands from Orissa to south Assam; Burma, Thailand, Indochina and peninsular Malaysia south to 5°N. Mask black, tail green, lower throat chestnut, sides of breast golden-green.

(2) *M. l. andamanensis* Andaman Islands. Larger than nominate race: mask rufous (blackish where it borders cheeks) and sides of breast chestnut.

(3) *M. l. quinticolor* Java and Bali. Mask entirely rufous, tail blue, lower throat yellow, sides of breast golden-green; smaller than nominate race.

ADDITIONAL DESCRIPTION

(Nominate race) ADULT ♂, ♀ Mask black and all feathers above and behind mask rich rufous. (Unusually, this species does not have contrasting forehead or supercilium or cheeks.) Back, rump and uppertail coverts azure blue, the shade of a Kingfisher's back, with azure tips overlying white bases. Tail green, dusky toward tip except for central rectrices, which may bleach blueish. Wings green, with blackish trailing-edge band 6–7 mm wide. Chin and throat pale yellow; a triangle of chestnut on lower throat pointing forwards and backed by narrow black gorget; 5 mm band behind gorget yellow, merging into apple- or golden-green breast. Belly and undertail coverts very pale green-blue. Axillaries and under-wing coverts rufous. Underside of flight feathers (wing and tail) dark grey, shafts white. JUVENILE I have not seen nestlings of this species, but from May–June skins of juveniles (although there is considerable variation among them) it is clear that very young birds sometimes or always have forehead, crown and mantle green, and nape and sides of crown, rufous washed greenish. Bases of green forehead and crown feathers are brown. Remainder of upperparts a bluer, less golden, green than in adults. Chin and throat are paler yellow than in adult; gorget is either dusky and irregular or almost lacking, and merges into yellow of throat

Plates and Maps

Adults of 42 species and subspecies of bee-eaters are portrayed, and a few juveniles. Ten subspecies not illustrated are barely distinguishable from others that are. Maps show breeding ranges, detailed better – according with the better information available – for Africa, Europe, central Asia, New Guinea and Australia than for south, south-east or east Asia. Winter ranges of a few, not all, migrants are shown. Projections: Africa, zenithal equidistant; globe, as viewed from 75,000 km.

Plates and maps are shown together to emphasize the crucial relationship of systematics with geographical distribution.

PLATE 1

Blue-bearded Bee-eater *Nyctyornis athertoni*   1   *N. a. athertoni*
                                                 2† *N. a. brevicaudata*
Red-bearded Bee-eater *Nyctyornis amicta*   3
Celebes Bee-eater *Meropogon forsteni*   4
                                                 († not portrayed)

In ranges shown, species inhabit only forested areas.
Note overlap (arrowed) between the two *Nyctyornis* species.

PLATE 1

1

3 juv

3 ♂

3 ♀

4

PLATE 2

PLATE 2

Black-headed Bee-eater *Merops breweri* 1

Blue-headed Bee-eater *Merops muelleri* 2   *M. m. mentalis*

3   *M. m. muelleri*

Black Bee-eater *Merops gularis* 4   *M. g. gularis*

5   *M. g. australis*

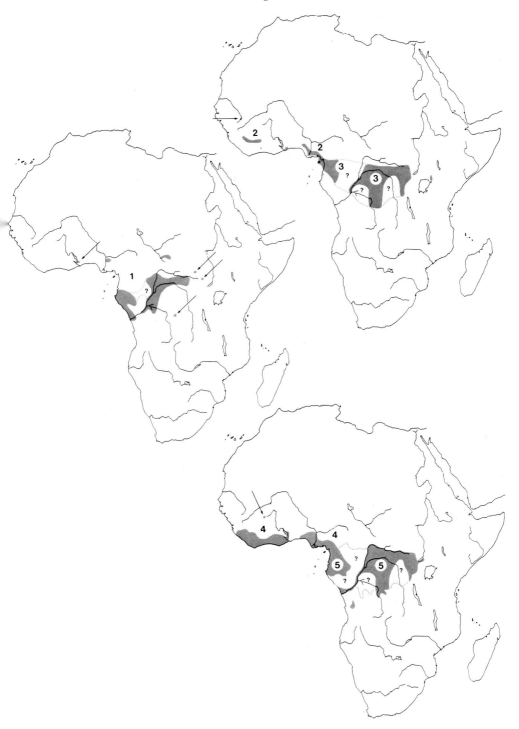

PLATE 3

Swallow-tailed Bee-eater *Merops hirundineus*

1   *M. h. chrysolaimus*
2†   *M. h. heuglini*
3   *M. h. furcatus*
4†   *M. h. hirundineus*

* extralimital records

Little Bee-eater *Merops pusillus*

5   *M. p. pusillus*
6†   *M. p. ocularis*
7   *M. p. cyanostictus*
8   *M. p. meridionalis*
9†   *M. p. argutus*

Blue-breasted Bee-eater *Merops variegatus*

10†   *M. v. loringi*
11   *M. v. variegatus*
12   *M. v. bangweoloensis*
13   *M. v. lafresnayii*

Cinnamon-chested Bee-eater *Merops oreobates*   14

(† not portrayed)

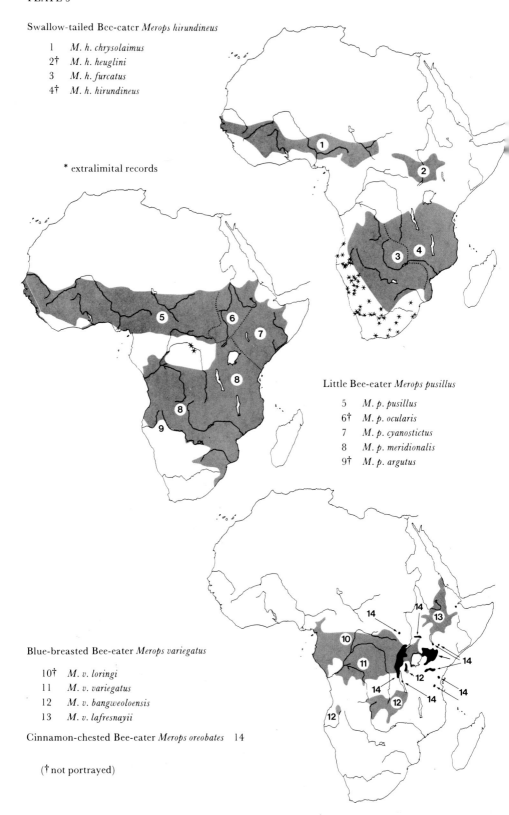

PLATE 3

PLATE 4

PLATE 4

White-throated Bee-eater *Merops albicollis*   1
Red-throated Bee-eater *Merops bullocki*   2   *M. b. bullocki*
                                                     3   *M. b. frenatus*
White-fronted Bee-eater *Merops bullockoides*   4
Somali Bee-eater *Merops revoilii*   5

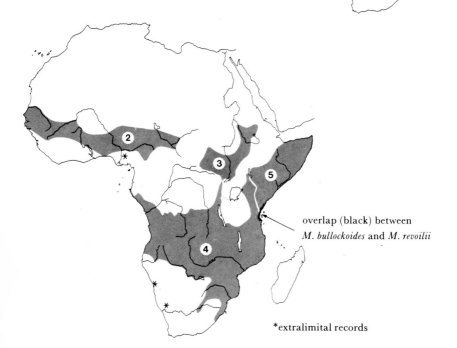

black – known breeding localities
dark grey – probable breeding range
pale grey – winter range
*vagrants

overlap (black) between
M. bullockoides and *M. revoilii*

*extralimital records

PLATE 5

Little Green Bee-eater *Merops orientalis*

1   *M. o. viridissimus*
2   *M. o. flavoviridis*
3†   *M. o. cleopatra*
4   *M. o. cyanophrys*
5†   *M. o. najdanus*
6   *M. o. beludschicus*
7†   *M. o. orientalis*
8   *M. o. ferrugeiceps*

Boehm's Bee-eater *Merops boehmi*

9

(† not portrayed)

*non-breeding records

PLATE 5

PLATE 6

6 ♂

6 ♀

6 juv

1

3

4

5

PLATE 6   Blue-cheeked Bee-eater *Merops persicus*   1   *M. p. chrysocercus*
                                                         2†   *M. p. persicus*
           Madagascar Bee-eater *Merops superciliosus*   3   *M. s. superciliosus*
                                                         4   *M. s. alternans*
           Blue-tailed Bee-eater   5   *M. s. philippinus*
           Rainbowbird *Merops ornatus*   6   († not portrayed)

*other breeding records of *M. persicus chrysocercus*
in West Africa and of *M. superciliosus
superciliosus* in eastern Africa

M. ornatus (6):
dark grey – known breeding regions
*other breeding localities
pale grey – probable breeding range
           Winter range not shown

Data courtesy RAOU *Atlas of Australian Birds*

PLATE 7

European Bee-eater *Merops apiaster*   1
Bay-headed Bee-eater *Merops leschenaulti*   2   *M. l. leschenaulti*
    3   *M. l. andamanensis*
    4   *M. l. quinticolor*
Blue-throated Bee-eater *Merops viridis*   5   *M. v. viridis*
    6   *M. v. americanus*

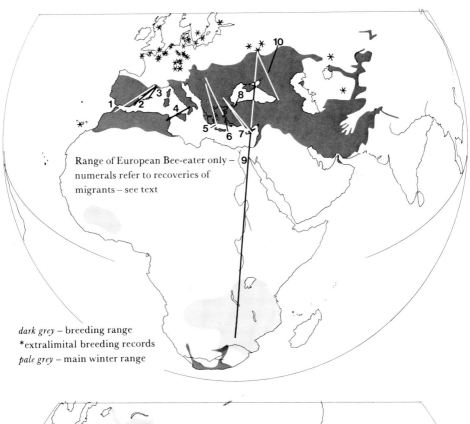

Range of European Bee-eater only –
numerals refer to recoveries of
migrants – see text

dark grey – breeding range
*extralimital breeding records
pale grey – main winter range

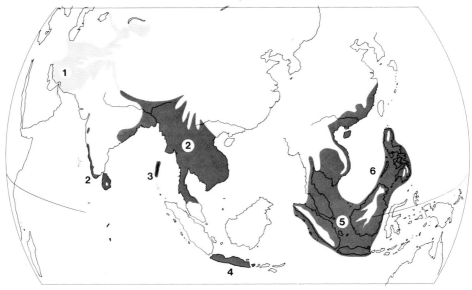

PLATE 7

1

1 juv

6

3

5

2

4

5 juv

2 juv

PLATE 8

1 juv

1

2

3

PLATE 8   *145*

Carmine Bee-eater *Merops nubicus*   1   ***M. n. nubicus***
                                        2   ***M. n. nubicoides***
Rosy Bee-eater *Merops malimbicus*   3

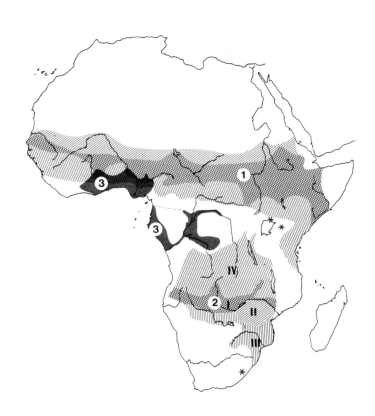

     breeding

     wintering

[post-breeding dispersal pattern]   post-breeding dispersal

*vagrants, *M. n. nubicoides*

Zones I-IV, see text

via a variable small area of obscure rufous. Breast and belly paler and more olivaceous than in adult, silky white feather centres showing through. BARE PARTS Probably as Blue-throated Bee-eater. MOULT A single annual moult, synchronously in adults and juveniles; primary moult starts with innermost primaries, which are shed very soon after (or even before?) young have fledged. WEIGHT 27.2 (23.0–33.1, n = 65, Penang, Malaysia, March, Lord Cranbrook pc). MEASUREMENTS *M. l. leschenaulti Beak* 33.0 to feathers and 37.0 (34–41.5, n = 15) to skull, ♂s averaging 0.6 mm longer than ♀s (n = 66[392]). *Wing* ♂ 107.4 (104–113, n = 32), ♀ 106.0 (100–112, n = 29). *Tail* ♂ 80.9 (78–85, n = 29), ♀ 79.6 (75–84, n = 30); *M. l. andamanensis Beak* each sex 2.4 mm longer than *leschenaulti* (n = 20[392]). *Wing* ♂ 111.2 (107–115, n = 14), ♀ 108.7 (107–112, n = 8). *Tail* ♂ 88.5 (81–94, n = 14), ♀ 90.1 (85–97, n = 8); *M. l. quinticolor Beak* 30.3 to feathers and 34.3 (32–37, n = 7) to skull. *Wing* ♂ 99.4 (95–105, n = 8), ♀ 99.0 (97–102, n = 4). *Tail* ♂ 79.2 (75–83, n = 9), ♀ 81.5 (80–82, n = 4). *Egg* 22.00 × 19.2 (20.0–23.5 × 18.0–21.0). STRUCTURE Folded wing projects 16–31 mm beyond tertials, which are rather long. P10 minute, 13 longer than its covert; p8 longest, p9 0–2, p7 4–9, p6 14–18, p5 25–26, p4 31–32, p3 34–35, p2 37–38, p1 40–41 and s1 40–41 shorter.

European Bee-eater *Merops apiaster*   (Plate 7)

Merops Apiaster Linnaeus 1758, Syst. Nat., ed. 10, 1, p. 117 (southern Europe).

FIELD CHARACTERS

One of the largest and most aerial of bee-eaters, a robust bird with long pointed wings and short, acutely pointed tail streamers. Length 23–25 cm (9–10 in), excluding 2 cm streamers. Constantly used voice a pleasant *pruuk-pruik*, far-carrying and with a rolled, trilling quality *en masse*. A plumage feature which is unique amongst bee-eaters is also a good field feature: scapulars, back and rump are pale gold or flaxen, making a V-shaped mark in flight contrasting with chestnut crown, mantle and secondaries. Wings translucent in overhead birds, looking pale rufous with heavy black trailing edge band. Dorsally, lesser coverts green and primaries and tertials blue-green. Clear yellow chin and throat and narrow black gorget are like several other bee-eater species; rest of underparts pale green-blue; forehead pale yellow, mask black, tail green, eye red.

Breeding birds can often be sexed by plumage[477]; females tend to have scapulars and lower back greener (less flaxen), lesser wing coverts less intensely green, the rufous median and greater coverts edged green, and yellow throat and turquoise breast and belly paler than male. Young birds have a distinctive dress with all of the adults' chestnut and rufous suppressed by green (except sometimes on the crown), and the V-mark on scapulars and back light green.

Breeds in small colonies and very gregarious at other times. Sallies after insects often from high perches, but feeds mainly in continuous flight, hawking with an easy, graceful action, flapping flight alternating irregularly with long swoops and with sailing around high in sky on rigid, acute-triangular wings. Often plunges momentarily onto still water survace, by steep descent or from easy low glide. Non-foraging flight is direct and a little undulating, the wings being briefly closed after a series of rapid beats. Perches freely on vegetation and wires, low near nests, otherwise high, two or more sitting shoulder-to-shoulder.

HABITAT

In its Palaearctic breeding grounds broad river valleys, pasture and cultivated land with shelter-belts and scattered trees; sunny hillsides, plains, dissected steppe often near rivers, along shrubby riverbanks in semi-desert, and in practically any open but well-timbered country: cork-oak woods, olive-groves, tamarisks, *Artemisia* scrub; also by ricefields, cereals and root crops and in Mediterranean *maquis* or *macchia*. Breeds from sea-level up to 2,500 m altitude (in Armenia[157]). Nests mainly in sandy cliffs or steep slopes: river and canal banks, gullies, ravines, quarries and cuttings; sandstone, and sand sea-cliffs reported in South Africa.

Birds on migration and wintering in Africa commonly forage high in the air. Coming nearer the ground they mostly avoid dense evergreen forest (but see Curry-Lindahl[147], p. 478) and desert (except for migrants crossing the Sahara) and are found in and over grassy and wooded savannas, plains, steppe, lakeshores, large rivers and cultivation at all altitudes up to 2,250 m and occasionally up to 3,000 m[79].

DISTRIBUTION

Map facing Plate 7. Intercontinental migrant, breeding in Palaearctic from Mahgreb and Iberian peninsula to Kuybyshev Reservoir region (Tatar ASSR) and from Mesopotamia to Pakistan, Kashmir, Kirgiz steppes and upper Irtysh and Ob rivers, and wintering mainly in Africa south of Sahara. There is also a small breeding population in South Africa, presumed to winter in the tropics.

BREEDING RANGE

In North Africa breeds commonly throughout the Maghreb from coast to southern slopes of Anti Atlas Mts (Goulimine, 28°50′N 10°00′W; Assa, 28°35′N 09°06′W), High Atlas and Saharan Atlas Mts (Tafilalet, Colomb Béchar, Figuig), south in Algeria to Wadi M'Zab (Oued N'Ça) (32°20′N

05°00′E) and Touggourt, in Tunisia to Gafsa, Tatahouine (33°00′N 10°30′E) and Ben Gardane (33°55′N 11°25′E), and in Libya to Jebel Nafusa and the coastal plain east to Garrabulli (32°46′ 13°34′E)[95,293]. Breeds on all larger Mediterranean islands from Balearics to Cyprus. Breeds throughout Iberian Peninsula northwest to southern drainage of Cantabrian Mts (common in León and Old Castille Provinces[575]) and throughout Italy (only irregularly in the north[157]). In south of France nests regularly in Hérault (lower Hérault river), Gard (upper Vidourle river), Bouches-du-Rhône (Arles, Camargue, Crau, middle Arc river, etc), Vaucluse and Var (lower Gapeau and Argens river, formerly lower Verdon river)[487,546]. Elsewhere in western Europe (west of 14° E) sporadic nesting has been reported at numerous localities (see STATUS SHIFTS AND EXTRALIMITAL BREEDING) among which three German sites are important: Vorderen Kraichgau, south of Heidelberg, where a colony lasted from 1965 until at least 1977; the Lech valley north of Augsburg which was colonized in 1964; and an area of former open-cast brown-coal mining at Hohenmolsen–Zeitz in the Elster valley south of Leipzig which was colonised in 1974[259,357].

Northern breeding limits coincide quite closely with the 21°C July isotherm and, in eastern Europe and Russia, run more-or-less parallel with, and up to 100 km north of, the northern limit of grassland and steppe. The central European headquarters is the Great Hungarian Plain, whence the species ranges through the Balkan Peninsula, Turkey, Syria, Lebanon, Israel (not south of about Beer-Sheva, nor in Sinai) and Iraq from Euphrates valley northward, and Azerbaijan.

Bee-eaters are widely distributed in those parts of Austria and Czecho-slovakia bordering Hungarian Plain to west and north[264]. In Austria there are colonies at a score of sites in Burgenland north of Mur and Raba rivers (eg Feldbach) and in Danube Valley west to Tulln or perhaps Krems. In Moravia (Czechoslovakia) bee-eaters occur in Morava, Svratka and Bečva valleys and lowlands north to Přerov and also in Pollauer hills; in 1976 there was also a small colony near Opava in Moravice valley (tributary to Odra river)[52]; in 1968 some bred near Lysá (50°11′N 14°51′E) in Elbe valley and in 1952 some at Ceska Lipa on the Ploucnice river, tributary to the Elbe[264]. But the centre of Czechoslovakian distribu-tion is Vychodoslovensky Province (eastern Slovakia), in Torysa valley, and doubtless in plains further east and Carpathian foothills to the north. Across the Carpathian border into Poland, pairs and small groups of bee-eaters nest in upper Wista tributaries, south of about 51°N (Jaslo, 49°45′N 21°30′E, Przemyśl, Rzeszów, Jarosław, and formerly Olawa, 50°57′N 17°20′E)[264]. To the east bee-eaters breed throughout Moldavia and Ukraine, north regularly to Zhitomir, Kiev and Chernigov, and from Caucasus north to Dmitriev Lgovski (52°10′N 35°00′E), Tambov and

Penza. The northern breeding limit shown in the map crosses south of the northern grassland/steppe limit in this region, but several sporadic nestings are on record to 55½°N here (Morshansk 53°30'N 41°45'E, Tula in at least five consecutive years, Ryazan, Mozhaisk 55°30'N 36°02'E, Murom[157]). Not far south of Ryazan and Murom there are numerous colonies on Pry, Moksha and Tsna rivers and along 100 km of River Oka from Shilovo (54°25'N 41°08'E) downstream to Rubetskoye; from 50 to 200 pairs have nested every year since 1957[471] (S.G. Priklonskiy pc). Further east again, they breed north to Gorodishche (53°13'N 35°40'E) and commonly on Samara bend of Usa river; also near Syzran. In Tatar ASSR they nest north to Laishevo, Spassk and Kama river estuary (and possibly 450 km further northeast, near Kued[361]) and in the east to at least Buzuluk.

East of the Caspian, in Kazakhstan[164], Bee-eaters breed with varying regularity in northwest of that land in Dzhambeity province (50° N 52½° E) and commonly on Khobda, Sari, and lower Kara rivers, also at mouths of Bolshoi Ik and Chaida rivers and sparsely on Ilek, Karagal, Tandy, Zharyk, Sakmara and upper Embe rivers. Nesting occurs all along lower Ural river and on Mangyshlak peninsula on eastern shore of Caspian Sea, but otherwise they are entirely absent between Ural river and Aral Sea and between the Caspian and Aral Seas. Except for Syr Darya river they are also absent from all low-lying land (<200 m) of whole Aral basin. But they breed on east coast of Aral Sea and on the lower Syr Darya, and on numerous small islands south of its mouth. They are commoner on upper Syr Darya and numerous in the near-by Tien Shan foothills and particularly in Golodnyi ('hungry') steppe between Dzhizak (40°20'N 68°00'E) and Il'ich, 90 km to the northeast. They nest in most western valleys of Ferganskiy range at head of the Syr Darya, about 1,500 m, and in valleys and foothills of Chatkal'skiy, Talasskiy Alatau and Kirgizskiy ranges to the north, also around Chimkent and Dzhambul and on southwest and northeast slopes of Kara Tau ridge. Further east they breed on upper Chu river and there are isolated colonies in Chu-Iliskiye mountains.

Bee-eaters nest in places along the south shore of Lake Balkhash and numerously on distributaries and mainstream of the lower Ili. They occur unevenly all along Ili river, including Panfilov only 30 km from the Chinese border, and are certain to nest inside China in its upper valley. They occur all around the Kazakhstani sides of Dzhungarskiy Alatau range up to at least 1,100 m, and particularly in its northern foothills and valleys, and along all rivers draining them into Lake Balkhash. There are a few on southern and northern slopes of Tarbagatai Range and they are quite common at Zaysan and in Lake Zaysan basin[164]. (Again, it is impossible to believe that they do not enter China[197] in this vicinity and my guess is that in reality they are quite common in western and northern Dzungaria, Sinkiang.) They are found in western foothills of the Altai, and breed or have bred on Irtysh river (which feeds Lake Zaysan) at Ust-Bukona and northest to Semipalatinsk and Bolshoi Narymskiy[164]. North of Kazakhstan they occur at 53°20'N on upper River Ob at Barnaul.

To the south of Kazakhstan the breeding range has not been documented in the same detail, but eastern breeding limits probably follow contours—at approximately 1,000 m in the north and 2,000 m in the south—of the Kirgiz steppes and the mountainous salients of Tadzhikistan and Hindu Kush range in Afghanistan. Common throughout Afghanistan below about 1,000 m, and also throughout Iran and Iraq to the Euphrates[307]. Nests on north Batinah coast, Gulf of Oman[250]. In Pakistan and India the bird does not breed in lowlands but nests near Quetta at 1,800 m, in upper Kurram valley (33°50'N, 70°00'E) between 900 and 2,100 m, and throughout North West Frontier Province and Kashmir almost anywhere above 1,500 m (eg Srinagar, Gunderbul, Garhwal, the Punjab, and the region called Kuman or Kumaun, the most easterly breeding location of the species and not far west of Nepal border)[6,26].

In Namibia and South Africa, European Bee-eaters breed sparsely from sea-level up to about 1,500 m in Cape Macchia zone and toward periphery of desert and sub-desert zones, east to 27°E and north to 25°S (see Appendix 3). Most nests have been reported near the coast immediately north of Cape Town, from Lambert's Bay (32°05'S 18°17'E) to Cape Town itself and at eight or more sites west of a straight line between them. They breed in Namaqualand and Little Karoo east to Port Elizabeth, Great Fish river near Grahamstown, and near Bloemfontein, and north to Vierfontein (Vaal river), Wagenhoutskop (Elands river), 80 km northeast of Kuruman and at Aarnsluit on Kuruman river (L. Gillard and P. Hockey pc). Five hundred km to the west, colonies of 20 and 40 birds have been found at two or three localities in Keetmanshoop District (C.F. Clinning pc).

WINTER RANGE

There are December–January records in Bahrain, Kuwait, and the Saudi Arabian Eastern Province, so a small population evidently winters in Arabia. There are one or two old winter records from Canary Islands, southern India[492] and Maldive Islands[463], and even, for that matter, from England[283], but none of these are regular wintering areas, which are all in sub-Saharan Africa. In West Africa European Bee-eaters occur sparsely and are known mainly as passage migrants, locally frequent in south Nigeria, rare in neighbouring Cameroun, Benin, Togo and Ghana. They are common over rainforest on Mt Nimba, Sierra Leone, particularly in February and March and in 1976 500–600 birds were present then[135A]. Further east, they abound in Tchad on migration[501]. West of Ghana they winter in some abundance, from savannas of north and south Ivory Coast[556] to open grasslands and hilly savanna woodlands in Sierra Leone (G. Field pc). Status in Guinea unknown, but in Senegambia only a scarce visitor, some wintering[324] but most on passage[267], occasionally in abundance[424]. A few may overwinter in Nigeria[185].

Almost entirely avoids forested Congo basin and even Zaire savannas except in southern Katanga and along eastern borders[118,497] but on same latitudes small numbers winter in Western Rift Valley north to about Lake Edward, in most parts of Tanzania, central and west Kenya and southwest Uganda[79]. Abundant in Rwanda and Burundi, especially in the wetter western areas (J.P. Vande weghe pc); a few winter in Zambia and Malaŵi (where they are much commoner on passage)[55,551,603] and in Zimbabwe it is common in the three or four 'mid-winter' months[286,535]. The European Bee-eater is generally distributed throughout the interior of Angola from October to April, most commonly in southern Huila Province[565]. It winters south to Caprivi Strip, northeastern and all eastern Botswana and western highveld of Transvaal at Barberspan (26°35′S, elevation 1,400 m) where it is common and widespread from October to mid March[200], and to about Mfolozi valley at 28°30′S in Zululand[148]. In Zimbabwe often occurs over montane habitats at elevation 2,200 m[312].

Elsewhere in Transvaal the species is absent in northern-mid-winter months of December and January but is widespread and quite common on passage, mainly in October and March–April. Because birds arrive at their Cape breeding grounds in September it has been inferred that they are not the same population as the Transvaal passage migrants[84]; but egg-laying in the Cape is later (from late October through November) than was then supposed, and in my view Cape and Transvaal populations are probably in large part one and the same. Otherwise, it is hard to understand where October passage migrants in Transvaal go; "vast flocks" and "cloud-like masses" used to arrive near Port Elizabeth in the 1950s, which would have suggested Palaearctic birds were it not that many of them promptly settled down to nest[325] (they are much less abundant there nowadays[198]).

We have little idea where the southern African breeding population winters; but July records from Malaŵi and July–August specimens in fresh plumage from Angola are suggestive[55,151A]. It seems very improbable that they go to Europe or Asia and breed again there[see 83].

STATUS SHIFTS AND EXTRALIMITAL BREEDING

The species seems particularly sensitive to environmental (probably

Comfort. Little Green Bee-eater rain-bathing; Carmine scratching head with foot and rubbing nape beneath wrist; European stretching wings and preening back feathers; Little preening preen gland and under wing; Rosy Bee-eater dust-bathing.

Rain-bathing

Head-scratching

Head-rubbing

Wing-stretching

Preening

Dust-bathing

temperature) change and during the course of the last 100 years its range has fluctuated considerably.

When it first invaded southern Africa as a breeding species is unknown; the earliest nest record I know of was in 1886, but it might well have been established there centuries earlier (although probably not many millenia, since southern African birds are taxonomically indistinguishable from Palaearctic ones). Between about 1958 and 1964 a sharp decrease occurred in several southern Cape nesting areas[491], not reversed by the late '60s[570].

In Europe, records of the invasion of bee-eaters as breeding birds in one or another region go back to 1517 (Heydenreich 1635[in 264]), but they are insufficient to draw any safe conclusions. By the 1840s, however, they were clearly extending their range northwards; they were then as common and widespread in Great Hungarian Plain as they are to-day, were nesting in south of France and occurred north to Abbeville in 1840, Prague in 1842, Pardubice (50°03'N 15°45'E) and Moravske Krumlov in Czechoslovakia in 1846. Many nested on Gran Canaria, Canary Islands, in 1856[71]. The great recession began about 1875, and by 1890 the species had completely disappeared from lower Austria and western Hungary and had largely vanished from France (except Gard)[264].

Recovery began in the 1920s and '30s and the European Bee-eater has continued to consolidate and slowly to extend its breeding range northward ever since. Birds settled March valley in lower Austria in 1924, the Tullner Feld in 1930 and lower Svratka valley (at Břeclav, Czechoslovakia) in 1932; at the same time they were expanding in Hungary and had invaded Lesser Hungarian Plain again by the early '40s. Nesting colonies were established in Camargue in France in the '30s and in Départements of Hérault, Vaucluse and Var in the '40s[375,487,546]. From 1940 the small Camargue population began to expand substantially, and the number of colonies in southern France has slowly increased from that time until the present. In 1946 and 1947 a major thrust to the north began in central Europe, with consolidation in Hungary, Burgenland and lower Austria and irruption into Slovakia and later Moravia (Czechoslovakia)[354,474]. The mid and late '60s saw considerable northward extension in France with invasion of Ariège, Haute-Garonne, Ardèche and Isère, and prospectively Ain and Vendée[260,353]. At the same time Bee-eaters established themselves in Ryazan Province near Moscow[471], and started breeding in West Germany and in Poland (see Breeding Range), although the Hungarian population became sparser in the '60s than it had been in the '50s[208,550]. Within the latest decade the northward trend in Europe has continued, with colonization of more of Austria[252], southern East Germany (Eisleben 1971 and Nordhausen 1973[264], Weissenfels 1974[357] and Zeitz 1974[258]), northern West Germany (Hofgeismar 1971[505], Bielefeld 1978[264]), northern France (Soissons 1970, Fontainebleau 1977, Manche 1980, Brest 1981, Boulonnais 1982[144,153,564]), Denmark (several islands[476]) and Sweden (Öland 1976[584], Jönköping (58°N) 1977[486]).

Ground lost at the turn of the century has been more than regained, and

European Bee-eaters are now breeding further north than ever before. Because of its vicissitudes, defining its continental limits is risky, but the following notable nestings of recent decades can be treated as 'extralimit-al'. Scotland: Musselburgh 1920[607]; England: Plumpton, Sussex 1955[33]; Alderney Island 1956[543]; Belgium: Stambruges 1956[36], Assebroek[264]; Netherlands: Haelen Limburg 1964[7], Terschilling Island 1965[553]; Denmark: Bornholm Island 1948[366], Jutland 1961 and later years[479]; West Germany: Stormare, Hamburg 1964[42,43]; Finland: Lappee (61°N) 1954[520].

MIGRATION

I have details of nine distant recoveries of European-ringed individuals, shown on the map. An adult ringed in the Camargue, France, in June was recovered next April in Morocco (1 in map) and two Camargue juveniles ringed in August were recovered two and four weeks later on Majorca, Balearic Islands and in Murcia Province (Spain) respectively (2, 3). A migrant caught in northern Tunisia in May was picked up *the next day* in Potenza Province (Italy), 520 km northeast (4)[194]. A Hungarian bird was found on Syros, Cyclades Islands three years after ringing (5) and another on Khios (6)[502] and two Bulgarian birds on Cyprus one year after ringing[455] (7, 8). An adult from Oka Reserve, Ryazan (54°45′N 41°00′E) was recovered after 20 months at Hartley, Zimbabwe (18°10′S 30°07′E) (9)[287]. Huge numbers of bee-eaters have been ringed on River Oka in and near Oka Reserve—nearly 10,000 since 1969[369,472], and in addition to this well-known recovery from Zimbabwe there have been 20–30 recoveries from Georgia and 30–40 from Cyprus (S.K. Priklonskiy pc), but I have not been able to obtain the details.

Few as these recoveries are, they tell us something about European Bee-eater migrations other than the capability of flying 520 km in a day. They provide evidence for a 'migratory divide', western European birds moving SW/NE and eastern European ones heading SSE/NNW or perhaps S/N. They suggest both that the Mediterranean may be crossed on a broad front and that many birds skirt it at either end. The Zimbabwe recovery locality is 7,850 km south of the Russian ringing station, which is much the same minimal distance—say 8,000 km—that must be travelled by Siberian birds migrating to their nearest African wintering grounds in the Western Rift or by Caucasian populations if they winter in Transvaal. The two Bulgarian birds recovered in Cyprus suggest some constancy of route by a population.

Field observations confirm such inferences. European Bee-eaters often migrate in loose association with Blue-cheeked (qv) and their migrations are similar[310]. They fly mainly by day, usually high and sometimes so high as to be barely visible, calling frequently and travelling in loose flocks of 20–40 birds[376,552]. Hundreds congregate at oases and on islands and 'leading' topographic features like peninsulas, coasts, rivers such as the Tisza flowing south through Szeged in Hungary, and passes like Chokpak in Kazakhstan (42°31′N 70°38′E) (E.I. Gavrilov pc). With their young, the French population in autumn is 4–6,000 birds, of which at least 15–20% coast southwest and skirt the Pyrenees 50 km inland at Prats de Mollo[155]. Spectacular concentrations occur at Gibraltar in autumn, when tens of thousands cross the Straits[376,552] and then coast southwestwards[466]. Migration through the eastern Mediterranean is less remarkable[310] although flocks of hundreds cross Cyprus in spring[32]. They were formerly common on Malta on both passages but are now very rare[422]. Although most seem to concentrate at the ends of the Mediterranean there is clearly plenty of passage directly across it. Migrants are common in all parts of Saudi Arabia[323], and they cross the Red Sea[131] but evidently not the Gulf of Aden since there is, unaccountably, an almost total dearth of records in Somalia (J.S. Ash pc).

The scatter of Saharan records from Morocco[19,531], Tunisia[374], Mauritania (P.W.P. Browne pc), Mali[363], Libya[95], Tibesti and Ennedi in Tchad[261,272,273,386], Egyptian oases[419,421] and the Nile valley[310], combined with the want of any report of great concentrations in the region except from Tchad[501], suggest that Bee-eaters cross the Sahara on a broad front too. In Asia large flocks cross the Black and Caspian Seas and Atrek Desert, travelling southwest in September. They readily cross mountain passes, in the Caucasus up to the level of glaciers[157]. In Africa it is one of the few birds directly to cross the equatorial rainforest block[424].

Saharan migrants are compelled to travel by night as well as by day, and night flying has been quite widely noted elsewhere[31,157,310]. At Gibraltar flights regularly commence half-an-hour before sunrise and continue (with a lull at mid-day) until half-an-hour after sunset[376]. I would think that families keep together in parties, and some evidence for that comes from Zambia, where newly-arrived adults have been seen feeding accompanying young birds in September[489]. Migratory flights are frequently punctuated by feeding, the birds hunting aloft or from perches; such breaks are usually only for an hour or two, but at a particularly productive spot a flock may stay for some days. Characteristic of Bee-eater migration is what H.P.W. Hutson[310] described as "regular staging by successive bands". In Cairo particular clumps of big trees were used for roosting night after night by different flocks of migrants in succession, in the springs and autumns of several years.

A spring bird in Cameroun was said to have much migratory fat[424], but Bee-eaters usually do not fatten themselves at all before migrating.

Timing After breeding and before emigrating Bee-eaters roam widely, far from nesting grounds. Departure from the Soviet Union has been minutely detailed by Dement'ev & Gladkov[157] (although their claim that adults emigrate rather in advance of juveniles needs substantiating). The most northerly breeding latitudes are vacated mainly in early August; further south locally-bred birds depart in the second half of August but passage by birds from the north continues into late September, for instance in the Caucasus. Autumn passage at Gibraltar is from mid or late August until the end of September, with 90% of migrants crossing the Straits in 18–25 days and with peak passage during 7th–12th September[376,552].

In East Africa the bird is numerous on passage in September to November[79]. First arrivals in Zambia are in late August; passage there begins in September and is heavy in October and early November[551]. In Zimbabwe first arrivals are in September and the bird is widespread by November, remaining until March (exceptionally, May)[535]. Visitors to Botswana, western Transvaal highveld and Zululand occur at those times too.

Passage in the rest of Transvaal—of Cape rather than Palaearctic migrants?—is from late September to mid November and again from late February to the end of April. Some Cape birds arrive in August but most not until mid September or even October[84]. Most young have fledged by late December and nearly all birds have departed by mid February.

'Spring' passage in Zambia is very evident during March and ends by mid April, and in East Africa it is from late March to early May. In Ethiopia spring migrants are common or abundant in April[573] (J.S. Ash pc) and in lower Egypt they travel north in the Nile valley and along the eastern desert littoral and Suez Canal from the second week of April until mid May[310]. At given localities in Russia there are considerable differences in arrival times in different years; but arrivals are usually in mid April at lower latitudes and mid May at higher ones[157].

In Senegal migrants are seen almost daily in April and early May[428] and the many records of arrivals and migrants in the Maghreb are from the same period, with two records as early as the first half of March[293]. Arrival in Camargue (France) is from early April to early May[546] and in Burgenland (Austria) nest sites are occupied in May, usually in the second ten days[264].

Migrations are of course affected by weather, and at any one particular European locality the time of spring arrival and autumn departure varies from year to year by about three weeks. Sometimes the first bee-eaters are seen as early as March, a few birds or large flocks, and Glutz and Bauer[264] cite a number of instances documented as long as 200 years ago (1770, 1791) and others more recently. Perhaps such vanguards are brought north by the vagaries of subtropical high pressure air cells. Nest sites are occupied two or three weeks after an early arrival and immediately following a large appearance at the breeding grounds[41,298].

POPULATION

Breeding densities have been monitored best in Hungary. Before 1940 bee-eaters occurred mainly in the southwest, in the triangle between Lake Balaton, Drava and Danube rivers. Thereafter they spread and, in 1949, 59 colonies with 1,271 breeding 'pairs' were counted[548] (at that time it was not realized that one in three pairs has a helper and is a trio); and in 1955 about 2,000 pairs[549]. In the early 1960s the population was low again[208,550] but by 1977 had recovered to 1,350 pairs in 39 colonies of which five each held 100–200 pairs[264]. The real Hungarian population might be 2–3 times these values. On several autumn days thousands of birds have been seen migrating down Tisza valley: 5,000–5,500 were counted on 11 August 1971[264]. Autumn counts of migrants at Gibraltar gave 37,000 birds in 1972, 36,000 in 1974 and (over a different sector of coast) 34,000 in 1977[376,552]. Probably 150–250,000 birds cross the Straits between Tarifa and La Peña, and thousands more further west, so that the total Iberian population has been estimated to be in the order of one million birds[376]. Bee-eaters are protected in Portugal but not in Spain, where there is no reason to suppose that their density is greater than elsewhere in the breeding range[608]. To arrive at a value for the world population I have therefore simply multiplied the Iberian figure by 13.0, the ratio of the world/Iberian breeding range areas. The world population will be in the order of 13 million, soon after breeding. About four young birds fledge on average[51,208,352], so the pre-breeding world population would be a third of that number, say 4,000,000 birds.

Fifty years ago C.R.S. Pitman, impressed with the large number of flocks which he encountered in East Africa, with the breadth of the migratory front and its two-month duration, thought that millions of European Bee-eaters must pass there in spring[467].

Adverse influences on the species' abundance are human persecution and cold weather. In several Mediterranean countries large numbers of Bee-eaters are killed every year for fun, for food and for taxidermy[608], while there and elsewhere—wherever apiculture is important—they are killed as pests (Chapter 5). In Cyprus, for instance, 3–5,000 are killed each year by hunters and bird-limers (P. Neophytou pc), and thousands are killed in the Nile delta. Hardly surprisingly, for a bird of tropical origin, the species is not very cold-hardy, and from time to time large numbers perish in unseasonally cold weather on their breeding grounds[157] and even on their African wintering grounds[540].

FORAGING AND FOOD

Most food is obtained by hawking from a perch, usually a branch or a wire but also buildings, stumps and even, in unrelieved terrain, dried camel-droppings. Insects are taken one at a time[356A] and each item is carried back to the perch for treatment (devenoming and immobilization) before being consumed there. A sally flight may be anything from a few metres to a few hundred metres, and 68% of short sallies are successful[293A]. Like Blue-tailed Bee-eaters, this species seems able to discern some flying insects 50–100 m away, and pursuit of a fast-flying butterfly or dragonfly may take bird and insect a further 100 m or so. A bird carrying an insect back to its perch and encountering another insect in flight, has been known to swallow the first item and immediately catch the second[505].

European Bee-eaters also freely hunt aloft, sailing around at height and making sudden twists and dashes, presumably catching small and soft insects like termites and ants, many of which appear to be eaten in flight without the bird returning to perch. Bee-eaters occasionally hover momentarily by wasps' nests or bee-hives and have been known to pick honeybees off the hive[264]. They often swoop for food close to the ground or herbage, evidently sometimes take grounded prey (see below) and when starved will pick insects directly from herbage[357,461] and even eat berries[540]. In France they regularly follow tractors, cattle, and flocks of Starlings, in order to exploit the insects they disturb[145] (J. Krebs pc); similarly a party of schoolchildren was attended by a flock of European Bee-eaters in Zimbabwe for two hours during a ramble (R.M. Harwin pc).

Hunting is generally well within 1 km of the nest, but parents will sometimes forage up to 12 km away[564].

Bee-eaters' food is well known from numerous studies of pellet-, nest- and gizzard-contents which have been made in Europe, Russia and Africa*. In addition to such analyses there have been one or two experimental studies in aviary and field, discussed in Chapter 4.

The food is almost exclusively medium-sized flying insects caught on the wing. Of 10,000 insects eaten in Ukraine, 28% were 5–10 mm, 51% 10–15 mm and 17.5% 15–20 mm long[461]. In Germany only 9% of prey were less than 10 mm long[293A]. Seasonal and regional variations in diet show that birds avail themselves of whatever insects are flying, within certain size limits and with the exception of some noxious insects which they seem to ignore. But at the same time there is some preference for bees, wasps and other Hymenoptera, which always predominate in diet samples although in nature they appear seldom to form the majority of insects flying at large, except near their hives and nests. In the six most extensive analyses, involving over 14,000 insects altogether, proportions of

* See references 36 (Belgium), 43, 293A (Germany), 366 (Denmark), 375, 546 (France), 298 (Spain), 498, 574 (Austria), 277, 388 (Czechoslovakia), 208 (Hungary), 352 (Rumania), 609 (Moldavia), 321, 461 (Ukraine), 50 (Turkmenia), 448 (Ciscaucasia), 351 (Kazakhstan), 457 (Uzbekistan) and 231 (Zimbabwe).

Hymenoptera varied from 52%[321] to 91%[366] (those percentages refer to the numbers of prey items but also apply to weights: 66% numerically of mixed hymenopterans happen to be 65% by weight[352]). The highest percentages on record, 83%[574] and 91%[366], were from adult pellets as well as nest contents (adult and nestling pellets); since nestlings evidently are fed a diet containing up to one-fifth more Hymenoptera than the adults themselves eat[574], the proportion of Hymenoptera eaten in an adult's lifetime is probably less than 80% and perhaps no more than 62%[245] or even 56%[321].

For bee-eaters—adults and their nestlings—living near clover fields and flowering grassland in the temperate zone the most important single prey is *Bombus*, bumble-bees. *B. hortorum* and five congeners comprised 33% of items and 43.5% by weight of food in Rumania[352], and half to three-quarters of the diet during June and July in Austria and in Ryazan, USSR[472,574]. Elsewhere honeybees *Apis mellifera* predominate; around Harare, Zimbabwe, I found that termites and honeybees were numerically each a quarter of the diet; and in shrubby farmland with olive and oak woods in Spain just over half of the food items were honeybees[298]. The Rumanian study showed nearly as many honeybees as bumble-bees to be consumed, but most of the honeybees were light workers rather than heavy drones and by weight were only half as important as bumble-bees[352]. Drone honeybees are preferred to workers; although greatly outnumbered by workers in nature, drones are sometimes eaten in greater abundance[245,352,395,574] and also fed commonly to nestlings[574]. A great many other hymenopterans are eaten: social and solitary, venomous and non-venomous, and small and large species like hornets *Vespa crabro* and carpenter-bees *Xylocopa* (Appendix 8). When Common Wasps *Vespula vulgaris* are most commonly on the wing—in August—they can constitute over 60% of the entire diet[461].

Beetles and odonates are the next two most-commonly-eaten insects. Observational studies in the field generally record a preponderance of odonates over beetles, because such large and showy dragonflies as *Anax*, *Aeschna*, *Sympetrum*, *Orthetrum*, *Gomphus* and *Libellula* (all of which are preyed upon) are easy to recognize when carried to the perch or nest. But in pellet studies odonates are usually outranked by beetles; odonate remains are easily overlooked since only their mandibles and pieces of wing are regurgitated and the rest is digested. Longhorns, scarabs, chafers, dytiscids and an unending variety of smaller beetles are taken numerously.

Butterflies and moths are frequently preyed upon, including large and fast-flying forms like Swallowtails *Papilio machaon*, Camberwell Beauties *Nymphalis antiopa*, Peacocks *Inachis io*, Striped Hawks *Hyles livornica*, Hummingbird Hawks *Macroglossum stellatarum* and elephant hawks

Deilephila sp. Flies feature commonly as well, particularly hover-flies *Eristalis* sp., horse-flies *Tabanus* sp. and soldier-flies *Stratiomyia* sp. Besides these principal groups a great variety of other insects is eaten, including Orders Orthoptera (grasshoppers), Dermaptera (earwigs), Dictyoptera (mantises), Isoptera (termites) and Heteroptera and Homoptera (bugs) (Appendix 8).

Opportunism leads the birds to prey on a single species only, where it is abundant: bumble-bees over turnip-fields, honey-bees at apiaries, dragon-flies over swamps, a hatch of termites or a swarm of locusts[467]. Adults feed themselves as well as their young on such sources. But nestlings almost certainly have diets rather different from those of their parents at the same time. Although no study has yet proved the point incontrovertibly, they may be given more odonates[65], fewer odonates[321], more wasps and honeybees and fewer bumblebees and chafers[574] than the parents take for themselves. Certainly youngsters are given larger insects, on average, than the adults themselves eat[293A], particularly when the latter are foraging more than a few hundred metres away from the nest (J. Krebs pc).

Experiments have shown that captive European Bee-eaters prefer black-and-yellow insects to plain ones (even if larger), and that amongst black-and-yellow insects they select large ones more frequently than small ones[339]. In the aviary they can be induced to eat dead insects, hydrated fresh-water shrimps, live meal worms, spiders, scorpions, centipedes, small lizards and even cut lettuce[107]. Captive birds deliberately seek to vary a monotonous diet, catching insects flying into the aviary, including the aposematic burnet-moths (Zygaenidae) and noxious Blister-beetles *Lytta vesicatoria*[107]. Other aposematic and noxious insects (tigermoths Arctiidae, ladybirds Coccinellidae, cantharid beetles and glow-worms Lampyridae) may be rejected[107].

In nature flightless arthropods are taken very rarely, such as *Lethrus apterus* and other flightless ground beetles (Geotrupidae)[293A,366,461]. A Bee-eater shot on a dung-heap by a Kazakhstani village contained fly larvae as well as flies[351]. A harvestman (Opiliones), a woodlouse and seven spiders were found in gizzards from the lower Volga[448]—although the last may have been taken not from the ground but parachuting on silk in the air. Hawking bee-eaters in Spain were noted to be trailing silk[434], and in Zimbabwe I found the remains of numerous small caterpillars in pellets, which might also have been in the air since caterpillars often suspend themselves on long silk threads.

They may rarely feed from water. Two records refer to a bird splashing onto the surface and rising with something in its beak[33,568]. While some other bee-eater species undoubtedly do take fish, the majority of similar claims for the European probably refer to bathing[239].

VOICE

The pleasant, liquid voice is employed constantly at all times and seasons. In the field it can sound rather monotonous, but analysis shows that small variations of the basic note, usually given in English as *prruip, crick-wicka, pruuk-pruik* etc, produce calls with at least 15 different 'meanings'. There is evidence, moreover, that birds can recognize each other individually[326]. *En masse* the sound is far-carrying, rolling and melodious, very distinctive in Europe where there are no other bee-eaters, but elsewhere hard to distinguish from the voices of Blue-cheeked, Madagascar or Rosy Bee-eaters.

Austrians—and the only analytical studies have been in German— render the voice differently, as *rüpp, drüh, dää* etc[326,340]. Main voices are: (1) *contact* call *rüpp* (resembles ∧ in sonographs[264,326]); (2) high-intensity contact or *annoyance* call *drüh* (∧ with up to five peaks), an urgent, rolled note; (3) *greeting, rüp* or *didirüp* (∧ rather than ∧); (4) *threat, dää;* (5) *alarm, dick-dick-dick-dick* . . .; (6) distress or *anxiety, dä-dä-dä,* like the threat call but each *dä* falling in tone; (7) *song,* of 2–3 secs duration, a phrase involving *drüh* (2), *rüp* (3) and other notes lasting 0.6 sec and repeated rhythmically four times or more. Two birds can sing together in duet, but whether that is strictly antiphonal singing has not been established. (8) *Copulation-intention* (both sexes), a throaty *rüpp,* like (1) but lacking harmonics, becoming in the ♀ an excited gobbling *grrp* or *grrrüüüüp* of low energy and high or very high frequency; (9) *copulating* ♀, a long, quiet, very low frequency gurgle; (10) another ♂ *copulation* call, *dick* like (5) but lower-pitched; (11) a call *raaaah* given during *courtship feeding,* structurally similar to the ♀'s *grrrüüüüp* (8) but sounding very different. It is evidently directed generally and its significance is not understood. *Nestling* voices are (12) *djüpdjüpdjüp* at a few days of age; (13) a fluty *dluiuiu* from about 9 days of age; (14) *dickadadickada* towards fledging; and (15) a long trill, *drüüüüüüü.*

Newly-fledged birds use adult calls but they sound rather different and sonographs show that they are strongly frequency-modulated and have two quite significant overtones (harmonics).

SOCIAL ORGANIZATION

Gregarious throughout the year, strongly so on migration and in winter quarters, when flocks may be quite dense and comprise hundreds of birds. In winter they huddle shoulder-to-shoulder in cold weather, and roost packed tight against each other in rows. Towards sunset up to 100 arrive at a roost in Nairobi and up to 200 at roosts in Addo near Port Elizabeth, having foregathered 90 min earlier in tall trees not far away; they sleep in groups of 4–6 on the leeward side near the tops of the trees[198,458]. At other times they maintain a perching distance of about 10–15 cm, or (except with mate) more when nesting, and in non-foraging flight of about 1–2 m.

Bickering by perched birds is commonplace but seldom seriously prosecuted. Territorial at start of breeding season, defending one or two favoured perches near nest rather than the nest itself.

Sometimes a pair nests solitarily (8% of Camargue nests[546]), but colonial breeding is the rule with colonies in USSR reaching several hundred nests, once 400 at Simontornya in Hungary and 700 (old and new nests) in Yugoslavia[271]. Only a quarter of colonies in Camargue have over six nests (average 17[546]), and in Ryazan, USSR, the overall average is eight[471]. Flat-ground colonies seldom have nest-entrances packed more densely than 1/m²; more generally they are 10–20 m apart[62]. Likewise they are well separated in cliffs, averaging 10 m[459] or even 35 m[375] apart, but holes dug in a long line just below the cliff-top may be only 0.5 m apart.

Males evidently predominate: 60% of sexed skins in the British Museum collection and 59% of those in Vienna[264] are male. One nest in about five has a helper, and helpers have been noted at nests in Spain[108], Corsica (my observation), France (O. Biber pc and J. Krebs pc), Germany[505] and Hungary[176]. They are always males, and in contrast with some other bee-eaters they turn up at the nest only after the clutch has hatched (J. Krebs pc). Nomadic flocks of non-breeders have been noted in Kazakhstan[351], and the birds seem not to be those destined to become helpers.

Bigamy is known but monogamy is the rule; and there is every indication that pairing is life-long (J. Krebs pc). There is some evidence that one bird may, over the course of a breeding season, visit several nests in its colony, again as happens with other bee-eaters.

European Bee-eaters survive much less well than do tropical species, Red-throats for example, which do not have to face the rigours of migration. A population on River Oka, not far east of Moscow, has been studied for years, with up to about 500 birds ringed each year since 1969; and although many have been caught there again after 2–3 years, the best-survivor so far has been for only 7 years (S.K. Priklonskiy pc).

SOCIOSEXUAL BEHAVIOUR

Territorial behaviour is shown mainly in defence of particular perches within the area chosen for the nest. It is quite strongly developed whilst the nest hole is being dug, waning in subsequent weeks and being scarcely evident when the young are well grown. A territory-holder threatens an incoming bird by lunging towards it with opened beak, the crown feathers depressed and throat, neck and mantle feathers raised (cuffing with a wing has also been observed[266]); the incomer either flies off or adopts a defensive posture at perch with the body stiffly upright, head held back and beak opened wide. They may grapple for a moment with interlocked beaks, and

fighting can continue on the wing. Other intruding bird species, like Rock Sparrows which try to usurp bee-eaters' nests[408,445], may be aggressively driven off.

On arrival on breeding grounds from their Afrotropical wintering range European Bee-eaters are already paired. Courtship behaviour has not been studied in Africa, and no-one has recorded any elaboration there of the commonplace greeting display between two birds at perch: excited *didirüp* calls and rather upright posture with vibrated, fanned tail and slightly raised crown feathers. But in Europe, in spring, birds may additionally half open one wing if coming to perch sideways on[277C] (A), or both wings if facing the partner (B), displaying the rufous under coverts*. I construe this as high-intensity greeting behaviour probably with sexual overtones. Such greeting may be followed by a rather more ritualized behaviour (C), in which a bird perches erect, tail and folded wings pointing straight down, crown feathers flattened, and yellow throat a little puffed accentuating the black gorget as the bird voices call (8), a throaty *rüpp*. The act is concluded by the bird rather slowly and emphatically banging its beak, as if with a non-existent insect, against the perch at its partner's feet.

Interesting behaviour peculiar to the nest-excavation phase is calling in duet. Volker Hahn, working in Greece, has shown that when one bird (of either sex) is digging deep in its hole it calls two or three times a second, each time prompting its mate outside to respond[277B]. The notes of the digging bird sounds very like a nestling's begging call.

Commoner than the greeting display, and altogether a more conspicuous sexual behaviour, is courtship feeding. In Africa it has been recorded only on Cape nesting grounds[602] and not in the wintering grounds, but in Europe it can be seen immediately the birds arrive. The

---

* The open-winged greeting was first figured by Dr Lilli Koenig in 1951[340] but the drawings mistakenly showed the tail being wagged sideways, rather than fanned and vibrated. The delightful figures 149A and B in U.N. Glutz von Blotzheim and K.M. Bauer's *Handbuch der Vögel Mitteleuropas*, Band 9 (1980), redrawn from Koenig, exacerbate the error.

male catches an insect in full view of his mate[264] and lands beside her facing in the same direction, taking an upright stance with tail held down, fanned and violently vibrated, calling loudly despite his beakful. He passes her the morsel which is usually a large insect[395] but may be a small one. The female nearly always accepts the offering, quickly eating it, and in so doing she can display either equanimity or excitement—greeting the male on arrival, and after being fed inviting copulation by lying almost horizontally against the branch and uttering the gobbling copulation-call *grrrüüüüp* (D, E, p. 165). Copulation sometimes follows so quickly that she does not have time to swallow the insect. It lasts up to 10 sec[477]; the female lowers her head and the male presses the tip of his beak onto her forehead (F). This assertive-looking action may in fact only help him to balance, which is clearly sometimes a difficulty for him. Copulations increase in frequency up to about ten times a day[264] until the clutch has been completed, and then they cease. If there is a helper he courtship-feeds the female and may also copulate with her; but if the strength of their attachment is not great she may not encourage his copulation attempts[505]. Copulation takes place on a branch or on the ground, at one of the spots defended by the pair.

During the egg laying period the female is courtship-fed often. The male calls her from egg chamber to tunnel entrance and feeds her there or nearby; she often disappears into the nest immediately afterwards. Prey items presented to the female are on average larger than those eaten by the male; probably at this time he provides her with almost all of her daily energy needs (J. Krebs pc).

COMFORT BEHAVIOUR

Bee-eaters sleep either with the beak tucked beneath the mantle feathers, or with head sunk into shoulders and the beak pointing forward and upward at an angle of about 45°. In the pre-breeding and incubation periods they roost in the nest and after eggs have hatched the female continues to spend the night in the nest; after breeding male and female roost in the nest only uncommonly. Otherwise they sleep roosting gregariously, high in foliage of clumps of trees or waterside shrubs, packing themselves into a row all facing in the same direction[207]. They have been noted roosted also on electricity wires, unlikely as that seems[278A]. They yawn, and with head lowered stretch both forewings above the back, with the wrists practically touching (figure p. 153). Then they stretch one wing at a time, downward and backward, spreading wide the same half side of the tail beneath the wing (figure p. 72). They scratch the neck and the back of the head by means of a fast scrabbling with the foot, reaching over (not under) the wing. They preen often, at any time of day when not actively foraging; but never preen each other. One side of the beak is sometimes vigorously rubbed against the perch and less commonly the tip of the closed beak is rapped sharply against the perch. They have the same sun-bathing attitudes as their congeners (see under Carmine Bee-eater). In hot weather they sit with the beak slightly or half open, but panting by means of gular fluttering is not evident. They bathe by splashing down onto a still surface from flight (p. 223) and in captivity—although not, as far as I am aware, in nature—they are known

Sun basking. All bee-eaters commonly sit back-to-sun, with mantle feathers fanned and raised acutely (top row). Less commonly, many species use the 'broken-necked' posture (one of pair, centre right). Red-throats, and doubtless other species, occasionally adopt a variety of improbable basking postures on cliff or ground.

to rain-bathe using spread-eagled horizontal and compact vertical postures[340].

BREEDING

A bird can breed in its first spring[258,264]. The male is said to select the nest site[264] but both sexes dig the burrow. Sometimes an old nest-hole is refurbished[208] and there are records of Bee-eaters using abandoned cliff-holes of Sand-Martins and ground-holes of susliks (ground-squirrels)[refs. in 264], and an old report of them nesting in a cavity in the wall of a house in the Canaries[71]. But nearly always a new nest is excavated. They favour cliffs and steep banks of dry loamy clay, firm sand, soft sandstone, laterite or gravel. In the Mediterranean, sloping hillsides are used and sometimes quite flat ground, bare or grassy, for instance in Andalusia, Camargue, Corsica and Vojvodina (Yugoslavia), also once in Hungary. Hungarian cliff nest-burrows mostly face southwest[176], and Oka valley ones (Ryazan, USSR) south[472].

In their first spring males tend to return to their natal colony but females usually disperse elsewhere; in subsequent years both birds of a pair return to nest in the same part of the same colony (J. Krebs pc). A ringing study in Ryazan showed that at least 80% of birds return to their previous-year's colony[471].

Nest site selection takes about three days, paired and unpaired birds gliding back and forth over the spot, often perching nearby, calling excitedly. On level ground initial scrapes are made with the feet, but at a vertical cliff digging starts with the bird repeatedly striking the cliff-face with half-open beak in hovering or swooping flight. When the indentation is 4 cm deep the bird can obtain a foothold and digging thereafter is much more rapid. At a hole-length of 10–12 cm the bird no longer supports itself woodpecker-like with spread tail at the cliff-face but can work with the body horizontally, beginning to use the legs to scrabble backwards soil loosened by scraping with the half-open beak[433].

Burrows are oval in section, up to 7 cm high and 9 cm wide, straight or curving gently to one side, horizontal or slightly inclining (7°) in a cliff and declining (15°) in flat ground, and about 0.7–1.5 m long in hard earth and 1–2 (exceptionally 3) m long in soft earth. The terminal egg chamber is about 8–15 cm high, 15–20 cm wide and 25–30 cm long[264], usually bending to one side and with its floor 1–2 cm deeper than the burrow floor. Sometimes it has a 'chimney' extension up to 40 cm long, leaving the egg chamber more or less upwards. Shapes of such 'chimneys' have been neatly and precisely demonstrated using plaster moulds[8], although whether they really do function as "air reservoirs useful in the event of a flood" is far from certain. The birds dig in alternating bouts, dislodging earth with the beak (which becomes noticeably worn in the process) and kicking it backward with a bicycling motion while supporting the body on carpal joints and beak. They can dig 38 cm of tunnel in a day. A mound of finely-divided earth appears outside the hole entrance, weighing up to 7 or even 12 kg[157]. If a major obstruction is encountered the burrow is abandoned and a new one started adjacently; whether or not for that reason, two or three short 'false-start' burrows within a metre or two of the definitive nest burrow are commonly found. A pair starts digging two or three holes at the same time, eventually concentrating on the definitive one. Small obstructions are bypassed; a soft root of 4 mm diameter was reported to be pecked through[264], and small pebbles and lumps of earth are carried out in the beak[348].

Complete excavation takes 10–20 days[157], and in a colony the later a particular pair starts to dig, the shorter the time it takes to complete the task[277A]. There is no nest lining; the eggs are laid onto bare earth, but a dry carpet of trodden-down pellets soon forms. Up to 2 litres and 1 kg of such frass may have accumulated by the time the brood fledges.

In northwest Africa laying starts in late April but is mainly in mid May. In Europe and the Middle East laying is from mid May, usually finishing in early June but delayed by adverse weather up to the end of that month[264]. Over much of the Russian range laying is through June, and in Uzbekistan desert steppe is as late as the first half of July[157]. South African clutches are completed by late October or exceptionally not until late November (P. Hockey pc). From the first egg laid to the last young bird fledged takes about 55 days, so fledging occurs in early July in Caucasus and in mid or late August in central Asia. In east Hungarian plain breeding is habitually late and the young do not fledge until the second or third week of August. There, fledging from river banks facing northeast is about a week later than from those facing southwest[208].

The completed clutch has 4–10 eggs, generally 5–6; 41 Hungarian clutches averaged 6.0 eggs, 270 Russian ones 5.8 eggs[472], and 10 South African ones 6.0 eggs (range 5–7, P. Hockey pc). In 1980–1981, 57 French clutches averaged 5.0 eggs, varying significantly from a mean of 4.4 in one colony to 5.8 in another nearby (J. Krebs pc). If the clutch should be destroyed a full replacement can be laid and, if the season is not too advanced, a new burrow even dug to receive it[549]. Eggs are laid at 24 hr and 48 hr intervals. Incubation begins sporadically with the first egg and is persistent from about the third egg or even the penultimate egg[50] (rarely, the last egg). The incubation period is about 20 days[334] (19[50,366], 22[293] or 24[350] days). Both sexes incubate and generally have brood patches[334], by day alternating in shifts varying irregularly from 10 mins to 2 hrs or more. At night the female is usually in the nest alone. The relieving bird finds where the eggs are, in the completely dark nest chamber, by passing the tip of its beak over them[264]. Embryos call just before hatching and the parent responds with soft notes[344]. Hatching of the clutch takes 2–6 days[50,180,475] and eggshells are later moved by adults to one side of the chamber[50] or are sometimes carried out[344].

Eggs are sub-spherical and lustrous white, fine-grained and porcelain-like. The shell is thin and so the new-laid egg looks pink with transmitted light.

DEVELOPMENT[345,475]

The hatchling is blind, completely naked and pink, with dry, wrinkled skin, drooping wings and swollen belly. There is a chalky white egg tooth and the lower mandible is fractionally longer than the upper. For some hours the head is too heavy to be held up, and rests on the floor; the body is supported on the belly and on the tibiotarsal (heel) joint of the splayed legs, which is swollen and yellow with whitish papillae. Soon the head can be lifted, and the bird responds to beak touching with unsteady lunges, grabbing a food morsel but swallowing it with difficulty. Locomotion is unco-ordinated, with shuffling on the heels. By day 3 it eats strenuously but the wings still trail. By day 5 the skin is no longer matt but has become shiny, and the eyes are beginning to open. The abdomen can be raised off the ground, and the shuffling gait becomes better co-ordinated—about this age the nestling sometimes wanders far along the burrow. At a week the eyes, oval behind their fleshy lids, are opening. The bird shuffles positively on its heels, quite fast both forwards and backwards; it snaps greedily at proffered food, and seems quite aggressive towards its siblings.

During its second week the upper mandible overtakes the lower and the young bee-eater, like a young kingfisher, is at the hedgehog stage, covered in pointed grey spines, the elongating feather papillae in discrete tracts. On the head the spines are short and sparse, but the flight feather papillae are up to 20 mm long, thick and precision-packed in neat rows. Feather colour begins to show before the papillae break open, at about two weeks. Secondaries, scapular and tail feathers are the first to sprout, and by about 17 days nearly all of the plumage has sprouted and is growing quickly in its definitive colours. At 3 weeks the normal (ie well-fed) youngster looks and behaves like a fledgling except that the feathers are yet only half grown. Its eyes are fully open and it is alert and mobile. Its egg-tooth is lost or vestigial; its toes grip; it is highly vocal; it preens, and moves plumage tracts in what will become the functional contexts of crown- and mantle-raising and neck-fluffing, and it comes to the nest-hole entrance to await its parents bringing food. Nestlings are quarrelsome, and one blocking the burrow can be tugged by its tail until it yields its place, the best for securing incoming meals first.

Until they are about a week old the young are brooded in spells of 10–30 mins totalling about one third of the daytime. A brooding bird may spread its wings out over the young. Both parents feed the nestlings, at rates varying greatly according to weather, brood size and age, and the presence of a helper. A pair brings about 12 feeds per hour to a newly hatched brood of four or five, and 35–45 feeds per hour to a 1–2 week old brood of six[176]. With a helper the rate can exceed 50 per hour, with 130 and 175 on record[375,477]. In its last nine days in the nest each young bird was found to receive 30–80 (average 53) feeds a day, by weight totalling 7–20 (average 14.2) g per day[352].

A nestling achieves the adult weight of around 55 g in 15–17 days. It is heaviest, at 60–70 g, about 20–25 days (sometimes 30) and thereafter its weight gradually declines by a few grams as feeding diminishes and plumage growth continues, until food is sometimes refused on days 30–31, when it fledges at 2–3 g above adult weight[50,475]. The whole brood fledges rapidly, within 1–2 days[50]. For the first day or two out of the nest young birds do not catch food for themselves at all; adults feed them with decreasing frequency for three weeks, and beyond that time begging youngsters are ignored or repelled[344].

ADDITIONAL DESCRIPTION

Monotypic. ADULT ♂ *Summer* Forehead white merging into chestnut crown via yellow then green; short yellow-green or blue-green supercilium; mask (lores, line of feathers below eye, ear coverts) black; yellow throat narrowly green where it borders mask and white or nearly so below ear coverts. Rump flaxen or tawny; long uppertail coverts same olive green as tail. Wing silvery grey below with very pale buff lesser and median underwing coverts, dusky tips to remiges, and buff marginal coverts; above, inner wing is mainly rufous and outer wing green, with primaries dark tipped and secondaries black tipped forming trailing-edge band 15 mm wide. Tertials green. Primaries olive green or blue-green; alula, primary coverts and wrist region green. Secondaries, greater, median and lesser coverts (except green outermost ones) rufous. Shafts dark brown dorsally, white ventrally. Forepart of folded wing looks chestnut and hindpart green, with green wrist, small central black patch made by secondary tips, and blackish primary ends overlying tail. ♀ *Summer*, see FIELD CHARACTERS. ♂, ♀ *Eclipse* (August–October) Gorget narrow, dusky with little black, feathers green-tipped; crown and scapulars green-tinged; mantle, back and rump green; eclipse adults can be distinguished from juveniles by their streamers, yellower scapulars, chestnut secondaries, and worn flight feathers. *Midwinter* Overall, plumage duller by wear; scapulars and rump greener and duller than in summer; the chestnut tracts with occasional greenish feathers. JUVENILE Recently (up to four weeks) fledged birds readily distinguished from adults: dull olive where adult is chestnut—mantle, back, greater, median and lesser wing coverts; nape and crown generally dark rufous but may also be mainly olive green with dark rufous feather bases showing through; secondaries dull olive narrowly edged warm brown. Folded wing looks olive with brown secondaries and dull blue primaries. Very narrow pale fringes may give scalloped appearance to crown and wing coverts. Forehead dull pale green, chin and throat paler yellow than adult, black gorget absent or only vestigial, scapulars pale green or buffy ivory, rump green not gold; no streamers, tail duller and underparts duller and paler than in adult. BARE PARTS Beak black, inside mouth flesh pink, iris crimson or red (adult), red-brown (fledgling) and brown (nestling), legs and feet purplish-brown, frosted grey or whitish. MOULT Only a few weeks after fledging many juveniles in France have growing contour (body) feathers in August[264], probably representing the gradual initiation of the complete moult which gets properly underway on wintering grounds, in October–November. Flight feather moult begins in October, and it and contour moult are completed by March, bringing young bird directly into nuptial plumage.

Adults in southern Europe begin to moult some contour feathers in late June or early July, accelerating the process to completion in August or September when they acquire transiently an autumn or eclipse[392] plumage feathering rather like the juvenile's. In Africa, adults change into breeding plumage by a second complete contour moult about November–February. Flight-feather moult commences soon after nesting is over, with about one third of adult birds in Camargue (France) replacing some remiges in mid August[264]. Wing moult starts with 13th (innermost) secondary and about same time with 3rd (inner) primary feather. In Kirghizia (Kazakhstan), moult of contour plumage begins in late June and early July and of primaries, starting with p1 or sometimes p2, in August[501A]. When primaries 1–4 have been renewed, moult of the primary series is suspended while the birds migrate to Africa. Percentages of 832 adults caught when migrating through Chokpak Pass in Kazakhstan were, respectively in each of the 4 ten-day periods from 21st August to the end of September, Not moulting 2, 13, 10 and <1%, Starting to moult <1, 2, 2 and <1%, and in Suspended moult 3, 30, 33 and 4%[501A]. Generally, males begin moulting a few days before females, and first-year birds do not start moulting before their autumn emigration. In Africa, about the time that 6th primary is shed, outermost secondary moults; thereafter primary series continues to moult outwards and secondaries to moult centripetally from each end of the series[264], and wing moult is completed by March. Rectrices (tail feathers) are moulted from inner then outer centres about October–January. The sequence of events for European birds thus approximates to the schedule[264,281,607]:

		Aug	Sep	Oct	Nov	Dec	Jan	Feb	Mar
First year	contour	–	–	– – – –	––––––	– – – –	–	–	–
	primaries			1 2 3 4 5 6 7 8 9 10					
	secondaries			12 11 13 10/1 9 2 8 3 7 4 6 5					
	rectrices			1/2 6/3 4 5					
Second year (adult)	contour	– – – – ––––			– – – – – – – – – – –				
	primaries	3	2/4	1/5	6 7	8	9		10
	secondaries	13	12	11	1 10	2 9	3 8	4 7	5 6
	rectrices			1/2 5/6 3/4					

The moult regimen of South African breeding birds has not been studied; to do so ought to be a simple way of resolving the vexed question, whether they migrate annually to the Palaearctic. WEIGHT ♂♀ Kazakhstan 56.9 ± 0.3 g (n = 322; moulting birds 54.1 ± 0.9 g in August and 59.1 ± 1.2 g in late September, and non-moulting birds 56.2 ± 1.1 g in August and 61.3 ± 0.9 g in late September[501A]); ♂ May–July, France 55.7 (n = 97), August, France 58.9 (n = 10) (combined range 48–78[264]); ♀ May–July, France 53.8 (n = 116), August, France 57.0 (n = 14) (combined range 44–72[264]), unsexed September, Ethiopia 44.1 (43.6–45.0, n = 3, J.S. Ash pc), November, Zimbabwe 54.8 (51.5–58, n = 3[14]) and (starved to death) 42.5 (39–46, n = 19[540]), April, Morocco 48.7 (36.5–60, n = 46, 3 g heavier after than before noon[19]); hatchling 4.15–5.55 g and nestling just before fledging 65–72 g[475]. MEASUREMENTS Europe *Beak* to feathers ♂ 36.2 (29–42), ♀ 34.7 (31–38.5), to skull ♂ 43.1 (36–50.5, n = 25), ♀ 39.5 (35–43.5, n = 25); depth 7.4–8.2. *Wing* ♂ 151.3 (145.5–158, n = 15), ♀ 146.4 (144–150, n = 13). *Tail* ♂ 89.4 (85–95, n = 10), ♀ 84.7 (81–88, n = 10) with ♂ streamers up to 24 and ♀ up to 18 mm longer. *Egg* Europe 21.85 × 25.63 (20.0–23.6 × 24.0–28.0, n = 100[607]), India 22.4 × 26.6 (19.9–23.3 × 24.1–28.7, n = 100[26]); weight Czechoslovakia 6.3 (5.9–7.1, n = 14[264]), Azerbaijan 6.5 (5.3–7.7, n = 167[334]), Turkmenistan 6.9 (6.2–7.9, n = 15[50]) including weight of shell, 0.38 g[264]. STRUCTURE Rictal bristles well developed. Middle toe nail flanged on inner edge. Uppertail coverts rather long (45 mm). Primaries project 40–55 beyond tertials in folded wing. P9 longest, p10 pointed, 12–14 mm long and 94–100 shorter than p9, p8 3–5, p7 14–17, p6 26–27, p5 35–38, p4 45–49, p3 53–57, p2 59–63, p1 64–68 and s1 69–71 shorter.

Rosy Bee-eater *Merops malimbicus*   (Plate 8)

Merops malimbicus Shaw 1806, Naturalists' Miscell., 17, text to pl. 701 (Malimba, Portuguese Congo).

FIELD CHARACTERS

Unmistakable: dark grey above, shocking pink below with broad white cheek stripe extending forward to chin. Length 22–25 cm (9–10 in), excluding streamers of 4 cm. A long-winged and fairly large species, about the proportions and nearly the size of European Bee-eater. Highly gregarious; breeds in huge colonies in sand-bars in great West African rivers and winters in flocks in rainforest zone. The most aerial of bee-eaters; feeds in continuous flight high in air, and by sallying from tree tops. Vocal; calls quite like European Bee-eater. Tail dull carmine, bleaching same dark grey as back. Eye bright carmine red. Juvenile grey above, dirty dull pink below, the white cheek stripe poorly defined. Adult and juvenile easily distinguished from Carmine Bee-eater (the only other pink one) by grey not red wings, grey not blue crown and rump, and quite different voices.

HABITAT

Airspace above rainforest and moist savanna woodland, feeding around emergent trees and in and above open canopy and (except when breeding) seldom coming near the ground or perching under 15 m high. At all seasons commonly near open water, hawking from secondary forest or a large solitary tree by a reservoir or broad river. Flies (and forages?) much lower over water than land and sometimes touches surface. Nests in coastal bluffs at Malimba, but the few other breeding colonies discovered have all been in large shelving sand-bars in rivers passing through low-lying savanna country. The tens of thousands of birds in such a colony forage mainly along the river's fringing forest, with distant roosting flights following its course; others disperse by day across a variety of wooded habitats away from the river.

DISTRIBUTION AND MIGRATION

Map opposite Plate 8. Migratory, at least in part. Evidently two populations, separately in Upper and Lower Guinea. In Upper Guinea ranges from western Ghana to southeastern Nigeria. Nesting colonies have been found on Rivers Niger and Benue between 5°45' and 10°E and 6°30'N, namely at the Kaduna river confluence at 5°48'E, Eggan about 6°00'E[91, 224], a site between those two[222], on Simanka river near Ibi at 9°45'E[29], "on the lower Niger in May 1898"[29], at Nzam about 6°30'N near Onitsha[135], and probably near Loko 7°50'E[508]; at these localities birds are present in April–June. After breeding there is a rapid dispersal, probably responsible for the most northerly sightings of the species, at 10°00'N near River Niger in August and September[585]. But normally birds disperse or migrate southwards, to the forest and coast and (in Ghana) coastal savannas, which they visit from late June to early April being common from September to March[186,254]. In forest areas of southeastern and southwestern Nigeria they are well-known migrants of predictable occurrence, but in savannas between the forest and River Benue, for instance, they appear only erratically. At some forest-zone localities they occur all year (presumably non-breeding birds in April–June). West of Ghana recorded only twice, in Ivory Coast, as far as 5°00'W in March[556]. To the east, never yet recorded in Cameroun[378] (although common just west of border in Calabar Province, Nigeria[512]).

In Lower Guinea found along the Congo from its mouth upriver to about 23°E, ranging west, in savannas rather than forest, to the coast north to near Cameroun border, and south to about 6°S in Kasai Province, Zaire. It has not yet been found nesting on River Congo, although almost certainly does so, at low water from February to April[118]. Not migratory on upper River Congo, but at Malimba (for which the species was named) on coast 80 km north of Congo mouth it is a breeding visitor, arriving in May, nesting soon after, and staying at least until August[118]. Much further north, on Fernand Vaz coast of Gabon, they occur especially in September–November[118]—migrants from Upper Guinea?

POPULATION

On its wintering grounds widespread and, although somewhat erratic, often common. So few nesting colonies have been found and aggregations there are so great, that the species seems likely to breed at only a relatively few locations. In 1942 the Eggan colony was estimated to hold 18,500 nest holes. In 1965 the Kaduna confluence colony had about 23,700 nest holes; allowing for some being unused false starts the colony would have numbered between 25,000 and 50,000 adults. Two other 1965 colonies were each about one-third that size, while in 1933 the Nzam one may have been much larger.

FOOD AND FORAGING

Exclusively flying insects, caught mainly in wheeling continuous flight; also in fast sallying forays from an elevated perch or in graceful swoop. Small insects appear to be eaten aloft; larger ones are carried to a perch to be immobilized and devenomed.

Flying ants greatly predominate in diets and constitute 70% of 1,250 prey items in pellets from River Niger breeding colonies in May. Of eight birds shot on River Congo in July "every one had its gizzard well filled with large brown winged ants"[118]. Honeybees are next most abundant, at 17% of the Niger sample (numerically; the proportion by weight would be greater). Gizzards of six birds shot at three (non-riverine) localities in southeast Nigeria contained nothing but "bees"[512]. The rest of the Niger sample was other Hymenoptera (11%) and other insects: including true (vespid), spider-hunting and sand wasps, dragonflies and damselflies, flying termites, grasshoppers and crickets, flies and squash bugs. Larger prey include a scoliid wasp *Campsomeris collaris* 20 mm long, a 16 mm dytiscid water-beetle, an acraeid butterfly *Bematistes vestalis* and the fast-flying nymphalid *Charaxes jasius*.

VOICE

Flight call "a hoarse *chick-k*"[118]; I recorded it independently as "a rather hoarse *crrrp*", not unlike the commonest voice of European Bee-eater. Alarm call, *wic*.

BEHAVIOUR

Whether there are helpers at the nest is not known. As in Red-throated Bee-eaters, nest visiting is 'promiscuous', ie one bird will enter several nest holes. Courtship feeding consists of a very small insect being ceremonially proffered by male to female. The male arriving at its nest with such food (the female being inside) often faces the entrance and digs in the tripod stance a few cm away, moves forward a few cm and digs again, progressing likewise into the tunnel a few cm at a time until out of sight. Sometimes food exchange occurs on sand by the nest entrance. Then facing each other, the male holding the insect in its beak-tip, both birds jerk the beak upwards through a few mm to alternate sides. The female's display is less intense than the male's and she accepts the morsel after a few seconds. I have not observed copulation to follow this display but have seen it at other times when it was not immediately preceded by courtship feeding. The male in coitus presses the female's head down, gripping forehead feathers in his beak.

As with colonial terns and with Carmine Bee-eaters, 'panics' at a nesting colony are commonplace. At intervals all birds sitting outside the

nest holes and many inside suddenly fly away, for no apparent reason but as if frightened. They return more casually soon afterward.

Neither the usual bee-eater greeting ceremony nor any form of sun-bathing have been noticed in Rosy Bee-eaters. Evening water-bathing or drinking is frequent—a glide down to the surface, brake and stall a few cm above it, splashing down and immediately rising clear with only a momentary break of flight. Behaviour interpreted as grit-eating was once seen after an evening wind-storm, when 50 birds alighted on smooth sand far from the nesting colony; each ran upwind a few paces, pecked at the sand surface, and flew on a few metres to join another group and repeat the process. I observed no insects but there were scattered pieces of grit 2–3 mm long.

BREEDING

Nests gregariously in huge colonies (see above) in coastal bluffs[118] and, more generally, in large shelving sand-bars exposed by falling waters of broad rivers. Nest holes are evenly scattered, at 195–240 holes per 100 m² or about two per m², on bare flat sand. One such colony measured 330 m × 33 m. Gently shelving sand banks with a thin growth of sedges and annuals are also used. Nest length is 180–195 cm (mean of ten, 190 cm), the burrow declining at 16° to horizontal and being straight or slightly curved to one side, or declining to a depth of 25 cm and then levelling off. Nest chamber is typical shape, aligned or angled with tunnel, the floor averaging usually 50–55 cm below (flat) sand surface. Nests are aligned, with 80% of entrances facing same quarter of compass. Sand-bars are submerged by rising water after the breeding season, so nests have to be dug anew every year. In one case the same sand bar was used for at least four years.

Laying is in third and fourth weeks of May on middle River Niger and was about a month earlier on lower Niger. On River Congo probably nests at low water, from February to early April; on Cabinda coast breeds soon after arrival in May[118]. Clutch is 2[91]; doubtless single-brooded. Rest of breeding biology unstudied.

ADDITIONAL DESCRIPTION

Monotypic. ADULT ♂, ♀ Forehead and crown dark dove grey, in some specimens with barely perceptible mauve wash; nape, sides of neck, mantle, back, rump, uppertail coverts, and exposed surfaces in upper side of folded tail the same or fractionally paler; upperwing coverts and exposed surfaces in folded wing darker sooty grey. Bases of rump feathers, uppertail coverts and larger upperwing coverts dull carmine, which colour sometimes shows through and lends purplish tinge. Tail, except central pair of feathers, dull purplish carmine, each feather narrowly edged dark grey so that no red shows when folded. Central pair of rectrices dark grey, but dull carmine exactly where overlain by uppertail coverts and where one rectrix of pair is 95% overlain by other. (It is obvious that the tail is, basically, carmine throughout and turns dark grey where exposed to light.) Mask (ie lores, ear coverts and connecting line of feathers below eye) black. Chin and cheeks pure white, forming broad line below mask. Throat, breast, belly and flanks Bengal Rose pink, grey feather bases and buff centres sometimes showing. Undertail coverts mid dove grey with pink wash. Underside of tail black, a little shiny, shafts whitish. Underside of wings dark grey, lining coverts sooty with mauve wash. JUVENILE Upperparts as adult but (except flight feathers) slightly paler, and wing coverts, tertials, back and rump feathers very narrowly pale-fringed and with blueish or greenish wash according to direction of light. Tail dark grey-brown with dull carmine wash towards central axis of each feather. Mask dark grey rather than black. Cheeks below mask narrowly buffy white, chin and intervening feathers pale grey. Underside dull dirty pink, buffy toward belly. Undertail coverts as adult. BARE PARTS Beak black; adult iris red or red-brown; legs and feet yellowish brown. WEIGHT Unrecorded; my guess is about 45 g. MEASUREMENTS *Beak* to feathers 38 (35–40), to skull ♂ 43.0 (40–46, n = 10), ♀ 42.3 (40–45, n = 10), depth 6.7 (6.2–7.3, n = 10). *Wing* ♂ 137 (128–141, n = 10), ♀ 132 (123–140, n = 8). *Tail* ♂ 78 (74–83, n = 10) and ♀ 77.5 (76–81, n = 8), excluding streamers up to 47 mm long in ♂ and about 35 in ♀. *Egg* 20.9 × 25.6 (19.8–22.0 × 24.9–26.15, n = 5, M. Walters pc). STRUCTURE In folded wing primaries project 40–45 beyond tertials. P9 longest, p10 minute—12–16 long and 88–89 shorter than p9, p8 2–5, p7 12–17, p6 25–27, p5 33–38, p4 45–48, p3 52–55, p2 56–61, p1 61–65 and s1 67–72 shorter. Tail of recently-fledged juveniles markedly graduated with outer feathers progressively up to 12 mm longer than central pair (which is round-ended, without an incipient streamer). Outer three rectrices hook-tipped, ie outer vane 1 mm and inner vane 0.4 mm longer than shaft.

Carmine Bee-eater *Merops nubicus* (Plate 8)

Merops nubicus Gmelin 1788, Syst. Nat., 1, pt. 1, p. 464 (Nubia).
Merops nubicoides Des Murs and Pucheran 1846, Rev. Zool., p. 243 (Port Natal, probably in error for Ouri River, Transvaal).
Merops nubicus nubicoides, White, Revised Check-List Afr. Non-Pass. Birds, 1965, p. 232.

FIELD CHARACTERS

Unmistakable in all plumages—few birds are more readily recognizable. A large, long-streamered, highly gregarious blue and shocking pink bee-eater, more aerial than others and with an unique *tunk-trunk* note. Length 24–27 cm ($9\frac{1}{2}$–$10\frac{1}{2}$ in) discounting streamers up to 12 cm ($4\frac{3}{4}$ in) long (adults of northern race and juveniles of northern and southern races rather smaller).

Found throughout African tropical savannas in two populations which have often been treated as specifically distinct, the Northern Carmine Bee-eater *M. n. nubicus* with a green-blue throat and the Southern Carmine *M. n. nubicoides* (which is the largest *Merops* bee-eater) with a pink throat, transiently blue in juveniles. Mask black; whole head-top greenish blue; rump and undertail coverts light azure; wings and tail crimson; and rest of body brilliant carmine pink. Long, pointed wings have a black trailing edge and are warm buff below. Beak relatively stout and decurved. In juveniles blue parts are duller, and remainder of plumage is buff and earth brown with back rufous and throat pink-buff or pale blue. Adult Northern Carmines have chin and sides of throat clearer blue than the centre—in some lights the effect can be of a triangular blue-black gorget and pale blue cheeks.

Nesting colonies are compact, usually in sand cliffs by large rivers, and the several hundred birds disperse daily to a radius of several kilometres. They feed aloft in continuous flight, or by means of fast sallies from a tree perch; strongly attracted to bush fires, swooping and wheeling through smoke to catch fleeing insects, and northern birds often ride on backs of antelopes, domestic stock and large cursorial birds, to feed on flying insects they disturb.

HABITAT

Open bushy and woody savannas, farmed river flood-plains with oxbows and stands of trees, open pasture and tilled fields having shade trees or wind-break hedges, grassy plains carrying ungulates, swamps, marshes and lake-shores with scattered leafless trees, arid *Acacia* steppe, mangroves. In addition, airspace above all of these habitats and on occasion practically any lowland habitat except rainforest, and airspace over large open waters. Nests are nearly always in perpendicular or steep-sloping river banks, but occasionally a colony spreads over the cliff top into flat ground above[315]; rarely nests are in hot sand flats (Mali, Somalia, Kenya) and coastal dunes (Somalia, J.S. Ash pc). Breeds below 1,000 m altitude in northern tropics and 1,500 m in southern.

DISTRIBUTION AND STATUS

Map opposite Plate 8. Wholly or partially migratory in mesic African savannas. Discrete populations, with northern and southern tropical breeding ranges 1,900 km apart at their nearest point, each moving to lower latitudes after nesting. At higher latitudes each is a regular summer visitor; but birds travel widely and, particularly at lower breeding latitudes, tend to be of irregular and unpredictable occurrence except near established breeding colonies. All known nesting localities are listed in Appendix 4.

In the northern tropics Northern Carmine Bee-eaters range in all savannas between desert and rainforest, but are absent from Somalia east of Webbi Shebelle river, and are not known to nest nearer to rainforest edge than about 200 km. Southernmost breeding localities are: in The Gambia upper Gambia river, in Ghana Black Volta river near Lake Volta; in Nigeria Niger and Benue rivers immediately upstream of Lokoja, In Cameroun Galim, in Zaire Garamba or perhaps Kibali rivers, in Kenya Lokichokio, Audache and Ileret in Lake Turkana basin, in Ethiopia near confluence of Gonale Dorya and Webbi Gestro rivers, and in Somalia near mouth of Juba river. South of a line connecting these localities (see map) the species is a dry-season (winter) visitor, south sporadically to northern limit of rainforest zone in West and central Africa. In East Africa it is a non-breeding visitor in September–April south in Uganda to Kabalega Falls National Park, in west Kenya to the Equator (occurring sparsely and mainly below 1,200 m), and in eastern and coastal Tanzania to about 10° S[79]. From November it becomes very common at the coast and large numbers roost in mangroves north of Mombasa, a few non-breeders remaining all year[79].

In Inundation zone of River Niger in Mali they are summer visitors only, north of about Bamako[363]. The same goes for northernmost Nigeria[163,303] and for Eritrea north of Tacazze river[530], and the bird is likely to be mainly absent in winter from Saharan fringe shown hatched on the map. The picture is obscured, however, by the tendency for birds to appear in summer far from and in some cases north of any known breeding grounds, as about $13\frac{1}{2}$° N in Tchad[439].

Southern Carmine Bee-eaters range from Rwanda to Swaziland and from southern Huila and Cubango Provinces of Angola to Western Rift Valley and in southern Mozambique to Indian Ocean seaboard. Within this vast area their southern-summer-breeding and wintering ranges somewhat mirror those in the northern tropics, and I can best describe them by reference to the four zones marked I–IV in the map.

The breeding range (zones I and II) extends north generally to about 15° S, and to $13\frac{1}{2}$° S on upper Zambezi tributaries and $12\frac{1}{2}$° S in Luangwa valley, Zambia. To the south it is bounded by middle Okavango and Chobe rivers[534] and reaches 21° S in Zimbabwe and Mozambique. Most colonies are in hot lowland savannas receiving 50–80 cm annual rainfall, but broad rivers with suitable nesting cliffs take birds into adjacent higher ground with greater rainfall, particularly in Zimbabwe and western Zambia. Breeding is in September–November; within breeding range birds occur north of Zambezi (zone I) in all months, but south of it (zone II) only as summer visitors from August to March. Important breeding rivers are the Luangwa, upper Zambezi, and Zambezi below Lake Kariba (Appendix 4). But the middle Zambezi, between Lake Kariba and Victoria Falls, has basaltic not sandy banks and is unimportant (J.D. Huckabay pc).

To zone III (northeastern Namibia, northern Botswana, Transvaal south to $25\frac{1}{2}°$ S, southern Mozambique, Swaziland, and northern Zululand south to Richards Bay—R.M. Harwin pc) Carmine Bee-eaters are irregular non-breeding summer visitors from August, their numbers being supplemented in December by post-breeding dispersal—especially from Zimbabwe to Transvaal. They all leave in March.

Zone IV is the principal wintering ground, migrants arriving in mesic savannas north of 15° S and visiting as far north as northern Angola, Kasai Oriental, Kivu, eastern Burundi and Rwanda (J.P. Vande weghe pc) and western Tanzania[79] from March to August.

MIGRATION

At many high-latitude nesting stations and at fewer low-latitude wintering ones the species is known as a regular and prominent visitor. Little is known about the journey in between, because of the difficulty of distinguishing migratory from roosting and even foraging flights. In places, seasonal movements may be determined by those of Migratory Locusts (see FOOD). Nowhere has this species been reported to migrate with the regularity and conspicuousness of White-throated or European Bee-eaters.

In Zambia (zone I) there are very few June records. Birds arrive at breeding cliffs in the upper Zambezi, Kafue National Park and Luangwa valley in mid July. Immigration from the north is in August and (mainly) September, when small southbound flocks are commonly seen all over the country. Nesting sites are vacated in early November, birds dispersing widely. Most December-to-April records are south of 15° S, in Southern and Barotse Provinces, and there are sporadic reports from all provinces of northward movements in March, April and May[551].

In Zimbabwe (zone II) the birds are breeding summer visitors arriving in August–September. Post-breeding dispersal means that many colonies, including the celebrated one formerly on Umfuli river near Beatrice, are deserted in December. Many birds remain in Zimbabwe—not at the breeding sites—until March but others move into Transvaal; they have been noted at considerable altitude, at 2,200 m in Inyanga Highlands[312]. Two adults ringed at Beatrice in November have been recovered 500 and 650 km south, in Transvaal, in December and January (R.M. Harwin pc).

In Transvaal (zone III) two more adults ringed at Beatrice in November were recovered in August and in September (R.M. Harwin pc). Presumably they had just arrived from Congo basin and were going

to remain in Transvaal for the summer as non-breeding visitors (or, improbably, were about to back-track to Beatrice to breed there).

The March migration through Zimbabwe is largely across the eastern lowveld (M.P.S. Irwin pc).

Southernmost records, from Transkei[148], are of vagrants, not breeding birds. At the other extreme there are East African records of vagrants from 00°03'N 34°10'E and 01°10'S 36°30'E in Kenya[79] and at about 8°S on Tanzanian coast[538].

POPULATION

Cliff-breeding colonies are generally of about 100 to 1,000 nests[186], rarely as few as 15 or as many as 5,000[363] (12,000 nests given for a Nigerian colony[185] is in error for 1,200[91]). Flat-ground colonies probably average larger: 200[441], 300[304], 650[441], 2,000[342], 3,000[342], 3,000–4,000[539] and 10,000[382] nests. All past and present nesting stations which I can trace are listed in Appendix 4 but probably represent no more than 10%* of the true number of colonies throughout Africa in any one year. At 5%, say, and an average of 1,000 adults per colony the total pre-breeding population would be about three millions; at 10% and an average of 500 adults per colony it would be only 750,000. Roosts are of comparable magnitude, eg 700 near Jappeni, The Gambia[267], and up to 4,000 at Mida Creek, Kenya[165]. Foraging flocks are often in thousands, too[324]. Admitting that it is easy to exaggerate the abundance of so spectacular a bird, I guess that a total population of at least five million Carmine Bee-eaters is a possibility.

---

* Observers tend to travel by road and in the dry season; if they travelled by river and during the rains it might reveal one Carmine Bee-eater colony every 10 or 20 km, at least on the great West African rivers. From Tchad to Sudan hardly any nesting colonies have been found, although the birds are clearly common and widespread in the breeding season[114,501].

FOOD

Airborne insects: particularly locusts and grasshoppers, also ants, honeybees, bugs, etc. Three major studies, in Mali, Nigeria and Zimbabwe, gave different results, in part due to evident specialization by Northern Carmines upon locusts. But the species forages opportunistically and at times feeds exclusively on a single swarming prey species, so that many further studies are needed before generalizations can be made safely.

Shortly before breeding commenced at the Beatrice (Zimbabwe) colony in 1964, 80% of prey items in a large pellet sample were honeybees, 15% other hymenopterans and 5% grasshoppers, bugs, lacewings, flies and beetles. But later in rainy weather nestlings were fed largely upon cicadas *Ioba leopardina* (at a time when the adults were themselves feeding on termites)[75], and on another occasion almost exclusively upon one species of chafer (D. Jackson pc). 1,600 insects from adult pellets collected at breeding colonies in three parts of Nigeria were 86% flying ants, 4% other hymenopterans, 3.5% grasshoppers, 3.5% beetles and the remainder bugs, dragonflies and flies. (The three samples were about the same size and ants comprised 36%, 89% and 93% of them.) Nestling gizzards from a Kaduna river colony (Nigeria) were packed with 18 mm long shield-bugs *Coridius viduatus* and also grasshoppers, wasps (*Campsomeris, Liris, Bembex*), bees (*Megachile, Apis,* and carpenter-bees *Xylocopa*) and dung-beetles (*Gymnopleurus*). Remains in their nests were mainly the same shield-bug and honeybees; also grasshoppers, water bugs *Riptortus*, and assorted hymenopterans.

At least in Inundation zone of River Niger, in Mali, locusts seem to be the staple of Carmine Bee-eaters. Recognition of that region as a major hatching ground of Migratory Locusts *Locusta migratoria* promoted studies of their predators, amongst which bee-eaters were found to feature importantly[478]. From January to May locusts move northeastwards down the Niger flood-plain between 6° and 4° W, following the retreating waters and breeding as they do so. At the same time Carmine Bee-eaters appear to move with them[363,441] (perhaps co-incidentally, since all over the northern tropics they migrate north in spring), feeding on *Locusta migratoria*, Desert Locusts *Schistocerca gregaria* and at least ten other genera of locusts and grasshoppers[441].

FORAGING

Feeds mainly aloft, in effortless sailing flight—not undulating—straight or in wide circles, flapping (to gain height, change direction, or chase an insect) for only one tenth of the flight time. Often soars falcon-like, rising on thermals. Forages at a height of about 50–100 m, in bouts of 5 or 10 mins alternating with rather longer resting periods at a perch. A few powerful flaps take the bird in a steady climb to the desired altitude, where it sails around on rather rigidly-held wings, nearly straight, a little anhedralled, the upper surface slightly concave towards the tip. A quick acceleration with wings flailing, ending in a sudden swerve or swoop, must denote the capture of an insect. Usually such prey cannot be seen by the observer, and presumably it is eaten immediately. Once I watched Southern Carmine Bee-eaters feeding in this manner on what I felt sure were high-flying honeybees; I managed to net some of the birds coming to perch and found that their beaks were sticky with a liquid with the characteristic smell of honeybee venom. Thus it seems that this bee-eater has mastered the problem of devenoming bees—by mandibulating them, I suppose—without having to interrupt its flight.

Perched Carmines commonly chase a passing insect, either returning with it to perch or continuing up to foraging altitude for a further feeding session. Large and resistant insects are beaten against the perch (generally a dead branch; occasionally the ground, M. Dyer pc) but I am unsure whether venomous ones are bee-rubbed. Sometimes—probably when high-flying small prey like ants and termites are scarce—they feed mainly in sallying flights from perches. In Zimbabwe I watched one bird for $7\frac{1}{2}$ hrs; it foraged high in the air for a total of 2 hrs 6 mins and made 100 prey-pursuit dashes, and perched for 5 hrs 25 mins making 41 feeding sorties.

This bee-eater has an interesting and well-known association with large ground-birds, wild and domestic mammals, people and vehicles, using them as 'beaters' to flush insects from grass. They commonly sit on the highest point of backs of walking Ostriches, Kori and Sudan Bustards and of grazing sheep and goats[113,318,381,576]; and they have also been seen on

Marabou and Openbill Storks[145], Saddle-billed Storks[29,40], White Storks[137], Abdim's Storks[25,145], a Black-headed Heron[73], Cattle Egrets (momentarily), Sacred Ibises, European Cranes[145], Crowned Cranes[272], Secretary Birds[73], cattle[554], camels, donkeys[145], Zebra, Wart Hogs, once a dog[145], and four antelopes: Beisa Oryx, Gerenuk, Grant's Gazelle and Topi[73,270]. They seem to avoid the common Soemmering's Gazelle, and Guinea-fowl will not let them take a ride[73]. From such animate perches birds not only swoop after insects flushed from the ground but also sally after any distant flying insect they see. Confiding birds, they fly slowly behind or swoop around a human and catch insects disturbed by his walking through grass[407]. Bee-eaters fly alongside galloping Beisa Oryx at shoulder height or up to 10 m behind them, occasionally swooping down as if after prey[73], and similarly fly alongside or behind cars, trucks and tractors (rarely, even perching on them), keeping station except to swoop now and again for an insect. Whether having caught a grasshopper they ever try to beat it against the back of an animal is not known, although one did "eat its prey on the back of a sheep"[443].

This foraging association is commonplace in Northern Carmines and may be related with their evident predilection for grasshoppers. It is rare among Southern Carmines, which have never been seen riding animals (unless Guinea-fowl, a second-hand report[413]) but have been recording following behind storks, bustards, elephants and other mammals[214], people in vehicles[152] and pedestrians[73].

Carmine Bee-eaters everywhere are strongly attracted by bush fires, a column of smoke signalling them perhaps from several kilometres away. They hawk around its edges, in and out of smoke and near to flame, seizing fleeing insects. Their Mandinka name (in The Gambia) means "cousin to the fire"[115].

A film of this bee-eater in Ethiopia shows several diving to the surface of swirling water and one rising with a small fish (see p. 222), the only known instance of Carmines fishing.

WATERING
Bee-eaters chasing each other over water sometimes touch the surface and momentarily completely submerge; at other times birds from a flock perching nearby make leisurely glides low over water and suddenly dive onto or into the surface, rising with a shake of the plumage (see p. 222).

VOICE
Flight call a brief, bass, rather throaty syllable, loud and far-carrying, clamorous *en masse*, rather different from voices of other *Merops* species although like them sometimes faintly rolled. Commonly given twice, or repeated with same intonation up to six times, at frequency of 4/sec. In

southern African literature usually rendered *terk* (following J. Vincent in 1934[582]). I find that my field notes have given independently *ok, klunk, chung* and *tunk*; and *krunk* or *trunk* suggest the faintly vibrant quality sometimes quite audible. Perched call a loud, clipped *ga-ga-ga* (or *gro-gro-gro*). Alarm, a subdued, or harsh, low chatter different from alarms of other bee-eaters. Threat, a sort of combination of alarm and flight calls. Copulation note, a quiet nasal *bro-ro-ro-ro-ro*. Begging call of nestling, a persistent note like that of Red-throated Bee-eater nestling (qv).

BEHAVIOUR

Breeds in large aggregations; at other times they are usually in flocks of tens but roost in hundreds or thousands. Casual observation shows that a third adult sometimes makes provisioning visits to a brood, but whether there are regular helpers is unknown. W. Serle was told by local Nigerians in the 1940s of their firm conviction that Carmines lay indiscriminately in adjacent burrows[509].

Near the start of nesting long aerial pursuits are common, two birds sometimes grappling with their beaks and twirling down to the ground together; one can be forced onto the surface of water. Threatening a neighbour at a perch, the bird adopts a hunched posture, body nearly

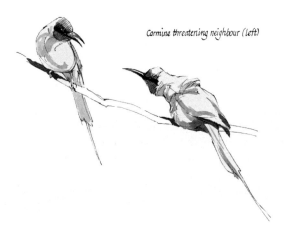

Carmine threatening neighbour (left)

horizontal, head low, crown feathers flattened and throat feathers puffed. An uncommon mutual display between two birds is rapid alternate jerky bowing of heads, with the beak touching perch near partner's feet. A female (or two together) solicits an insect proffered by a male with juvenile begging posture; it may be followed by copulation, which is accompanied by a quiet nasal call also heard from within nests, suggesting that copulation occurs therein. Shortly before laying commences 'panics' are as frequent as eight per hour, nearly all of the birds suddenly flying fast out of nest holes and away from cliff perches, for no obvious reason, but soon returning.

Egg chambers are not lined; but twice I have seen a Northern Carmine Bee-eater carry a beakful of grass-bents into a burrow during the laying period.

Preening may be accompanied by rapping the perch hard with part-opened beak. Scratching is over-wing. Frequent sun-bathing postures are: sitting with mantle feathers raised and fanned to expose their dark bases; perching in 'broken-necked' attitude, the head bent sharply to one side and neck feathers fluffed to the sun on the other side; sitting on sloping ground at a nesting cliff with wings held outstretched against the earth; and (rarely) sitting on the ground with wings folded and body rolled to expose the flanks on one side to a low sun.

Early in the breeding season, in the late afternoon, birds eat sand, pieces of snail-shell and other calcareous matter on the ground (see Fig. 15 in[342]), and in the process often pick up, toss in the beak, and discard bits of dead leaves, grass bents and grit in a seemingly playful manner.

BREEDING

Nests are excavated in river cliffs (the usual site) at densities up to 60 per m². Colonies are often associated with smaller ones of Red-throated, White-fronted and (in Somalia, J.S. Ash pc) Madagascar Bee-eaters. Burrows are straight or slightly and evenly curving to one side, the egg chambers not angled, and are horizontal or decline at as much as 8°. They are generally 100–210 cm long (average of 40:150 cm) but one of 12 ft (3.7 m) is on record[509]. In Inundation zone of River Niger and also in Lake Turkana basin, colonies are in flat ground with nest densities of 1–6 per 2 m², the tunnels 6 cm in diameter—slightly wider than deep—and declining at 18–26°[342,539].

In places, Carmines excavate their nest holes 4–5 months before laying; in Nigeria, for instance, digging was in late October and laying began in late March (J.F. Walsh pc). Such behaviour may be the rule at lower latitudes but presumably that is not the case at higher latitudes where the birds are only summer visitors. The same cliff face (the same holes?) may be used for years and in the late 1950s the well-known colony of 1,500

Northern Carmines courting

birds near Beatrice, Zimbabwe, had been known to farmers for decades[328]. They were still there in strength in 1965, but failed to breed and then abandoned the site in 1966. In Harare the desertion caused a stir, with recriminations and blame falling in turn on the activities of ringers in the previous three years, on the Beatrice Intensive Conservation Area Committee (who had withdrawn a guard at the site), and on nest parasites. At any rate, they resumed breeding in 1967, not at Beatrice but at Inyondo, 7 km away, staying there until 1971 when they returned to Alsace. In 1976 part of the breeding cliff at Alsace collapsed in a violent early storm, and there were many casualties of birds and eggs. The following year the colony removed itself back to Inyondo, nesting in gently sloping bank with a number of nests 'overflowing' onto flat ground at its top. In 1979 a few bred back at Alsace but there were none there in 1980 (D.V. Rockingham-Gill pc).

Egg-laying is about the beginning of the rainy season at low latitudes and some weeks before it at higher latitudes. North of the Equator laying on Garamba and other upper Uele tributaries is from early February[580]; at Lake Turkana it is from late April through May*; in Nigeria south of 10° N in early April, from 10° to 12° N from mid April to early May and north of 12° N in May and early June [92,231,509]. In the southern tropics the breeding season in Zambia is September to November[58], and further south in Zimbabwe a little later. At Beatrice birds arrive in late August and lay in late September and October; most young fledge in late November and the colony is deserted by mid December.

The clutch is 2–3 or sometimes more. In Nigeria eight completed clutches were of two and nine of three eggs at Zaria[176], but at Yelwa there were two clutches of two and two of four eggs, and broods of two, three or

---

* The late L. H. Brown wrote that the breeding of Carmine Bee-eaters "is not necessarily annual" (*Bull. East Afr. Nat. Hist. Soc.*, 1976: 128–129), and he referred to data in Urban and Brown's Ethiopian checklist[573]. As far as I can gather (E.K. Urban pc) the data there do not support his claim, however.

four nestlings[509]. Further north the clutch may be 3–5[382]. In a clutch of two the eggs are laid 48 hrs apart; in a clutch of three the second egg is laid about 43 hrs later and the third egg about 53 hrs after that[176]. As with Red-throated Bee-eaters, laying in different parts of a colony is out-of-phase, by up to three weeks. Incubation period not certainly known. With at least six days separating the oldest and youngest nestling in a brood of four, and a 14-day youngster able to gain 8–10 g in a day[176], the size discrepancy can be remarkable. In broods of three the youngest often dies of starvation, at seven days of age[176]. Nestling period 30 days ± 1 day[176].

SUBSPECIES

(1) *M. n. nubicus* Northern Carmine Bee-eater. From Senegal to Webbi Shebelle river in Somalia and from Eritrea to Kenya, wintering to 10° S in

East Africa. Chin and throat green-blue.

(2) *M. n. nubicoides* Southern Carmine Bee-eater. Southwest Angola, Okavango and upper Zambezi tributaries to Luangwa and Shire valleys and Transvaal, wintering mainly west of Western Rift north to Katanga and Rwanda. Chin and throat pink; heavier than *nubicus*.

ADDITIONAL DESCRIPTION

(Nominate race) ADULT ♂, ♀ Green-blue parts of plumage change colour dramatically according to direction of light. Viewed against the light crown, chin, cheeks and uppertail coverts are mid blue, forehead, back, rump, vent and undertail coverts azure blue, and throat blackish or greenish blue. Viewed directly down-light these parts are beryl green with throat dark olive green. The difference is as between ultramarine and aquamarine. Since in the field one can rarely see birds directly down-sun next to one's shadow (when they would be pink and green), they usually look pink and blue or greenish blue. A few forehead feathers next to beak sometimes pink. Tertials dull green-blue where exposed. Black trailing edge band of wing about 9 mm wide, passing to carmine of remiges via a barely perceptible, narrow green zone. Four or five longest primaries have a subterminal blue spot several mm long on outer web. Tail nearly uniform carmine, browner or blue-washed dark brown for 2–3 mm at tip except for central pair, which grade from carmine to black 1–2 cm beyond tail proper. Male streamers up to 105 mm longer than tail, not steeply attenuated, and 4 mm wide at tip. Underside of tail silvery grey and of remiges silvery grey distally but warm buff proximally; underwing coverts and axillaries warm buff, marginal coverts often pink, and rufous. Pink mantle, breast and belly feathers have buff bases often showing through, and flanks can be more buff than pink. Pre-nuptial moult gives some individuals pale tips to pink and carmine contour feathers; lower mantle and whole underparts except cheeks then look pink irregularly streaked pale chalky buff, and lesser and median wing coverts look carmine, scalloped ochre. JUVENILE Forehead and crown mid blue, black feather bases often showing through; merging to earth brown nape and upper mantle; lower mantle fox red; scapulars and tertials dun brown with olive tinge and pale blue edges; rump and uppertail coverts greyish azure blue; tail dull carmine, brown distally, central and outer feathers with dull blue-green fringes. Remiges dull ochreous carmine, tips not as markedly black as in adults, and coverts dun brown with pink fringes. Head-top, scapulars and wing-coverts are narrowly pale-tipped, giving finely scalloped appearance. Mask black. Chin and throat mid blue, feathers with grey bases, merging indistinctly with shell-pink-fringed dun brown breast feathers; lower breast and belly very pale buff, silky; vent and undertail coverts greyish blue, very pale. (*M. n. nubicoides*) ADULT Like *nubicus* except

that chin, throat and cheeks are vivid pink. Male streamers up to 120 mm longer than tail. JUVENILE Like juvenile *nubicus* except either (usually) that chin and upper throat are pale pink and cheeks, lower throat and upper breast warm reddish buff, or (rarely) that chin, throat and cheeks are pale blue. Intermediate conditions occur. BARE PARTS Beak black; eye rich brown in juvenile, and in adult of both races seems to vary widely from blood red to red-brown; legs and feet black frosted grey or whitish, nails black. MOULT A single annual moult of flight feathers starts in adults about four weeks after end of nesting and in juveniles perhaps a week or two later[281]. WEIGHT *M. n. nubicus* (J.S. Ash pc) Ethiopia, October–December 42.4 (33.9–50.9, n = 92), January–May 44.1 (37.3–53.1, n = 40). *M. n. nubicoides*[75] Daily November values at Beatrice, Zimbabwe, on days when at least 30 birds were weighed, varied from 57.1 (51–68, n = 67) to 63.9 (55–72, n = 116) as a function mainly of ambient temperature. September weights were fractionally lower. Between dawn and dusk an individual can increase from 61 to 66 g. Recently-fledged juveniles (December) were 51.8 (39–61, n = 5). Luangwa, Zambia, October 54.4 (44.5–65.0, n = 105)[81], at dawn. MEASUREMENTS (*M. n. nubicoides*, n = 170[75]) *Beak* to feathers 37 and to skull 41 (36–46). *Wing* 151 (145–160), ♂ 148–158 and ♀ 147–156 (n = 20[29]). *Tail* 103 (91–121), ♂ 97–105 and ♀ 95–103 (n = 20[29]) excluding streamers up to 120 mm long in ♂ and about 105 in ♀. (*M. n. nubicus*) *Beak* to feathers ♂ 35–40, ♀ 34–38, to skull ♂ 41.9 (39–46, n = 15), ♀ 39.9 (38–42, n = 10), depth 8.6 (8.3–8.9, n = 10). *Wing* ♂ 149 (143–163, n = 25), ♀ 144 (140–149, n = 25). *Tail* ♂ 98 (92–107, n = 25) and ♀ 95.5 (92–101, n = 25) excluding streamers up to about 95 mm in ♂ and 80 in ♀. Birds larger in West Africa (wing, ♂ average 150 mm) than in East Africa (148). *Egg* 20.9 × 24.1 (20.3–21.5 × 23.3–25.0, n = 5[509]). STRUCTURE In folded wing primary tips extend 33–38 mm beyond tertials. P9 longest, p10 minute—11–18 long and 92–102 shorter than p9, p8 5–8, p7 17–22, p6 26–32, p5 35–42, p4 43–50, p3 49–58, p2 54–63, p1 58–68 and s1 63–71 shorter.

Black Kite raiding
Carmine Bee-eater colony

3:   The origin of species

Geographical differentiation among the bee-eaters

THE FACT OF EVOLUTION

In the years following the publication in 1859 of Darwin's *The Origin of Species by Means of Natural Selection*, Science and the Church were in shameful head-on collision; journalists and tract-writers had a field-day and the layman knew not what to believe. To this day the public has embraced the doctrine of evolutionary change and species multiplication only with considerable misgiving—witness that people still insist on calling it the *Theory* of Evolution, although evolution long since became as solidly entrenched a set of facts as any other in biology. In recent years a number of separate controversies about animal evolution have been aired in the scientific journals and even in court; they have been reported prolifically in the media, often in a decidedly partial manner. The result is that the public, its religious propensities still affronted by the implications of Darwinism, is now almost as bewildered and dubious as it was back in the 1860s.

Evolution seems to be in disarray. In the wake of a Sacramento, California, court ruling, legislative assemblies in Louisiana and Arkansas have enacted laws requiring that alternative notions about the origin of life in its myriad complexities be given equal time in school with the 'theory' of evolution. So for every hour that evolutionary biology is taught

there—and there are few areas of life science that can be understood
without regard for adaptation and similar evolutionary precepts—
children in these States now have to contend with an hour of creationism
or 'Creation Science', poor things. Britain has seen polemics about the
role of the London Natural History Museum and the politics of Darwinism, including an editorial in the world's leading science journal *Nature*
titled 'Darwin's death in South Kensington'*. On both sides of the
Atlantic there has been vigorous public debate, not without some
mud-slinging, as to whether evolutionary change proceeds smoothly or in
jumps. Immunological work has suggested that some acquired characters
can be inherited after all, temporarily rehabilitating the discredited old
idea of Lamarckism. People have sought to tar evolution science with
racism†; and, of course, frequent new fossil finds keep controversy about
human evolution ever simmering.

What has all this got to do with bee-eaters? Little, in the sense that an
understanding of them contributes nothing to Marxism, Lamarckism,
creationism or the philosophy of science. But a great deal, inasmuch as
bee-eaters provide classic evidence for the fact of evolution itself. Ask
anyone what is the best evidence for evolution and they will say fossils.
But to my mind the evidence from the geography of subspecies and species
is irrefutable and every bit as convincing. (Correction: nothing is logically
incontrovertible to the determined creationist, arguing that the Creator
made fossils in the rocks at the time that He created living species. While I
have not encountered a similar *reductio ad absurdum* respecting geographical
patterns of relatedness, one could surely be applied likewise. Scientific
reason can make little headway against such blind faith.)

As it happens a few fossil bee-eater fragments have been unearthed,
from Pleistocene deposits in Austria and recent Holocene beds in Russia
and Israel, but they have all been attributed to the living species *M.
apiaster* and tell us nothing about the Family's evolutionary history[320].
Geographical distribution tells a great deal, however.

MONOTYPIC AND POLYTYPIC SPECIES

Most bee-eater species with a large breeding range vary geographically
within that range (ie they are polytypic). The list on p. 22 shows that just
over half of the 24 species are polytypic: seven have 2 races each, two 3
races, two 4, one 5, and one 8 races. Of the species which are uniform and

* It all started with a letter accusing proponents of the evolutionary principles of cladism and
of punctuated equilibria in the British Museum (Natural History) of furthering the Marxist
concept of dialectical materialism (L. B. Halstead, *Nature* 288 (1980):208). The debate was
concluded with an editorial and correspondence in *Nature* 292 (1981), No. 5822.
† See rebuttal by R. Dawkins in *Nature* 289 (1981): 528.

without subspecies (ie monotypic), most are understandably so. **Boehm's Bee-eater,** for instance, has a relatively small and compact range in which any tendency for a peripheral population to diverge genetically in response to selection pressures different in kind or extent from those operating upon central birds, is likely to be continuously offset by gene flow (that is, interbreeding) between periphery and centre. **European Bee-eaters,** although they have a vast breeding range, are monotypic probably because populations from Europe and Asia intermingle on their tropical wintering grounds, with pairing between 'foreigners' sufficiently frequent to swamp any tendency for the populations to diverge morphologically. The fact that the South African population is identical with the Palaearctic one implies that they have not been apart for very long, probably for only a few hundred generations at most. (Although identical morphologically they do differ behaviourally, in breeding seasons and migration time, which would reduce the chances of each population picking up breeding partners from the other when they meet in tropical Africa.)

Boehm's Bee-eater may be the most closely related with the widespread, highly polytypic **Little Green,** and the European may be allied with the **Bay-headed.** But if so, neither relationship is close enough for me to be confident about, so these two species do not exemplify my assertion about distribution patterns as evidence of evolution. Such patterns begin to emerge among the polytypic species. **White-throated Bee-eaters** and **Rainbowbirds** are each monotypic in my treatment, but slight clinal variation is demonstrable respecting wing-length in the former, gorget-colour in the latter. Gradual geographical change in a character (ie a cline) is less commonly found than a rather abrupt change, where diversifying adaptations at distant extremes of the range are no longer completely negated by gene flow between those extremes. It results in geographical subspecies being arranged parapatrically, their ranges touching but not overlapping, the transitions sometimes well but usually ill defined.

The **Little Bee-eater** provides a good example. Its five parapatric races together occupy practically the whole of sub-Saharan Africa; they are well characterized although the differences between them are trivial—size, shade of plumage, presence or absence of a blue eyebrow streak, and so on. The common boundary between adjacent races is not as sharp in reality as on the map opposite Plate 3; in Ethiopia, for instance, the boundary is a zone some 200 km wide where birds are not safely attributable either to *M. pusillus ocularis* or to *M. p. cyanostictus*. Whether their differences evolved in strict parapatry or (more likely) during a period when the populations may have been quite distantly isolated from one another by some temporarily intervening topographical feature, I do not know. We have only a hazy idea as to the adaptive nature of these regional differences and we can only guess at, and generalize about, the immensely complex picture of mutation, allele frequency, gene flow and demographic processes which have gradually been developing over the last twenty thousand generations or so, involving in the order of 10^{11-12} individual Little Bee-eaters, originally monotypic and to-day highly polytypic. But no-one would or could deny the common ancestry of these subspecies, any more than he or she would deny the common ancestry of West African and fractionally larger East African White-throated Bee-eaters, or of South African and Palaearctic European Bee-eaters.

PATTERNS IN ALLOPATRY: SUBSPECIATION

Racial differentiation can continue apace when populations remain contiguous, although it is more likely to occur rapidly in distantly-separated ones, without the restraint of introgressive gene-flow. During the Pleistocene period, the last three million years or so, the world has seen great vicissitudes of climate, with the result in Africa that rainforest and desert have repeatedly supplanted each other. The tree-line has oscillated up and down mountains creating and submerging archipelagos of montane forest in a sea of lowland savanna; and time and time again great areas of woodland have been cut off from the main mass by isthmuses of rainforests or thornbush or some other vegetation equally inhospitable for woodland birds. This has meant that conditions in Pleistocene Africa have been ideal for speciation. Several times equatorial rainforest has extended from the Congo basin across East Africa to the Indian Ocean seaboard and then retreated again. Each time the savannas have been divided into two great blocks, and populations of every contained bee-eater species have become segregated north and south of the forest. The subsequent history of such isolates will depend on the duration and effectiveness of their insularity, which I can illustrate with Carmine and with Red-throated and White-fronted Bee-eaters, whose distributions neatly exemplify two further steps in species formation.

The map opposite Plate 8 shows that the two kinds of **Carmine Bee-eaters** have savanna breeding ranges north and south of the Equator and about 2,000 km apart. Although they 'winter' in low latitudes, that neither of them nests in the savannas between Lake Turkana and Lake Malaŵi suggests that the 'summer' climate there is unsuitable, presumably too warm and humid. Climatic conditions similar to the present day have prevailed for 10–11,000 years, but before that for a period of some 20,000 years Africa was up to 6°C cooler and far more arid, particularly at the time of the worldwide glacial maximum 17,000 years ago[160,456]. Then and until about 11,000 years ago Carmine Bee-eaters would have

Northern Carmine

ranged uninterruptedly across dry East Africa, and it would only have
been when forest began to spread from relict Congo patches eastward
through Lake Victoria basin[331] and probably all the way to the coast in the
warm pluvial period from 7,000 to 10,000 years ago[373], that bee-eaters
would have become sundered into discrete northern and southern populations. Before 11,000 years ago the continuous population may have varied,
perhaps clinally say from Sudan to Zimbabwe, or with northern and
southern races abutting parapatrically near the Equator. But my opinion
is that their differences in plumage and size and behaviour have arisen in
the short span of the last 10,000 or 12,000 years. Although they breed at
one year of age, a great proportion of the population is borne of
experienced parents aged 5 or 10 or more, so the average generation time
will be a lot more than one year. Considering that some authorities regard
Northern and Southern Carmines as different species (*M. nubicus* and
M. nubicoides), it means—if my opinion is right—that bee-eaters can differentiate practically to the level of species in much less than 12,000
generations.

The real arbiters of their taxonomic rank are of course the birds
themselves, or would be if they were to meet at the mating season. Since
that does not happen (and since it would be taxonomically meaningless to
show that the two races can successfully interbreed in the artificial
confines of an aviary), one has to fall back on the taxonomist's judgement.
My guess is that Northern and Southern Carmines would hybridize
if opportunity afforded; thus I treat them as one species, not two.
Incidentally, occasional juvenile specimens of the pink-throated Southern
Carmine have blue chins and throats, and they look very like blue-
throated Northern Carmines. The converse is unknown; so it is likely that
before the latest Pleistocene pluvial period, when Carmine Bee-eaters
were probably monotypic, they were *all* blue throated. (The best specimen
I known of is a juvenile collected a hundred years ago by J. Ayres on
Eland river, Transvaal, in February and deposited in the British

Museum—skin 90.6.10.140. Stray pink feathers in an otherwise uniform pale blue chin and throat, and the month, show that it is indeed a Southern Carmine Bee-eater and not a vagrant Northern.)

PATTERNS IN ALLOPATRY: SPECIATION

Red-throated and **White-fronted Bee-eaters** are not migratory to any extent, and their breeding ranges (see map facing Plate 4) are very like the breeding-and-wintering ranges of Northern and Southern Carmines respectively (except in Kenya). Similar distributional patterns indicate similar evolutionary origins; the difference is that Red-throated and White-fronted Bee-eaters are considerably less alike than are the two Carmine Bee-eaters. Moreover the Red-throated Bee-eater makes a close approach to the White-fronted in the Rift valley near Lakes Albert and Edward, and their breeding ranges *may* just overlap[112]. The birds differ in facial appearance more than do the two races of Carmine Bee-eaters, and they differ in rump colour, spread-tail colour, and very conspicuously in voice. However, these differences are not yet so accentuated that there has been unanimity with taxonomic treatment, for even some quite recent authorities have regarded the two populations as comprising a single species (eg[594]). If it should be shown that their breeding ranges do in fact overlap in the Rift valley without hybridization, then Red-throated and White-fronted Bee-eaters will unquestionably be separate species. In the meantime my opinion is that their differences are sufficient to preclude any likelihood of inter-breeding in nature (I doubt if they would pair even in the aviary) and for that reason I regard the two birds as of different species.

SUPERSPECIES

Two (or more) species like those, of immediate common descent and which are hence geographically separate (allopatric) are termed allospecies. Allospecies are at that stage of speciation where systematists often disagree about their taxonomic status, whether subspecies or species, and it is convenient to avoid the issue, in a sense, by grouping them into what is called a superspecies. The concept of the superspecies is extremely valuable; it became entrenched in zoology largely, as it happens, from mapping speciation patterns of birds in Africa[278]. Other bee-eater examples are the **Blue-cheeked** with the **Madagascar/Blue-tailed,** whose breeding ranges are just starting to overlap (in the Punjab)* and to which

---

* F. Vuilleumier[583] has called for research on the etho-ecology of speciation by means of studying Blue-cheeked and European Bee-eaters where they overlap in Iran; in fact such an investigation would be far more profitable with Blue-cheeked and Blue-tailed Bee-eaters in the Punjab.

superspecies the **Rainbowbird** surely also belongs; and the **Blue-breasted** and **Cinnamon-chested Bee-eaters.** Interestingly, the last two are separated vertically rather than regionally; they also present a taxonomic dilemma. Is the large blue-gorgeted bird in the highlands of Ethiopia (*lafresnayii*) conspecific with the large black-gorgeted one in the highlands further south (*oreobates*), or with the small blue-gorgeted one of neighbouring lowlands (*variegatus*)? I incline to the latter view[226] and think that the two highland forms are independent derivatives of the lowland Blue-breasted Bee-eater *M. variegatus*, the Ethiopian population more recently so than the East African highland form. I doubt if unanimity shall ever be reached with this problem; in any event it is a trifle academic to debate how the Ethiopian *lafresnayii* is derivative of lowland *M. variegatus*, whether at first remove or only at second remove by way of *oreobates*.

From time to time a continental superspecies will invade an offshore island, there to produce a further allospecies and eventually perhaps a form so distinctive that its nearest continental relative is no longer readily apparent. Here the bee-eaters do *not* provide good instances. The only populations endemic to islands are the **Blue-throated Bee-eater** *americanus* of Palawan and the Philippines, the **Bay-headed Bee-eaters** *andamanensis* of the Andaman Islands and *quinticolor* of Java and Bali, and the **Blue-tailed Bee-eaters** of Sulawesi, the Philippines and New Guinea-New Britain. The last, with three described races, are barely separable from the Asian mainland form; *andamanensis* is moderately distinctive; but only *americanus* is substantially different from its mainland counterpart and it is the only candidate for incipient allospeciation.

Virtually all emerging bird species are members of a superspecies, at least transitorily in the evolutionary time-scale. It follows that, if we wish to determine the closest relative of a particular species, we must first look for geographical distribution patterns in its genus; the closest relative is far more likely to be in a distant similar habitat than in the selfsame region[278].

Over the fullness of time two main fates may overtake surviving members of a superspecies, depending on the way their ranges change. They can remain in their original separate regions, continuing to evolve differences in allopatry to the point where resemblances and relationships may no longer be at all obvious. I suspect that the **Bay-headed Bee-eater** is in that category vis-à-vis the European, because it has a number of plumage similarities and suggestively allopatric, nearly parapatric, breeding ranges. Likewise **Boehm's** and **Little Green Bee-eaters** may be each other's closest relatives; and **Rosy** and **Carmine**. I suggested above that **Rainbowbirds** are surely the Australian derivative of the ancestral **Blue-tailed**; and if the affinities of Rainbowbirds with the *Merops* *superciliosus* superspecies are no longer obvious, it is at least true that their plumage features do not ally them obviously with any other bee-eater.

(Critics might wonder whether, apart from the evidence of distribution, postulated relationships at this level are based on anything less subjective than the eye of faith. I have tried to test my ideas by comparing feather proteins, which has proved a valuable method among other birds[238,338]; but, with the 24 bee-eaters, patterns resulting from protein electrophoresis have mostly been too indistinct for accurate analysis (A.G. Knox pc). Biochemical characters—especially nuclear, blood plasma, egg-white, eye-lens and feather proteins—have been treated by systematists as the best possible clues to the degee of affinity between species. They are basic, and less subject to misinterpretation than are gross anatomical or external appearances, where resemblances can owe as much to convergent evolution as to affinity. All the same it is worth emphasizing that even with proteins, as with plumage or any other characters, one ultimately has to fall back on simple comparison, enumerating the points of likeness and unlikeness. It means that, provided the systematist is ever on guard for the pitfalls of convergent evolution, such ready features as plumage are very nearly as useful as proteins, as indicators of relationships within genera and families.)

A further example of an allospecies—one which has had time to adapt to a climate and habitat very different from those of its putative ancestors—is the **Somali Bee-eater**. Appearances notwithstanding, it is probably quite closely related with the Red-throated/White-fronted superspecies. Not only is it accurately parapatric with the White-fronted Bee-eater, but such characters as the blue rump and vent and the peculiarly pointed mealy-white forehead feathers remind me forcibly of its geographical neighbour. Long after making that deduction I came across a corroborative, if slim, piece of evidence: a White-fronted Bee-eater specimen (1176.15.12.06 in the British Museum) with aberrant plumage. Its chin and throat are mealy white or greyish, not red, making it look much like a large Somali.

EVOLVING SYMPATRY: THE SPECIES-GROUP

Being of recent common descent, allospecies will usually be ecologically almost identical with each other and so, should they meet, competition will serve to prevent their ranges overlapping. But some measure of ecological distinction will sooner or later arise, permitting such parapatric species to pursue their second principal fate and slowly to evolve sympatry. The two species of *Nyctyornis* seem to be at this stage; although plainly not very closely related, the **Red-bearded** and **Blue-bearded Bee-eaters** just overlap, around Bilauktaung Range west of Bangkok, in an area which is only a tiny fraction of the total range of either species.

Extensively sympatric congeners never compose a superspecies, by definition; when they appear to be closely allied we call them a species-group. The four species illustrated in Plate 3 are a good example. They are the **Blue-breasted/Cinnamon-chested** superspecies and two 'independent' species, namely the **Little** and **Swallow-tailed Bee-eaters**. The last two have almost coincident ranges across Africa, and in many parts one or the other members of the superspecies occur too. Swallowtails are a fairly distinctive bird, although there are all sorts of pointers to their membership of this species-group[226]. But Little and Blue-breasteds are look-alikes to the extent that they can be confused in the field and even (to my knowledge) misidentified in museum skin collections. They differ a little in size and weight, but otherwise seem so amazingly the same that one might reasonably expect their ranges to be mutually exclusive as a result of competition. However, they are not only broadly sympatric but can also live cheek-by-jowl in the same grassland or marsh, and herein lies an etho-ecological mystery for field research to resolve.

Blue-headed and **Black Bee-eaters** have coincident ranges in the African rainforest zone, and I think that, different as they are, they have sufficient points of likeness (spiky scarlet throat feathers, red-brown remiges, dark plumage) to be treated as a species-group. In other words these distinctive birds, neither with any other claimed relative, probably have a distant common ancestry and many ten-thousands of years ago were allospecies of a superspecies found in disjunct patches of rainforest.

RATE OF EVOLUTION

Concerning the time scale of events in the differentiation of bee-eaters I can only make guesses. The races of Carmine Bee-eater differentiated with the coming of interglacial conditions, when a hot and wet climate served, as effectively as the physical barrier of equatorial rainforest which it created, to sunder the ancestral dry-savanna population into two. I have suggested that that was after the most recent glacial period, which was brought to an abrupt close when warming began 13,000 years ago. Before that African and world temperatures were varyingly low for 20,000 years and not much less low—certainly without any very warm intermission—for a further 35,000 years earlier. It appears, in fact, that temperatures like to-day's have never prevailed since the last interglacial period haltingly began to collapse 73,000 or 67,000 years ago[456] (although even then Africa was evidently arid, with the Congo basin composed largely of blown Kalahari sand[423]). That interglacial, the Sangamonian or Holstein, broke the preceding ice age as much as a quarter million years ago, and consonant with such antiquity is the greater degree of mutual distinction between Red-throated and White-fronted Bee-eaters, which differentiated from each other for the same reasons as the Carmine races did. And if the Somali Bee-eater indeed belongs distantly to the Red-throated/White-fronted superspecies we had better give it an age of one further interglacial period—a third or half a million years. That is as far as it is prudent for guesses to go.

Black-headed

TWO PROBLEMATIC BEE-EATERS

In this chapter I have been able to use all of the bee-eaters to illustrate stages in the process of differentiation, except the Celebes and the Black-headed. They are systematically isolated, each in its own monotypic genus, *Meropogon* for the Celebes and *Bombylonax* (formerly) for the Black-headed. By a lucky chance I was able to spend a few days studying **Black-headed Bee-eaters** at only the second group of nests ever found and described, in Nigeria in 1981, and its nesting, diet, foraging behaviour, voice and 'jizz' in the field all seemed well within the limits of variation of *Merops*, into which genus—in the absence of any morphological distinction by the Black-headed Bee-eater—I now unhesitatingly place it. All the same I have to admit that systematically it stands alone, without any immediate relative within the family. I retract the idea, advanced before I had had the opportunity to familiarize myself with the bird in the field, that it might have originated from savanna stock ancestral to the Little Bee-eater line[226]. There remains the possibility that its closest relative is the **Celebes Bee-eater**, improbable because of their great geographical separation. But there are some uncanny resemblances and at least one systematist has thought them to be quite nearly allied, even congeneric[69,70], a view which receives some support from there being one or two other genera of small land birds each with one southeast Asian and one west equatorial African species, for instance *Pseudochelidon* for the Thai and African River Martins *P. sirintarae* and *P. eurystomina*[560,611].

The two bee-eaters have similar wing formulae and almost exactly the same wing and tail colours and patterns; the Black-headed Bee-eater has quite long throat feathers, and the Celebes very long ones which are often puffed out to form a beard or ruff; they differ in beak morphology and in voice—moreover photographs show a Celebes Bee-eater skeleton to have one pair of ribs more than a *Merops* skeleton[409], although how constant a difference that may be, and what is the rib count of Black-headed Bee-eaters, I do not know. On balance it seems more realistic to ascribe their similarities to convergence rather than to affinity.

THE FAMILY'S ROOTS

Celebes Bee-eaters seem to have some distant kinship with the two other round-winged forest species of southeast Asia, the Red- and Blue-bearded Bee-eaters (genus *Nyctyornis*), but like so many other animals peculiar to that fascinating island—off-beat kingfishers, the curious Black Ape and the weird pig known as the Babirusa—it has been in splendid isolation there for a tremendous time, perhaps millions of years. What little is known about the lives of these three birds is set down in Chapter 2. It is clear that all three of them are eaters of bees (among other insects), so it is wrong to think of them as I formerly did, as antediluvian models for the superb flying machines that *Merops* are, a sort of atavistic, roller-like pre-bee-eater. In a study some years ago of the evolutionary and geographical radiation of the family[226], I concluded that *Nyctyornis* and *Meropogon* are generalized and relatively primitive and that the family originated in southeast Asian forest. Some time in the mid or late Tertiary, I thought, such primordial bee-eaters spread by way of then-continuous rain forest to Africa, where in due course they managed to adapt to the physically very different savanna environment. There they radiated into a spectrum of open-country-adapted forms, now genus *Merops*, varying from small sedentary flycatching bee-eaters to large, long-winged types foraging in uninterrupted flight aloft, some of which extended out of Africa to recolonize Asia, this time in open light woods and grassy valleys.

Despite my more recent conclusions[237] that, among kingfishers, the most primitive of the 87 living species are also confined to the southeast Asian region, and that from centres there the family spread into Asia and Africa evolving into open habitats on the way, I have less confidence than previously that that is necessarily the story for bee-eaters. We now know to what diminutive vestiges African rainforest was reduced, once or several times during the Pleistocene[143A]. Perhaps numerous forest species were entirely eradicated in the process, and that could account for the absence in Africa to-day of seemingly primitive types like *Nyctyornis*. If such a bee-eater had happened to survive there the notion of southeast Asia as the cradle of the Family would not be invalidated, but Africa—or rather the entire anciently forested palaeotropics—would become a rival candidate.

4: Food and foraging

The food an animal eats and the way it obtains it not only define its place in nature and its role in the ecosystem, but also determine most of those attributes which distinguish it from other species. Obviously adaptive to diet are 'tooth and claw', jaw and guts, beak and gizzard; so at a further remove are locomotion and its correlates in the skeleton, muscles and other systems; and so in the last analysis—as intensive field studies since the '50s have clearly demonstrated—are social organization, mating system and other life history properties.

As a rule each species in nature subsists on a more or less broad range of animal or plant 'prey', which is only a minute fraction of all of the organic matter in its environment. Within that range it has a narrow spectrum of preferred, sought-after prey which it excels in exploiting when available. Little is known about diets of the Asiatic forest bee-eaters, genera *Nyctyornis* and *Meropogon* (they seem to be like those of *Merops*). Most *Merops* species are well researched, although to what extent the seemingly trivial dietary differences between most of them have shaped their notable social distinctions, remains to be seen (Chapter 7). At this stage what *is* sure is that bee-eaters, despite a wide range of food, have an astonishingly narrow spectrum of preference: in effect, for most of them, only honeybees and social wasps.

To catch and consume such fearsome insects without being stung to death requires adaptive skills, in which the Family Meropidae is paramount. Thus in their forage and their foraging behaviour bee-eaters are extremely specialized; in fact the evolutionary history of the genus *Merops* seems to be inextricably bound with specialization upon a single resource, the ordinary hivebee or honeybee, *Apis mellifera*.

FLYING INSECTS

The field of prey which bee-eaters exploit is virtually the totality of day-flying insects, hundreds of thousands of species. In practice many that are too small or too large are ignored, although bee-eaters will occasionally eat fruit-flies (*Drosophila*) and diminutive flying ants, and such giants as carpenter-bees, cicadas, hawk-moths, some beetles over 4 cm long, spotted lace-wings of 7 cm and dragonflies up to 8 cm long[239]. I doubt if any insect is too fast for a bee-eater, although quarries often escape by erratic avoiding action or by disappearing into herbage; the birds' success rate is generally only one foray in three, varying from 25% to 70%. I wonder also whether the noxious properties which so many insects have evolved are as effective with bee-eaters as with other predators; they readily eat Blister-beetles *Lytta vesicatoria*, highly irritating to human skin, and on occasions when they apparently do discard a warningly-coloured, distasteful butterfly[107,225] it may only be because pleasanter prey abounds.

An insect flying by is such a powerful releaser of hunting drive that a perched bee-eater will almost invariably make intention movements, even if too satiated actually to give chase. So geared are the birds to gaining their livelihood on the wing, that an insect in flight is an almost irresistible stimulus; yet remarkably, the moment the same insect closes its wings and lands it signifies nothing. That was brought home to me forcibly when I kept Red-throated Bee-eaters in a sunny garden aviary, in Nigeria, and fed them flying worker honeybees by the simple expedient of blowing them one at a time, from my concealed observation point 10 m away, through a long polythene tube[225]. Each bee shot into the aviary, flying at its normal velocity, and was snapped up by a bird launching itself on the instant and curving back to its perch. There the unfortunate insect was beaten, devenomed, juggled and eaten. On occasion it was dropped during the process, and I noticed that if the bird's perch was higher than about a metre above the ground the bee could be retrieved in a lightning flurry of wings before it hit the earth. But if lower than that the bee-eater had insufficient time and the bee fell to the ground, where it was ignored whether it lay inert or crawled away. I had a hand-tame bird which I had reared from the egg. If I proffered it a dead bee held in forceps it was not taken, but it showed interest in a lightly-held live bee with whirring wings, sometimes taking it from the forceps and always pursuing it on release. It seemed quite disinterested or at most a little bemused if I allowed the bee to walk over the perch within pecking distance, and I have once or twice witnessed the same disinterest by other bee-eaters in natural situations (conversely there *are* records of wild bee-eaters snapping up insects which land at their feet[289]).

There are other exceptions to the rule that bee-eaters eat only flying insects, and, as it happens, they are of considerable interest. But first, some further points about the normal diet, which is known for several species in great detail because of their convenient habit of coughing up neat pellets of food remains. Nestlings at first produce one pellet every 24 hours, usually at night, and from some ten days of age they regurgitate two per day[347]. Adult pellet size does not vary greatly but frequency of regurgitation, depending on the sort rather than on the amount of prey eaten, varies from one pellet every $1\frac{1}{2}$ to one very 4 hours[574]. It may contain the remains of only a single large dragonfly or of hundreds of small ants (5 insects per pellet seems to be the average for European Bee-eaters and 12 for Red-throats). In any event it is easy to collect vast numbers of pellets, and careful microscopic analysis related with field observations of food show that virtually every insect eaten is represented in them in some shape or form.

OPPORTUNISM AND SELECTIVITY

Like most animals, bee-eaters are opportunists which cash in on any transiently abundant food. Examples from studies cited in Chapter 2 are the exploitation of localized hatches of termites, ants, locusts, dragonflies, cicadas, shield-bugs, corn-beetles, chafers, and wood-boring beetles. All were caught when swarming on the wing, and pellet analysis shows that one such species will be preyed upon, perhaps for hours on end, practically to the exclusion of all else. Studying Red-throated Bee-eaters in Nigeria, Humphrey Crick stumbled across and showed to me an isolated but diverting instance of individual opportunism: a single bird had learned to prey kleptoparasitically upon others in its nesting colony. Instead of flying several times each hour to the foraging territory a kilometre away, this genius provided for its nestlings merely by lying in wait at the breeding cliff and giving furious chase to any bird (other than its mate) returning with food to adjacent nests. The pursued parent, unless it won the race to its own nest entrance, dropped its prey item as will a skua-harried tern, and the thief-bird caught the morsel in mid air and directly fed its own brood with it. Crick found one other such thief at a colony elsewhere but those are the only cases in scores of *M. bullocki* colonies which have been intensively studied.

Hymenoptera—ants, bees, wasps and their allies—predominate in the diet. Of 20 separate studies involving tens of thousands of prey items, in 16 sorts of bee-eaters, the overall numerical (not weight) proportions of Hymenoptera were 20%, 24%, 40%, 52%, 73%, 75%, 75%, 75%, 76%, 79%, 79%, 81%, 86%, 87%, 90%, 91%, 94%, 95%, 95%, and 96%. In part these high values reflect the abundance and ubiquity of Hymenoptera in nature, particularly in the tropics. They are high in part because numerous ants, wasps and bees are gregarious, so that chance encounters with, say, ephemeral swarms of flying ants may inflate the hymenopterous proportion. But what contributes the most importantly to these figures is that bee-eaters select certain hymenopterans preferentially from the aerial insect fauna, such as honeybees *Apis*, bumble-bees *Bombus*, sweat-bees *Trigona*, and wasps *Vespa* and *Polistes*. I asseverate that prey species like those are singled out, eaten selectively, because that is what often seems obvious in the field. Why else do migrant bee-eaters congregate at beekeepers' hives, year after year and often in the face of persecution, if not simply because they are drawn to a prized food? The assertion is difficult to prove; but a recent field study by A. Helbig of a pair of European Bee-eaters nesting in Westphalia demonstrated that they fed opportunistically and also selectively, taking prey according to size and flight characteristics[293A].

Years ago I used suction traps to sample aerial insects in Red-throated Bee-eaters' foraging grounds. Samples contained much lower proportions of Hymenoptera than I was finding in the birds' pellets, but all sorts of factors conspired to bias them. I thought it prudent not to publish, and the work remains to be repeated with much greater sophistication. That bee-eaters are not just random aerial vacuum sweepers but are discerning predators selecting prey according to the needs of the moment, is proved by their feeding their nestlings and themselves on different prey on the same occasion, which has been amply demonstrated.

Robert Hegner has given some insight into the parents' decision-making process, by studying the foraging energetics of White-fronted Bee-eaters in Kenya[297]. In the case of an adult bird feeding close to the nesting colony, there was no difference in prey size between what is delivered to the nestlings and what it ate itself. But the further away from the colony it foraged the greater the size disparity between the insects it consumed and those it carried back for the young—in other words the more selective it became. (It was uneconomic to exploit territories much more than about 3 km away, for nestlings fed from them had markedly impaired survival.)

OTHER PREDATORS OF ANTS AND WASPS

By no means are bee-eaters the only birds that eat stinging Hymenoptera*. Probably a majority of insectivores take toxic ants from time to time; certainly a surprising variety of birds catch wasps and bees, even if very few exploit them to the extent of having acquired special adaptations. Passing mention is worthwhile here of two special relationships between birds and ants. There is that known as 'anting'; whatever its function it is certainly not nutrition[469]. And in a huge and diversified Family of songbirds, the neotropical antbirds (Formicariidae), many, like the genus *Rhegmatorhina*, attend upon columns of army ants, feeding on the insects they put to flight[598,599]; other antbirds are shrike-like, with massive hooked and notched beaks and strong bites, and I suspect that they freely take ants and wasps. In the western Palaearctic, nearly 40 sorts of birds are known to consume adult Hornets *Vespa crabro* and six species of social wasps *Vespa* and *Vespula*[66], while North America has 140 wasp-eating birds[397]. (An explanation for that disparity may well be the great preponderance of social wasps in the Neotropics, where numerous North American birds winter.) Besides bee-eaters, the most noteworthy wasp predators are Honey Buzzards, shrikes, corvids and jacamars.

Honey Buzzards *Pernis apivorus* (*apivorus* means 'bee-eater') feed at wasp and bee nests on pupae, wax and honey, and their heads are closely covered with small scaly feathers probably affording protection from stings[134]. They eat innumerable adult wasps yet do not de-sting them; whether they have immunity to venom, or perhaps some anti-sting adaptations of mouth or gut, is not known[66]. Several species of shrikes (Laniidae, and probably 'shrikes' of other Families too) eat wasps in abundance, and bees[104]; and at least three *Lanius* shrikes can devenom them by rubbing the insects' tail-ends against the perch very much as bee-eaters do[504]. Various corvids, the crow Family, and in the Palaearctic particularly the Jay[120], are wasp eaters, without any apparent behavioural or other adaptation for it.

Jacamars (Family Galbulidae, usually classed as piciform, but now thought to be coraciiform like Meropidae[101,518]) are the ecologues or ecological analogues of bee-eaters in the New World tropics. There are approximately as many species in each Family and the range of body sizes is about the same. They look alike—jacamars are mostly green above and

* After 50 years of collecting, W. L. McAtee and the US Biological Survey had examined, by 1932[397], the stomach contents of 80,000 American birds. They made a quarter-million identifications of animal prey of which 80% were insects. Hymenoptera comprised 14% of the insect identifications and were consumed by about 300 kinds of birds—they are "eaten by birds of all groups studied [and are] one of the most important elements of bird food". This monumental investigation was concerned with the efficacy of protective adaptations of animals and not with bird diets as such, so—unfortunately—identities of only a few of the birds were given in passing.

rufous below with contrasting throats, long-beaked, short-legged, burrow-nesting, alert-looking sit-and-wait 'flycatchers', and one species even has elongated central tail feathers. Even if they do belong to the same Order, the antiquity of their common ancestor would not be much less than Oligocene, so their similarities would owe far more to convergence than to affinity. The reason for convergence between jacamars and bee-eaters, which is of an astonishing degree and affects also a host of life history and nidification details[227], is that each has evolved as specialist predators of venomous bees and wasps. In 1968 I found myself in Mato Grosso, Brazil, at the head of the trans-Amazonian highway under construction through virgin jungles (an overworked phrase, valid then, but in the meantime those particular jungles have lost their virginity), and I made a study of the Rufous-tailed Jacamar. If and how it de-stings its prey, I never did ascertain (P.J.K. Burton[99] studied the feeding habits of Paradise Jacamars without ever seeing bee-rubbing, although one instance was reported to him and the technique seems the same as in bee-eaters. He could find no unusual features of the mouth or gut which might protect the bird against venom, and thought that they must have some physiological immunity.) But pellet analysis showed its diet to be startlingly like that of Red-throated Bee-eaters in West Africa, with the same insect Orders and Families and genera in much the same proportions. The jacamar's diet was 86% Hymenoptera and the bee-eater's 79%; representatives of nine hymenopteran Superfamilies were the same except that the jacamar was more of a social-wasp eater (expectedly, in view of social wasps' Neotropical abundance) and the bee-eater made good with flying ants. It is among the best examples in the animal kingdom of convergence between organisms differing taxonomically at high rank, and I am sure that it all owes to the coincidence of diet[227].

OTHER PREDATORS OF BEES

Bees as distinct from wasps, and in particular honeybees, are preyed upon by all of the birds so far mentioned and importantly also by honeyguides (Indicatoridae), swifts (Apodidae), swallows (Hirundinidae), Kingbirds (Tyrannidae), wood-swallows (Artamidae) and drongos (Dicruridae). At least 40 birds in North America alone take them, incidentally or in some cases regularly[269], which is quite surprising in view of the fact that honeybees are not native to the New World. Even such improbable birds as Kookaburras[296], Spotted Flycatchers and Verditer Flycatchers[37,120], Cactus Wrens[397], Black Wheatears[482] and Great Tits[572] can be quite significant honeybee predators (the last-named was known as a bee pest even to Aristotle and Virgil[493]).

Honeyguides are too sparse to have come much to the attention of beekeepers, which is as well for them since their lives revolve around honeybees as crucially as bee-eaters' do. They subsist on bee grubs and honey and on beeswax[217], and their adaptations include thick skin, cerases or wax-digesting enzymes, and in one species a polygynous mating system in a territory centred around a Giant Honeybee nest[143].

Swifts can be major predators of honeybees in Africa (Alpine Swifts[10]), Asia and elsewhere. In the Philippines, Spine-tailed Swifts raid apiaries to such an extent that boys are employed to net them; "on peak days as many as five are collected by each person" using a sort of gargantuan butterfly-net[432]. The gizzards of 14 swifts thereby killed contained ten Giant Honeybees *Apis dorsata* and over 1,200 Honeybees *A. mellifera* and Asiatic Honeybees *A. cerana*, an average of 88 bees per bird. One had consumed 162 *A. mellifera* and another 234 *A. cerana*: little wonder that beekeepers bear them malice. Most of the bees were workers, and it is of much interest that mouths and gizzard linings were barbed with scores of detached stings[432]. Surely these large swifts, of mean weight 180 g, are absolutely immune to bee toxins and are not even incommoded by the stings. More surprising still, several swallows and martins are also honeybee predators although they average smaller and lighter than swifts and, for that matter, than bee-eaters[269,299,368].

A TASTE FOR HONEYBEES

Heavy as the toll taken on honeybees worldwide by swifts and numerous other birds may be, there is little doubt that where bee-eaters occur they are far and away the bees' foremost avian predators[9]. All bee-eater species eat honeybees, and mostly they do so year-round and in preference to other hymenopterans. The same 20 studies referred to earlier showed the following percentages of *Apis* honeybees in the diets of the 16 bee-eaters: 0%, 2%, 3%, 5%, 16%, 17%, 20%, 20%, 25%, 25%, 25%, 45%, 47%, 50%, 52%, 54%, 67%, 80%, 83% and 89%. Honeybees are hawked wherever they are to be found, in wood and savanna, secluded garden and suburban park, over sunny hillside and flowering field and especially, of course, at apiaries. Bee-eaters shot by irate apiculturists can be stuffed full of bees exclusively, nothing approaching the swift's record of 234, but often a tidy 30 or more and once 100[609]. A breeding European Bee-eater consumes on average 39 g of food a day[472], or about 410 insects the size of worker honeybees; and one bird has been estimated to account for 9,000 honeybees during its summer stay in the Ukraine[461].

To large country gardens full of flowers and trees in blossom honeybees are attracted in profusion, and bee-eaters living there feed on them year-round practically to the exclusion of all else. Such is the case, I found, with Swallow-tails in the spacious suburbs of Harare and with Cinnamon-chested Bee-eaters in the Nairobi residential district of Karen. For the latter, honeybees form 96–99% of the volume of prey over the breeding season (see species account; this value not in the above 20). By contrast, they comprise only insignificant parts of the diet of rainforest and of desert edge bee-eaters, habitats alien to these insects.

DEVENOMING BEHAVIOUR

Nearly all of the honeybees eaten are workers, the stinging sterile-female caste, and it is fascinating to watch closely in the aviary to see how they are devenomed. Each flying bee is plucked adroitly from the air and the bee-eater carries it back to its perch in the tip of its beak. There it is mandibulated for a moment until grasped crosswise just behind the thorax. Bending to one side, the bird deals the bee's head a violent blow against the perch, then it transfers its grip to the tip of the abdomen almost too quickly for the eye to see, and bends the other way to subject the insect's tail-end to five or ten bouts of rapid rubbing. The beak is closed tight and held side-on to the perch, crushing both abdomen and sting, and while bee-rubbing the eyes are closed as venom and bowel-water are visibly discharged, and sometimes the sting itself, a needle-sharp sliver a millimetre long, is caused to stick into the branch. A couple of sharp raps to the head-end completes the process which lasts up to 10 sec, and the bee is swallowed. Whichever way a bee is held, facing right or left, the direction does not change during treatment, so that all head blows are to one side and all tail rubs (or sometimes blows-plus-rubs) to the other. Of the two distinct actions, the abdomen rub is used only for stinging Hymenoptera and the head blow, with variations, for all other insects.

Red-throated Bee-eaters eat harmless, soft insects like moths up to 2 cm long without beating them at perch, but larger, tougher prey items prove troublesome, especially if they do not easily disarticulate. Driver ants, *Dorylus*, are an example; their drones are large, winged insects called sausage-flies, brown, shiny and very hard. Since I could obtain them in quantity I used to feed a lot of them to my captive birds; they usually hit them against the perch more than 30 times, and once it took over 80 blows before a sausage-fly was softened-up to the bird's satisfaction.

Of honeybees taken by wild bee-eaters, stingless males or drones customarily form only an insignificant fraction. It reflects the facts that they are far less numerous in the hive than workers and do not normally fly outside, although sometimes great assemblies of flying drones occur at a traditional distant spot (functioning to prevent a colony becoming inbred). The few times when a predominance of drones has been found in

Bee-rubbing

European Bee-eaters' pellets, they had probably come across such a drone assembly. Drones of *Apis mellifera* are larger than workers, 230 mg against 95 mg, which should combine with their being stingless to make them more sought-after—when, for instance, they are thrown out of the hive in late summer. By means of aviary experiments I was able to show that Red-throated Bee-eaters can distinguish the two castes, partly by size and partly by some other property[225] (colour, flight pattern?). Despite that, the birds seemed not to know that drones are harmless since they nearly always bee-rubbed them. Maybe it was just a safeguard, for they were habitually rubbed less than workers, although their heads were beaten more, commensurate with their greater size.

Some further experiments using devenomed workers, bee-mimicking flies and so on, led me to deduce that the function of the bee-rubbing component of the treatment is to procure venom discharge and not to incapacitate the insect, which is what the beating is for. Mimics and other non-hymenopterans which are beaten but not rubbed, are recognized by the birds as harmless non-stingers.

One bird which I raised from the egg showed the rudiments of bee-rubbing the first time I ever gave it a bee to eat, so the habit must be innate. It was evidently stung in the mouth by the first, second, third and fifth bees it swallowed, obviously distressing it. But thereafter it was never stung again, and its bee treatment behaviour improved so rapidly that after only its tenth bee it was practically as adept as adult birds. (Photographs of bee-rubbing by captive Red-backed Shrikes show how like bee-eaters they behave, and, interestingly, the behaviour is clearly innate in them too[276].)

VENOM IMMUNITY

Are bee-eaters immune to the venom of stinging Hymenoptera? The only physiological study I know of affecting birds was by Phisalix in 1935[465]. He found that the poison of *Apis mellifera* administered at a dose of 0.60 mg per 100 g of body weight was generally fatal to mammals and to sparrows. Since a bee discharges about 0.2 mg of venom, any bird weighing less than 33 g and surviving one sting would probably have

partial immunity. My hand-reared bee-eater was that weight and survived three or four stings in quick succession, and barbs sometimes found
needling the oesophagus and stomach attest to adult bee-eaters being
stung from time to time (if the venom had not already been discharged
against the perch). Incidentally, nestling bee-eaters at a young age are
provided with worker bees although it is not known whether the adult
birds have devenomed them first. These facts suggest strongly that
bee-eaters, as well as many other small birds, have indeed evolved
physiological immunity. Endorsement for that comes from the fact that
insects even more toxic than *Apis mellifera* are commonly preyed upon by
bee-eaters. Some wasp venoms are at least as toxic, *Apis dorsata* reputedly
has high toxicity, and *A. cerana* venom was found to be twice as toxic as
that of *A. mellifera*[60].

LEARNING THE TRADE

For two or three days before young bee-eaters leave the nest burrow the
frequency of parental feeding visits falls and they lose weight. But as soon
as they fledge the parents and any helpers rally round and resume feeding
them at the old high rate. They are quite inept at dealing with larger
insects, however, and up to 40% of some kinds given to them are dropped
and abandoned[574]. The fledgling is entirely reliant upon the adults for
several days, until it starts to catch some insects for itself[574]; thereafter it
slowly learns how to immobilize a large beetle without dropping it and
how to devenom bees, and it may be several weeks before it is nutritionally
quite independent.

HAWKING STRATEGIES

The smaller, round-winged bee-eaters obtain their food by 'flycatching', choosing a perch overlooking open airspace where they can give
unimpeded chase to any suitable insect that happens to pass, a technique
which recently has been called 'sentinel feeding'[358]. Captures are brought
back to the perch never more than one at a time, to be immobilized and
consumed there. It is a sit-and-wait stratagem, and the birds do not
actively seek out insects; only by moving from time to time to other
lookout perches nearby can such bee-eaters be said actively to hunt their
prey. True flycatchers and other small insectivores can feed in this
manner within a leafy canopy, shading themselves from the sun. But to
catch fast-flying Hymenoptera bee-eaters need space to manoeuvre, so
they shun dense foliage and favour instead a tall grass stem, the top of a
bush, or an emergent branch. They seldom retire into shade, but spend all
day out in the open, the tropical savanna birds under the most merciless of
suns.

Little Bee-eaters are typical[167]. Their usual habitat is low grass sward interspersed with shrubs and clearings and they like perches commanding unobstructed views. Spying an insect, the bird instantly dashes after it and audibly snaps it up—or misses and gives up—only a few metres away, returning to its perch in a graceful glide. On average only one sally in three is successful. Prey taking evasive action may be pursued, but sallies or forays seldom exceed 20 m in length or 4 sec in duration. In low growth the commonest perch height is only one metre, which is close enough to the ground often to be unbearably hot for a person. These bee-eaters neither drink nor pant very much, and by what internal mechanisms they avoid cooking themselves I do not know. (On their Saharan nesting grounds White-throated Bee-eaters pant a lot and they also sit with the body held high exposing the featherless insides of the thighs, doubtless to dissipate heat. In hot weather European and Blue-throated Bee-eaters fly with trailing legs for the same reason[94,94A].)

Red-throated and White-fronted Bee-eaters hunt in bushier and more wooded places, searching for prey from an outer twig some 3 m above the ground in a leafy tree. With dashing flight they hawk after an insect up to 15 m away, or glide slowly towards the ground in order to glean prey in a momentary hover, snapping it up as it rises, disturbed, from herbage. With White-fronts, Robert Hegner found that a minor stratagem is to fly down to the ground to capture an insect[289], but Red-throats very seldom do that and then only in a passing swoop, without landing. Only rarely do these two species hunt in continuous flight aloft.

In open country the larger, pointed-winged species, namely the Blue-cheeked, Madagascar, Blue-tailed, European, Rosy, Carmine, Rainbow and Blue-throated Bee-eaters, forage by flycatching from a treetop or telegraph wire, and to varying extents they hunt also in easy wheeling flight on high, catching insect after insect (or so it appears) without coming to perch in between times. Flycatching forays can be in the immediate proximity of the perch or quite distant. In Malaysia I had a grand opportunity to make measurements where Blue-tailed Bee-eaters were feeding in a huge, 10 km² paddyfield divided into regular quadrants by power lines from which the birds hunted. They sat facing into the 2–4 knot breeze and flew one by one to intercept small wasps flying down wind towards them. Sighting a wasp, a bird flew fast, straight and level or slightly rising on a course to pass immediately below the insect, at the last moment reaching up with its beak to seize the victim with deft precision, the master craftsman using his animated needle forceps with admirable effect. Each wasp was borne straight back to the power line for treatment. Some strikes were 65 m away, a flight of 6.5 sec duration. In that time the wasp had moved 14–28 m, so it had been first spotted by the bird, against a backdrop of distant trees and rainy skies, at a distance of 80–95 metres[239]. What vision!

Although they do not always use the habit, Blue-tailed Bee-eaters and their close ally the Blue-cheeked are the only ones that intercept their victims from below. At the critical moment they throw the head back with the beak pointing straight up or even behind the vertical, an extraordinary posture made spectacular by being retained for a full second after the prey has been seized. I watched them feeding in this manner from mangroves at the edge of a tidal creek: numbers of the fierce and dangerous large hornet *Vespa tropica* were flying down the middle of the waterway and the bee-eaters flew out 50–70 m to attack them. Each was snatched from below, and possibly because of the hazard the bee-eaters held their beak-up posture for what I estimated was 1.5 sec, enough for several wing-beats on the return to the mangrove, where the hornets were bee-rubbed and beaten so vigorously that several times their heads flew off. Another time Blue-tailed Bee-eaters were feeding on Giant Honeybees flying low over a hockey pitch and what was then remarkable was that the birds attacked the insects from below with the sky-pointing posture momentarily sustained, when the insect was itself only half a metre above the turf.

FURTHER SPECIALIZATIONS

In Africa White-throated Bee-eaters are an exception to the rule that only the large, long-winged bee-eaters hunt in continuous flight. They are small, with wings more rounded than pointed, but on their wintering grounds they seem to do much of their feeding aloft in continuous flight. Food studies show that they prey largely upon ants, so doubtless they are then exploiting high flying swarms of stingless ants which would be crushed by a snap of the beak and could be swallowed forthwith, but I have found it quite impossible to see what actually happens whenever bee-eaters seem to be foraging high in the sky.

One unresolved problem concerns Carmines. I netted some in Zimbabwe whose beaks were sticky with honeybee liquids, and I deduced that they had been catching bees without coming to perch. If so, this species has made a portentous evolutionary innovation. But whether they really *do* cope with bees in uninterrupted flight, remains to be established.

This particular species, the Carmine Bee-eater, has a number of other interesting foraging habits, not concerning honeybees. They were mentioned in the species account but will bear repetition here. Along with Grasshopper Buzzards and Black Kites they are the first birds to arrive at a newly-started bush fire. It can burn so fiercely that carbonized vegetation is shot aloft, making even a small fire visible from 5 km away, and doubtless the bee-eaters are attracted from at least that distance. They seem excited, perching on charred shrubs and dashing about the flames and through the smoke to catch fleeing insects—probably mainly locusts, grasshoppers and mantises[557].

White-throated and European Bee-eaters have been noticed following behind people and vehicles moving through the African bush, catching insects disturbed from the grass. Carmine Bee-eaters do likewise but more frequently, and will use persons, grazing and galloping Oryx Antelopes, or motor vehicles as their beaters. As with bush fires, all manner of insects put to flight from the grass are doubtless captured but the main ones are probably grasshoppers and locusts, for studies of Carmine Bee-eaters in Nigeria and Zimbabwe have shown that those insects form about 5% of prey items (or perhaps over 10% of the diet by weight) while in Mali they seem to be the staple food. Carmines have progressed another evolutionary step in foraging behaviour, for in addition to following larger animals through the savannas they ride on them, using them as 'animate perches'. The habit is commonplace in the northern tropics, where one of these flamboyant birds may be seen on the back of bustard or stork, goat or antelope anywhere from Senegal to Somalia. For some reason it has barely been developed south of the Equator—perhaps it is because the birds do not rely on grasshoppers so much there. The vantage provided by an ostrich or a camel must be of particular value to the bee-eater in grass plains or desert steppe where there are no other elevated perches for it to use. As described by J. Boswall[73]: "I followed one very approachable lone Oryx with an attendant bee-eater for about ten minutes. Twice the bird sallied after prey obviously put up by the moving animal; once it flew a much greater distance in pursuit of prey obviously *not* flushed by the Oryx". Little Greens are the only other species which sit on the back of grazing cattle (recorded only in India, rarely).

If Northern Carmine Bee-eaters are diversifying their hymenopteran diet with an incipient specialization upon locusts, it may be remarked also that: Blue-cheeked and perhaps Blue-throated Bee-eaters are dragonfly specialists; Boehm's relies to quite an extent upon flies; and flying ants are major parts of the diets of Little Greens, White-throateds, Rosies, Carmines, and European Bee-eaters in Africa (see species accounts). Termites also figure prominently in the diet of European Bee-eaters in Africa, but in Europe their staple is the bumble-bee *Bombus*.

The Carmine Bee-eater riding around on Secretary Birds or gazelles makes a good story, but associations between small birds and large mammals are by no means singular and this particular one, of whatever import for the bee-eater, is actually little more remarkable than the humble robin using the gardener to good advantage. Truly exceptional, however, is the strange way in which White-throated Bee-eaters capitalize on squirrels. Like many other animals, squirrels relish the oily, fibrous and highly nutritious flesh of oil palm nuts. Tugging a damson-sized nut

from a cluster, the squirrel sits in the head of a palm tree and systematically strips away the epicarp in order to reach the pulp. Narrow strips of
epicarp, up to 16 mm long and 1–2 mm wide, rain to the ground and
bee-eaters, waiting animatedly on the drooping fronds, catch many in the
space beneath the frond umbrella as adroitly as they do wasps. Apart from
an isolated case of European Bee-eaters reduced to eating hard *Cedrela
toona* berries shortly before dying in an exceptionally cold spell in
Zimbabwe[540], it is the only known instance of a bee-eater ever taking
vegetable matter; moreover the habit is clearly commonplace in the
White-throated Bee-eaters' winter grounds. When I discovered it I was
tempted to relate the consumption of this lipid-rich food with the fact that
the bee-eaters fatten perceptibly just before they quit their forested winter
quarters and migrate 1,000 km or more to their breeding grounds[223], but
later observations suggest that there may be no connection[462].

GROUNDED PREY

Another oddity concerning White-throated Bee-eaters is that in their
Saharan nesting haunts they feed small lizards to their young. I have not
witnessed the moment of capture, but from an observation hide near Lake
Chad I saw, two or three times, parent birds arriving at their nests with
3–4 cm long lizards, *Mabuya* skinks I think. A similar record is of
vertebrate bones in Blue-throated Bee-eaters' pellets in Malaysia, probably small lizards (M. Avery pc[24]); and birds in captivity can be induced
to eat lizards[107]. Astonishing as it may seem, some bee-eaters catch fish;
but first, some further points about grounded prey.

Most of the limited number of records of wild bee-eaters taking
flightless prey are circumstantial or evidential rather than observational.
Spiders have been noted once each in gizzards of pellets of Little Green
and European Bee-eaters and Rainbowbirds. It is quite possible that they
were in fact captured in the air, for many spiders spin a thread of silk to
disperse themselves on the wind; a bee-eater feeding over a marsh in
Spain was seen to be trailing a long silk thread. Caterpillars often suspend
themselves on silk too, from herbage, which might account for the
presence of many small unidentified caterpillars which I found in a
European Bee-eater pellet sample from Zimbabwe. (Hirundines, aerial
insectivores like bee-eaters, also eat caterpillars probably caught hanging
on threads[571].) Caterpillars of the small moth *Sylepta derogata* were eaten by
Little Green Bee-eaters in the Punjab[309]*.

A Black-headed Bee-eater took what looked like grubs to its nest (M.

* Data in Husain & Bhalla's 1937 paper are rather ambiguous, but from a careful reading of
their text it seems that they found caterpillars and adults of this moth in two of the four
bee-eaters they shot.

In need of confirmation. A Little Bee-eater reported carrying another in its beak[399], Swallow-taileds roosting on each other's backs and taking insects from flowers[382], Little Bee-eaters breeding in a weaverbird's old nest[382], a Rainbowbird using a twig to assist in excavating[136], a Red-bearded taking a scorpion, and a Carmine taking an insect from a Kori Bustard's beak[113]. Probably all of these reports contain errors of observation or interpretation.

Dyer pc); European Bee-eater pellets from Denmark contained a flightless ground beetle and from Russia harvestmen (Opiliones), while Zambian pellets of Boehm's Bee-eater had a number of flightless soldiers of the driver-ant *Dorylus*. In Borneo Blue-throated Bee-eaters were seen on a lawn seemingly picking up termites or ants, but I am a little sceptical of bald assertions like that because it is not widely realized that when bee-eaters come to the ground to eat grit (for gastroliths) it looks very much as though they are picking up insects. Earthworms were given under "previous records" of Rainbowbirds' food by Lea & Gray in 1935[370], without comment. In the aviary almost anything goes, and when we read that bee-eaters can be reared on mealworms[119] or minced beef taken from a pan (K.A. Muller pc, *anent* his success with Rainbowbirds in Sydney Zoo) or can be induced to eat hydrated fresh-water shrimps and cut lettuce, it comes as no surprise to hear that they will also take scorpions and centipedes[106,107].

Some old claims that bee-eaters, the Swallow-tailed for instance, take insects "freely from flowers"[382] are surely not correct, but it is the case that flying birds will on rare occasions pluck an insect from herbage, which is attested for Black-headed, Blue-throated and European[357] and is a possibility with Blue-bearded Bee-eaters (again, hirundines do the same[279]). European Bee-eaters have also been known to pick off a bee crawling on the flight board of its hive[264], at odds with what I was asserting about captive Red-throats.

FISHING AND BATHING

Although a discussion of bathing is inapposite in this chapter, I am treating it with the surprising phenomenon of bee-eaters' fishing for reasons which will quickly become apparent.

Rather uncommonly, bee-eaters of various sorts can be seen splashing down in a leisurely-looking fashion onto the surface of still water. It is hard to tell whether they are bathing or drinking or, as has repeatedly been claimed, diving for food at or below the surface. A century ago H.E. Dresser wrote in his *Monograph of the Meropidae*, about Little Green Bee-eaters in India, that "Mr Blyth informs me that he had seen a number of them assembled round a small tank seizing objects from the water in the manner of kingfishers", and in recent decades there have been 15 or so further published accounts of water diving. In about half, authors have recounted some evidence of feeding although they could never be quite certain about it[33,109,284,480,499,568, Guthrie in 591]. In a recent description, R.A. Conant gives the feel of interpretative difficulties experienced in practice—his observations of Carmines in Zambia were made from a canoe[138]: "The flock was circling haphazardly low over the water and some birds were perched on exposed branches of *Syzygium guineense* at the water's edge. As the birds flew slowly about 2 m above the (surface), they periodically dived suddenly into the water at an angle of about 45°. The entire body of the bird seemed to disappear beneath the surface and at least a full second elapsed before the bird sprang from the surface and shook itself convulsively. . . . As many aquatic insects were observed about 5–15 cm beneath the surface, it seems likely that the birds

were indeed feeding rather than drinking or bathing".

The equivocation in the literature[269A] was such that, never having my-self seen any water diving behaviour which I thought might be fishing, I remained sceptical. After all, bee-eaters are so exclusively geared to feeding upon flying insects that it was unthinkable that they might stoop as low, so to speak, as to fish. In 1981 I was able to confirm and extend Conant's observations upon Carmines, by watching them critically in the field in Nigeria and on film in London; but not before I had proved accidentally but incontestably that bee-eaters really do eat fish. A few months earlier I was keeping watch on Blue-tailed Bee-eaters wintering on playing fields in Kuala Lumpur; I collected their pellets daily from turf below a goal-post cross-bar where, conveniently, the birds liked to perch. The pellets were the usual crumbly blackish affairs, but one day two were smaller, grey and finer-textured. They comprised 60 fish vertebrae each 1 mm long and other fish bones, almost certainly of the little mosquito-larva predator *Gambusia affinis* (Cyprinidontiformes, Poeciliidae)[239]. Males reach 35 mm long and females 60 mm; each has 33 vertebrae, so the pellets probably contained two males. A small shallow stream ran nearby, and the bee-eaters spent much time hawking alongside it from bushes. I expect the *Gambusia*—which commonly occur at the surface film—were caught there, although I did not see any birds splashing onto the stream.

So unusual-looking were the grey fish pellets that I wondered whether some other sort of bird using the same perch as the bee-eaters might have

regurgitated them. There was in fact a solitary White-breasted Kingfisher in the vicinity. But kingfisher pellets look quite different, and the clincher that the two pellets really were cast by bee-eaters was the rest of their content, insects practically diagnostic of *Merops*: namely two vespid wasps, two spider-hunting pompilid wasps, a scoliid (relative of the velvet-ants), three flying ants, a bug, a grasshopper, and a 10 mm long beetle—all 11 flying insects of different species.

The discovery prodded my memory and I eventually unearthed from store a similar greyish pellet which I had picked up with normal ones when watching Blue-breasted Bee-eaters on the Kenyan shore of Lake Victoria in 1972. Sure enough that too proved to contain fish remains, a few tiny bones and large numbers of scales, but this time no additional insects. The scales were ctenoid in form and so the fish was almost certainly a cichlid (Perciformes, Cichlidae), very probably of a small, surface-film-feeding vegetarian species not more than 30 mm long (P.A. Orkin pc). There were Little Bee-eaters nearby but at the time I thought that all of the pellets I had collected were from Blue-breasted Bee-eaters.

Then I found that the act of fishing had fortuitously been filmed. The bee-eaters *most thoroughly observed* in nature are the Red-throated and White-fronted and the one the most closely studied in the aviary and about which by far the *greatest amount has been published*, relating to breeding biology but mainly to diet, is the European. But the species for which much the *best visual reference* material is available is the Carmine Bee-eater, and that is simply because it is such a marvellous, attractive subject for still and motion photography. The spectacle of a thousand of these pink, red and caerulean birds wheeling about their river-cliff nesting colony, vivid beyond belief against the river's sunny sparkle, their flat *klunk klunk* calls mingling into a gladdening medley, is never to be forgotten, and it draws the cameraman in Africa almost as strongly as do herds of large animals.

So the archives have plenty of film of Carmine Bee-eaters. I arranged to view all of the holdings in the London film library of Survival Anglia Television, and found footage of over 20 diving episodes filmed by Dieter Plage in Botswana and Ethiopia and Cindy Buxton in Zambia. In one sequence four birds wheel then momentarily hover together a metre above the still surface of a broad river, falling in unison as if competing for prey they all saw simultaneously. The fastest splashes tern-like into the surface and 1/5th sec later emerges holding a 5 cm fish lengthwise in its beak. As it does so the other three disperse; unfortunately the camera did not record what happened next. Frame by frame projection, blurred as each frame is, leaves no doubt that this bee-eater species does indeed fish.

The analyser provided for my use permits 25 frame/sec film to be projected frame by frame, stilled or at variable speed forward or backward. It was interesting to measure wing beat rate with it, which for Carmine Bee-eaters proves to be up to 5.0 beats/sec in accelerating flight during chases between partners or rivals. 'Normal' flight has a lower rate, of 4.2 and 3.6 flaps/sec in two instances, and of course a lot of normal flight to and from the nesting colony or when feeding, is gliding with zero flap rate. Studying the other 20 dive episodes I found that they were mostly as I had described them in my field notebook a few weeks earlier, in Nigeria:

> From foraging altitude of about 50–70 m, descends to perch on waterside shrubs and trees in graceful leisurely swooping glide. From perch flies over water, losing height till gliding slowly ½ m over surface, then twists to splash onto surface immersing forepart of body, makes an immediate fluttering rise then returns with powerful strokes to perch (usually) or to foraging altitude. Shook plumage in flight but did not preen at perch. When first bird descended to water its dozen or so foraging companions came down too.

Much the same behaviour by European Bee-eaters was noted in Austria by J.C. Reid (pc), who added that his birds twisted through 180° the moment before splashdown, to enter the water in the opposite direction to the line of approach. From first touching the surface to submersion to breaking clear again can take as little as 7/25th sec, far too fast for the eye to discern its details without cinematographic aid.

Since bee-eaters take fish they will doubtless also catch insects on or below the surface, as some observers have claimed. Strictly, unequivocal evidence for taking insects has still to be produced: I have myself often identified aquatic insects in pellets but they have always been winged forms and I have assumed that they were caught when flying. Apart from the single fishing incident, none of the Carmine Bee-eater diving episodes show any evidence of feeding; so that the bird cooling itself, dislodging parasites, or even drinking, remain as alternatives to cleansing in what seems, in the gregarious bee-eaters, to be essentially some sort of social comfort activity[242].

Blue-breasted Bee-eater regurgitating pellet

5: Bee-eaters and apiculture

"Let your rich hives be free from bee-eaters . . ." VIRGIL, *Georgics*, iv 14.

So great is the reliance of bee-eaters upon the genus *Apis*, the honeybees which are their staple food, that one might expect the natural distributions of predator and prey to be as congruent as those of, say, the Palm-nut Vulture and the Oil Palm. Beekeeping has made honeybees practically cosmopolitan in tropical and temperate latitudes, but in pre-beekeeping times the geographical distributions of bird and insect evidently did in fact correspond closely. There is a little evidence that in recent decades the range (and doubtless local abundance) of bee-eaters has fluctuated with the fortunes of the bee-keeping industry, for instance in USSR and in the Punjab; and there is a lot of evidence for the animosity which beekeepers not unnaturally feel for the birds as pests. A few words on bee history may thus not be out of place.

There are four species of honeybees; all are valued for their products but only one, *Apis mellifera*, has been widely cultivated. In many respects the most primitive (or least advanced) species is the Little Honeybee *A. florea*, found in the Oriental Region from Iran to the Philippines, south to Sri Lanka and southeast to Java[410]. The Giant or Rock Honeybee *A. dorsata* has much the same range, from about Afghanistan to the Philippines, southeast to Timor. Both of them make a single exposed honeycomb, but *the* Honeybee or Hive Bee *A. mellifera* and its eastern relative the Asiatic Honeybee *A. cerana* construct multiple combs in dark cavities, a habit enabling them to exist in drier climates and predisposing them for domestication. *A. cerana* ranges from India to China and Japan, southest to the Moluccas. Man has been farming *A. mellifera* for so long that its natural range is difficult to be certain about, but from cave paintings and other sources it appears to have been parapatric with *A. cerana*, in Asia west of the Urals, warmer parts of Europe, the Mediterranean basin, southwest Arabia, and the whole of Africa and Madagascar except for rainforest and desert regions. Thus the ranges of bird and bee coincide except that bee-eaters do not go quite as far north, in western Europe or into Japan for example, and that *Apis* bees do not range naturally into New Guinea or Australia. Both *Merops* and *Apis* are of tropical origin and both have successfully invaded higher latitudes, bee-eaters giving rise to *M. apiaster* and bees to *A. mellifera* in the western Palaearctic, each with a population in the Cape[494,495].

Pleistocene man in his then home, Africa, almost certainly collected wild honey just as all pre-industrial peoples do at the present time[275]. When bees were first cultivated is not known—probably when man himself first became settled, 50,000 years ago. In the Mesolithic and Neolithic much importance was clearly attached to them, partly for their honey and wax and partly for symbolic reasons. The celebrated paintings in the Cuevas de la Araña in Spain, dated at about 8,000 years BP, depict scenes of honey hunting with ladders and combs and swarms[297], and there are similar rock shelter paintings elsewhere in Spain[150], in India and Australia[452] and in a dozen African countries from Morocco to the Cape (H. Pager pc). Particularly explicit are those in the Matopos Hills and Zombepata Cave, Zimbabwe, and Eland Cave, Anchor Shelter and Ndedema Gorge in the Natal Drakensberg Mountains[275,450,451].

Honey was greatly esteemed by the ancient Egyptians, as tomb art and hieroglyphics testify. Bee-eaters were also portrayed, for their magical and medicinal properties. A Middle Kingdom papyrus prescribed for a certain female complaint to "fumigate her eyes with the shanks of Bee-eaters", and another recommended Bee-eater fat as an unguent[151]. Whether any relationship between bee-eaters and bees was appreciated I do not know, but I would expect the omniscient Egyptians to know all about the depredations of *Merops*, for in Greece Aristotle—admittedly much later (about 350 BC)—noted their destructiveness to honeybees. So did Virgil[493]. The Romans were great beekeepers: near Rome the brothers Veianius had a commercial enterprise yielding 2.5 tonnes of honey a year[10]. In the tenth century there developed a flourishing Russian trade in beeswax, for Byzantine candles, and for 900 years thereafter beekeeping for wax and honey was an industry of enormous importance in Russia, employing perhaps a million people with 2.5 million bee-trees, and with bee-walks safeguarded by law and often specified in medieval wills and deeds[251]. About 1806, Peter Prokopovich, the renowned Ukrainian who gave apiculture a quantum boost by introducing the movable-frame hive, kept 10,000 colonies and ran a school for beekeepers[10]. In 1910, Russia (mainly the Ukraine) had an incredible 6.75 million hives producing an annual harvest of 32,000 tonnes of honey and nearly 4,000 tonnes of beeswax[251]. After the Revolution the industry waned to a fraction of its former size although the USSR remains the world's premier honey producer.

Early colonists took European races of *A. mellifera* with them to the Americas and to Australia. In 1956 the fierce African race *adansonii* was introduced to Brazil where, being itself tropical, it flourished; with aggressive 'africanized' hybrid bees now widespread in the New World, beekeeping there will never be quite the same. Nevertheless, in the early 1970s the four top honey-producing countries in the world, after the USSR, were all American (USA, Mexico, Canada and Argentina), each producing over 10,000 tonnes annually[10].

Apiculture is an integral part of the agricultural economy of many nations; in numerous others—especially in emerging tropical states—modern beekeeping is presently developing on a commercial scale[15]. But it will be a long time before organized apiaries overtake traditional, rural beekeeping in importance. Of the 6.75 million Russian hives, old-fashioned log hives and tree nests were five times as numerous as modern movable-frame hives arranged tidily in apiaries; and throughout tropical Africa to-day there are untold millions of hives traditionally crafted of clayed elephant-grass or wicker or hollowed logs, festooning trees across the savannas. It is that haphazard rural practice which over the millenia must have made a major (if unrecorded) impact upon the status of bee-eaters. Conversely bee-eaters have not been slow to extend their exploitation of bees, from scattered tree hives to commercial apiaries. Africa, constituting two-thirds of the autochthonous range of *A. mellifera*, holds enormous potential for apiculture, for the genetic variability of its 11 races of honeybee is commercially totally untapped[496]. Africa is also the home of two-thirds of the world's bee-eaters: it is hard to judge how they will fare in the future.

Red-throated Bee-eaters are occasionally troublesome at apiaries in northern Nigeria (although worse predators there are *Agama* lizards[222]), but none of the species is sufficiently pestiferous in tropical Africa to have provoked much remark. In South Africa, European Bee-eaters and also drongos and bee-pirates (sphecid wasps, *Philanthus* sp.) are 'rather serious' and Alpine Swifts a 'serious' nuisance[103]. European Bee-eaters can be pests at Algerian apiaries[322] and doubtless elsewhere in north Africa and around the Mediterranean. It is not regarded with any particular malevolance in the south of France, despite there being over 200,000 hives within its breeding distribution there. Bee-eaters are nominally protected by law in most Mediterranean countries but, probably in deference to the beekeeping lobby, not in Spain, Morocco, Greece or Cyprus[608]. In Cyprus their pest status is only an excuse; in fact the 3–5,000 killed there each year are for eating (P. Neophytou pc). Likewise about 2,500 are killed every year in Malta[608] and thousands in the Nile delta. They are regarded widely as pests throughout the rest of their breeding range[547], and in USSR are a nuisance at apiaries, particularly when migrating in autumn[609]. Blue-cheeked Bee-eaters are generally much less of a menace, except in Iraq[188], and in Russia are considered valuable[9]. In Pakistan and India agriculturists formerly regarded Little Green Bee-eaters as beneficial, but after the introduction of apiculture in one region the bird became commoner; 850 were shot, found to eat bees, and attitudes hardened[309,367]. Rainbowbirds are a considerable irritant to apiculturists in parts of Australia.

Bee-eaters tend to raid apiaries in dull, cool weather—probably because it keeps insects grounded and forces the birds to seek their food further afield. At their hives the bees themselves are then relatively inactive and the birds can behave with remarkable temerity, sitting on the hives and persisting to feed around the apiary even whilst half of their number is being shot[195]. Bee-eaters may sometimes affect adversely the working strength of an apiary. All the same it is probably only very rarely that so many bees are consumed that a beekeeper has to lament the loss of half of his honey harvest[400]; and it is the loss of queens (upon which the colony depends) that really plagues apiculturists[322,351]. The insects themselves take effective action against attack, simply by lying low: in a 5-minute period 450 bees flew into or out of a hive but when bee-eaters started harassing them flights were reduced to only 20 in the same period[351].

All sorts of control measures have been taken: stopping up nest burrows with earth, encouraging children to destroy nests by whatever means[367,609], and poisoning with strychnine, cyanides, carbon disulphide or chloropicrin[22,356]. Shooting is the most effective remedy and, having an immediate impact, is the most widely employed. At least let it be humane: one must deplore the use of "ordinary airguns, readily available in the Market" (in Pakistan)[367]. More bizarre efforts at control have been stringing bee-eater corpses on gibbets between the hives[322] and catching birds with 'fishing lines'. Hooks baited with live bees dangling from nylon lines threaded around an apiary caught 80 bee-eaters in ten days[22]. One senses rising hysteria when the editor of one bee-keeping journal, writing in another, advocates destroying by any means available these "fierce and cruel antagonists, (with) piercing and discordant cries which seem to strike terror into the bees (and which) even drum on the hive body to encourage the inmates to investigate"[322]! A more rational approach to the problem is one of evasion rather than destruction: simply shutting bees into the hive[195,271], or where possible moving the entire apiary out of harm's way[490].

As many apiculturists recognize, bee-eaters are in other ways beneficial to them. Bee genera like *Psithyrus*, *Sphecodes* and *Allodape* have numerous species which are themselves honeybee predators or parasites which bee-eaters readily prey upon[246]. Sphecid wasps *Cerceris* sp., bee-pirates or bee-wolves *Philanthus* sp., hornets *Vespa crabro* and particularly the eastern *V. orientalis* are bee predators which can seriously damage bee stocks, but all bee-eater species eat these wasps in quantity[351]. The same goes for robber-flies (Asilidae) and dragonflies. And in the wider context bee-eaters are valuable also for the inroads they make into locusts[122,467] and insect pests of stored products, cotton fields and other agricultural interests[309,393]. The most detailed investigation of their pest status ever undertaken was in Kazakhstan, in 1936; 500 European Bee-eaters were shot in order to evaluate their diet and, because they raid beehives only on rare cold, wet days and prey elsewhere at other times on 'harmful' insects such as Eastern Hornets, it was concluded that the species is, on balance, economically valuable and should be afforded protection[351]. Even when preying on hive bees they may be less harmful that at first appears, for in autumn they tend to kill old bees, which have high winter mortality stemming from bowel disease and other infections[356].

To make my own estimation of the ratio of honeybee-predators to honeybees consumed by bee-eaters, I tabulated the results of the Kazakhstan and all other studies, totalling 47,000 prey items identified in the diets of 17 *Merops* species in 25 countries[243]. I anticipated that the birds might take one bee-predator for every 100 or so honeybees eaten. But the ratio proves to be astonishingly high: for *Merops* as a whole approximately 6 : 100 and for *M. apiaster* up to 14 : 100 or even 25 : 100—one bee-predator to four honeybees.

It used to be fashionable to decide an animal's pest status by listing its pros and cons, in the case of an insectivorous bird the 'harmful' and 'beneficial' insects it eats. But with bee-eaters as with almost every other animal running foul of people's livelihoods, the web of ecological cause and effect is tangled. Bee-eaters eat bees and bee-eating bees; and the knotty problem of their real, long-term effect on apiculture ought to be properly disentangled before any further action against them is taken. Nor let it be forgotten by adherents of the view that bee-eaters ought to be shot on sight, that to many people honeybees are themselves a menace: world figures for bee sting fatalities are hard to come by, but 86 people were stung to death by Hymenoptera in the USA in 1950–1954, 52 by honey-bees[34,431], in a population of 200 million, so globally nearly 300 people are likely to die from bee stings *each year*.

Transcending these economic considerations is the inestimable worth to all but the apicultural world of these lovely birds as a part of nature. Their many kinds enhance the beauty of places wild and tamed, conspicuous for eye and ear to admire. Fortunately no species is endangered. Probably deforestation has affected woodland species adversely and some savanna ones (like Rainbowbirds) beneficially. With Carmine and many other bee-eaters dependent on river banks for nest sites, the drowning of valleys and other tropical water development schemes have been of concern for years[586]. Conservationists view some recent proposals with mounting apprehension—the Mupata Gorge dam on the Zambezi, for instance, where Carmine Bee-eaters would be hard hit, even if not as irreversibly as most other animals.

Aside from the adverse effects of some agricultural development, the birds suffer quite unnecessary persecution. Across Africa bored pastoralists mindlessly poke sticks or burning rags into the nest burrows of colonial bee-eaters, or entomb the living contents with a stone; in the name of fun, children from Morocco to Malaysia perpetrate even worse cruelties. It is at least a crumb of comfort, in the unlikely event of any species ever becoming seriously endangered, that they can be quite readily bred in captivity despite their feeding and nest-site specializations[107,343,346,355].

6: Social and reproductive life

It is generally held that nesting in holes gives eggs and young a better chance of survival than nesting in the open. In the tropics predators are legion, which is why so many birds there nest in holes, often roofed-over edifices of marvellous workmanship like the mud, cobweb, grass, thorn and leaf nests of oven-birds, swallows, penduline-tits, sunbirds, weavers and tailor-birds. All coraciiform Families are cavity nesters, some using rock crevices or tree holes and others excavating their own burrows in termite mounds or the soil.

Bee-eaters are all earth-hole nesters—unlike kingfishers they never use tree termitaria—and they dig a burrow anew rather than use last year's hole (rarely) or a suitable rodent burrow (very rarely). They seek a compact sandy or loamy soil but their strong, sharp beaks eventually penetrate even hard clays and laterites. All the same it doubtless profits them to avoid hard ground if they can—savanna soil is often so hard that a man needs a pick to break it—and, uniquely among all birds I believe, Red-throated Bee-eaters, and maybe Carmine, excavate their burrows three or four months before they are really needed, when the earth is still soft at the end of the rainy season. Perhaps this is in part adaptive to a secondary purpose, for some bee-eaters (if not the Red-throated) roost in their burrows all year. The softer the ground, the longer the burrow; the earth is pecked, scraped and granulated by the beak, which can become perceptibly worn and shortened by 2 mm, and feet are indispensible too, for scrabbling loosened soil backwards out of the lengthening burrow with an improbable bicycling action— the bird freeing both legs by supporting itself on the tripod of wrists and beak.

'False starts' or supernumerary nest holes are an unexplained curiosity. Woodpeckers begin and soon discard a number of holes, which serve importantly for rapid re-nesting in the frequent event of their definitive nest being usurped by other birds or squirrels[514]. But those bee-eaters which do re-nest[289,549] do not use their half-finished extra burrows for the purpose. Their false starts seem to be a pointless waste of effort, and a study of the problem is needed.

It is by no means the case that bee-eaters' hole nests always afford reliable protection. Rats and snakes often raid them, sometimes returning to a colony night after night to eat eggs, nestlings and roosting adults. In Africa, Egg-eating Snakes *Dasypeltis scaber*, Spitting Cobras *Naja nigricollis* and Nile Monitors *Varanus niloticus* are amongst their major nest-predators, the snakes adept at reaching holes even high on cliff faces, by descending from above using projecting roots, and the lizards lumbering up from the bottom and laboriously digging their way into lower nests. Varying proportions of Red-throated Bee-eater nests, about 5% overall, are predated. Burrows can also be expropriated by mice, agamid lizards, Rock Sparrows, Horus Swifts and whip-scorpions; I have known a true scorpion to take shelter in an occupied nest and to kill an incoming parent. One particularly nasty death which I have come across three or four times is by starvation when a bird accidentally wedges its head crossways in a narrow tunnel—any young and adults entombed behind it perishing too.

Choosing a site

Burrows dug into flat ground are more readily accessible than are cliff holes to a variety of reptilian and mammalian predators (the only avian predator of bee-eater nests, apart from parasitic honeyguides, is the Harrier-Hawk, an African crevice-raiding specialist[100] which can probably grab the odd youngster venturing too near its burrow entrance). Ground nests are at risk in cloudbursts and sandstorms—a small colony of White-throated Bee-eaters nesting in dunes at Lake Chad was immured under blown sand and entirely obliterated—and they are highly vulnerable to trampling by elephants or buffaloes. Since there is no shortage of suitable-looking cliffs, one may ask why the birds ever excavate in places other than the perpendicular walls of erosion-gulleys and sand-quarries and river banks. The answer is that when disaster strikes a cliff-breeding colony it can do so on the grand scale: it can be inundated by a flash-flood, or the cliff can be so undercut by a stream, or so riddled with nest holes, that it collapses destroying all eggs and young and many adults and—since bee-eaters are single-brooded and the survivors will usually not re-nest—nullifying one year's production of offspring. In fact bee-eaters are good parents with a strong attachment to nest and young, and instances are on record of them continuing to rear young in a wetted nest and in a brood chamber exposed by a cliff fall taking the tunnel away; Carmine Bee-eaters even "set about digging out their young" in an earth slip[268].

Most dangerous of all are the outer bends of meandering rivers which bite their cliffs back a little every year, keeping the face clean-cut and vegetation-free—which makes it appear ideal to the birds. Solitary species like Little Bee-eaters are drawn to these places, but their nests are sufficiently spaced for only a very small proportion to come to grief. Far more adversely affected, in terms of their total populations, are the gregarious species. Even in cliffs that are not regularly undermined by water, the very tunnelling activities of Carmine, White-fronted and Red-throated Bee-eaters enhance the risk of collapse; but in addition these species, needing plenty of space for their nesting colonies, are irresistibly attracted to the wide expanse of a fresh-cut meander cliff. Not infrequently the result is calamitous.

That their penchant for such sites has not been eliminated by natural selection—that colonial bee-eaters continue to use meander cliffs—can only mean that a capriciously lethal potential is offset by some benefits—relative freedom from predators, for instance. Likewise the risk of weakening a cliff by peppering it with holes must be outweighed by some advantages of aggregated breeding (advantages which are only speculative among bee-eaters but have been demonstrated in gulls, gannets and other birds[438]). Again, flat-ground nesting has pros and cons in relation to cliff-nesting: in nest-site selection as in all other areas of biology, alternative strategies can be adopted in the struggle for survival.

Cinnamon-chested, White-fronted and Red-throated Bee-eaters are the only obligate cliff-nesters, particularly the last[142], and their burrows have unique architecture: invariably the tunnel slopes steeply upward from its entrance for about half a metre and then angles down into the egg chamber. Doubtless it would serve better than the level or declining burrow of the other cliff-nesters to keep rain out—but Red-throated Bee-eaters are dry-season breeders and hardly ever encounter rain then! Paradoxically the other species nesting in rainy seasons have horizontal or declining nest holes. Many Red-throated Bee-eater eggs and young are lost by falling out of the burrow (I suspect more than in their cliff-nesting congeners), although a little protection is afforded to them by the brood chamber being sunken. Whatever adaptive value this burrow-form may have remains enigmatic.

Other species are more versatile and excavate tunnels by preference (I believe) in high cliffs, but will also use low banks and slopes and perfectly level land. Carmines certainly prefer cliffs (their densely-packed holes sometimes spreading up over the top onto more-or-less flat ground) although a few flat-earth colonies are known. Blue-throated Bee-eaters nest more commonly on flats than in banks and so perhaps do Blue-cheeks and Blue-tails; and the highly gregarious Rosy Bee-eater and solitary Boehm's rarely or never use cliffs. Rosies site their huge colonies, ten-thousands of nests strong, on sand-bars exposed by falling waters of the Rivers Niger, Benue and Congo, but that situation is probably neither more nor less safe than other bee-eaters' places. Maybe those Little Bee-eaters which drill their nest tunnel into the sloping roof within the entrance of an Aardvarks' deep lair have the safest site of all.

The 'milieu intérieur'

In the northern hemisphere, European Bee-eater nest holes tend to face south or southwest and, although explanations having to do with the direction of incident light are admissible, the true reason is probably its effect upon nest temperature. Hole nests may lend some protection from predators, but in addition they have the invaluable function of providing their occupants with a stable microclimate and protection from wide temperature variation at the soil surface. Like the physiologists' 'milieu intérieur' or core-temperature uniformity of warm-blooded animals, bee-eaters' brood chambers are in general excavated at the right depth in suitable topography to maintain a thermal environment for the nestlings at or near their thermally neutral zone.

Fred White and his colleagues found that bee-eater nests in southern Spain, with soil surface temperatures varying from 13° to 51°C, maintained their brood-chamber temperatures uniformly about 25°C[596]. Living deep in the ground might pose physiological problems in relation to water balance and gas exchange; but White discovered that high chamber humidity and a succulent insect diet combine with minimal thermal stress to ensure that nestlings do not thirst unduly. As for ventilation, the purging effect of wind gusting across the nest entrance was demonstrated by blowing tobacco smoke through a long tube directly into a chamber a metre from the nest entrance: "A few seconds after the next strong gust of wind, a vortex of smoke appeared in the centre of the tunnel and moved along the tunnel to its entrance in a series of slow pulses. Within a few minutes all traces of smoke were gone . . . (it) was repeatedly introduced into the next chamber, always with the same result". Moreover, adult birds' bodies fit snugly in the tunnel and every time they go in or out they act like a piston, pumping in fresh air and exhausting stale air. All the same on occasion the CO_2 concentration in a chamber with several nestlings rose above 6%, enough to make their breathing fast and laboured.

Bacterial decomposition of pellets, dropped whole insects, and faeces produces a pungent smell of ammonia in the chamber, and in windless conditions its concentration can rise and that of oxygen fall significantly, but there is no evidence that nestlings are ever affected adversely. Having taken plaster casts other investigators found four European Bee-eater nests, in level sand, also in Spain, had 'chimneys' about a third of a metre long slanting up from the chamber[8]. But I think they were artefacts and I very much doubt whether the birds dug them or whether they had any function in microclimate control.

Nest hygiene

The only concession to hygiene is that nestlings defaecate usually not on the floor but against the earthen walls. As more and more pellets are regurgitated the carpet of insect sclerites thickens—hatchlings sometimes sit in it up to the neck—and becomes alive with scavenging dermestid beetle larvae.

Any nestling which dies is rarely removed from the nest[344]; as a rule its rotting corpse is simply trodden underfoot. The scavengers are benign, but much less so are a number of ectoparasites that start to infest the birds about the same time. Minute larvae of harvest mites, a species of *Neoschogastia*, infect the skin around the cloaca and another microscopic mite, *Neocheyletiella*, causes quite large and unpleasant-looking lesions in the skin of the abdomen[249]. Large hippoboscid flies (*Ornithophila metallica*) are not uncommon, running fast over the body surface under and between feathers; stick-tight fleas (*Echidnophaga gallinacea*) occur[524] and so do feather-lice, including *Meromenopon meropis*, *Meropoecus meropis* and *Brüelia apiastri*[394]. My impression is that bee-eaters carry a heavier ectoparasitic load* than most birds; and in the case of the more densely gregarious species hole-nesting doubtless promotes infectious diseases like the epidemic which decimated S.T. Emlen's study colonies of White-fronted Bee-eaters at Nakuru in Kenya in 1979, killing 86% of his birds.

Brood parasitism

In the Palaeotropics, and especially in Africa, a variety of cuckoos, whydahs, indigobirds and a weaver parasitize open-nesting birds, but hole-nesters are not exempted and are parasitized by honeyguides (Indicatoridae). They parasitize *only* hole-nesters, mainly piciforms and coraciiforms: barbets and kingfishers are particularly vulnerable and one

---

* Endoparasites (nothing to do with bee-eaters being hole-nesters, of course) include the flatworm *Eumegacetes maliensis*[209], microfilariae, and the blood-cell protozoa *Haemoproteus* (three species[53]) and *Leucocytozoon*[446].

Fledgling

quarter of all Striped Kingfisher nests are parasitized (H.U. Reyer pc). In Kenya, Robert Hegner found no parasitism at all in 250 White-fronted Bee-eater nests, but in Nigeria I found plenty and I would estimate that Greater and Lesser Honeyguides between them account for the loss of 1–3% of all Red-throated and Little Bee-eater broods. The honeyguide pip's the host's eggs, killing the embryo[176], but if any do survive to hatching the young parasite, blindly lunging and snapping at everything with its needle-sharp beak hooks, soon lacerates and kills its foster siblings. In time their corpses are trodden into the nest floor litter, and the fast-growing honeyguide vociferously demands attention. Interestingly, it has the *Beau Geste* tactic, a literal duplicity, of a begging call that sounds not like a single bee-eater begging but two together—a supranormal stimulus for the food-bringing parent[232].

SOCIAL ORGANIZATION

Except possibly at the periphery of the species' range, Red-throated Bee-eaters are highly sedentary and the large majority remain within a few kilometres of their natal cliffs for the whole of their long lives. Such evidence as there is suggests that long-distance migrants are equally philopatric and come back year after year to the places where they were born. About 80% of European Bee-eaters return from Africa to the colony where they nested or were reared the previous year, many to the same part of the colony, and the ones that do go elsewhere are for the most part first-year females, but even they do not generally disperse much further than a few kilometres away. Carmine Bee-eaters' colonies can be as permanent as seabird rookeries: the large one on Umguza river near Sawmills, Zimbabwe, 100 km northwest of Bulawayo, has been there for at least 80 years (the only exception being 1955, when it might have been affected by adjacent farmland being left fallow—D.V. Rockingham-Gill pc).

The clan

When I began observing Red-throated Bee-eater colonies closely, in 1962, I soon found that at any stage in the breeding cycle several adult birds may enter a particular nest hole, and conversely that one bird will sometimes visit two or three nests in quick succession. My first description used the word 'promiscuity', but how far off the mark that was has now been shown by the long-term demographic study of White-fronted Bee-eaters begun in 1977 by Stephen Emlen and his Cornell University team in Nakuru National Park, Kenya. Its social organization proves to be fascinatingly intricate—"one of the most complex societies recorded among birds"[291]; the colony is as structured as that of human village society but with none of the random, transient relationships that promiscuity implies.

Like Red-throated Bee-eaters, their northern counterparts, White-fronteds breed in small, dense colonies, and they are monogamous—the pair usually staying together for life (although 'divorce' is not unknown). After fledging, juveniles commonly keep in close contact with their parents, roosting and foraging with them, and in the next breeding season they may become their helpers and participate in such duties as excavating the burrow and feeding the brood. Two-thirds of the nests in a colony have a helper in attendance (in Red-throated Bee-eaters it is only one-third: with one or sometimes two or three helpers). The 'breeding unit'—pair, trio, quartet or quintet—defends the nest entrance and the area immediately around it selectively, allowing the members of some other 'friendly' breeding units to make visits into its nest.

Those visits are not to bring food but are purely social, and the two to five friendly breeding units concerned comprise a commune or clan whose nest holes are not clumped together but are scattered throughout the colony—one of them may sometimes be in an adjacent colony. The key to clan membership lies not in the spatial relation of nests, but on the feeding grounds up to 7 km away. Early each morning a colony of bee-eaters departs from roost in waves which travel outward (often up- and down-stream) shedding groups as they go. With years of painstaking study of marked White-fronted Bee-eaters at Nakuru, the team has been able to demonstrate conclusively that in composition these groups are the same as the breeding clans and that each one defends a large, stable feeding territory from incursion by strangers[291]. Clans are quite stable too, although from time to time membership does change, of course (no bird is mortal!) and Robert Hegner found additions by birth within the clan and by 'marriage' from outside (both by first-time pairers and widows), and subtractions by death and by a mated pair moving away to become the nucleus of a new clan[289].

Clan territory

A foraging territory within 2 km of a White-fronted Bee-eater colony site is used by a clan year in, year out; a more distant one may be forsaken for feeding grounds nearer the colony only for the duration of the nestling period. Within their territory the half-dozen or dozen members of the clan space themselves out and forage essentially solitarily, keeping contact by infrequent but regular calling, paired birds—and usually their helper—never being far apart. Each pair hunts in its own favoured area but there is extensive overlap between such sub-territories of the various pairs and individuals. Whenever two birds make a close approach—two or three times an hour on average—they greet each other with more-or-less excited calling and tail quivering; less commonly one aggressively supplants the other, which is followed by mutual greeting. But if one of the birds turns out to be an interloper from an adjacent clan territory it is roundly chased well away.

Helpers

By virtue of its membership of a clan, a bee-eater maintains almost continual social contact with several other individuals; they roost in very close proximity and daily commute back and forth together to their clan foraging territory. Although some of the youngsters raised by breeding pairs within a clan disperse elsewhere, others remain with their parents and become members of their clan, and until a young bird finds a mate it helps at its parents' nest and sometimes at the nests of other pairs within the clan. Other non-breeding birds in the clan, widows or those whose nesting attempt has failed, also become helpers at their clansmen's nests. Within the clan social roles seem almost interchangeable, and Emlen and Hegner have documented numerous cases where a bird bred one year and helped the next, as well as several instances of helping reciprocity where bird A helped pair B in one breeding attempt and, having obtained a mate, nested itself in the next to be helped in turn by pair (or one bird) B—for not all pairs attempt to breed in any given season.

Stephen Emlen's current studies are revealing further complexities. It seems that many females are fertilized after forced copulations, not by their mates; that (like Red-throated Bee-eaters) some females lay 'parasitically'; and even that a bird may subvert its own nesting son into becoming its helper.

Helping only occurs within a clan, seldom or never between members of different clans even within the same colony, and despite the small size of a clan—from one to five pairs together with a few unpaired individuals—incestuous matings have never been recorded[291]. Although the clan foraging territory is permanently sited, the location of the nesting colony generally changes by some hundreds of metres between successive breeding seasons (even when the site does not change new burrows are dug amongst the old ones) and the helpers participate in the digging. Red-throated Bee-eater helpers sometimes copulate with the breeding female, which complicates matters and makes paternity impossible to determine; and White-front helpers (probably Red-throats too) also help with incubation. But their most valuable contribution is in feeding the nestlings, which I will return to consider below.

Bee-eater society is thus an elaborate weave of affiliations: the individual may be one of a mated *pair* or it may be a *helper*; a pair with its helpers temporarily forms a *breeding unit*; a few friendly pairs and helpers together constitute a commune or *clan*; several clans nest or roost gregariously to form a *colony*; and colonies every few hundred metres along a suitable river have a limited degree of exogamic interchange of individuals and can be said to comprise a localized *population*.

Aid-giving behaviour

At this point I need to put the helper phenomenon into zoological perspective, but in as few words as possible since voluminous discussion of its complexities is readily available in the literature[2,191,192].

Because of the implications of aid-giving behaviour for the evolution of animal (including human) society, its study has been a major growth point in zoology and a cornerstone in the young discipline of sociobiology. And because co-operative breeding among birds is easily its most widespread manifestation, ornithologists have been able to take a lead in what has become a fascinating field of investigation.

Some degree of aid-giving behaviour is found in almost all sexually reproducing animals, between mates and in their care of the young; its survival value and the mechanism of its evolution are readily understood in Darwinian terms. But in the complex societies of social Hymenoptera, some mammals and numerous birds, additional behaviour can be performed which in extreme instances is altruistic, placing its donor at risk and costing it the loss of reproductive privilege (sterile drone honeybees) or even of life (worker honeybees dying when they sting in defence of the hive). How such self-destructive genes might sustain themselves, and how abnegating genes for helping (the helper foregoing breeding) might spread in a population, was a formidable difficulty for evolutionists but has now been explained satisfactorily by the concepts of *kin selection* and *inclusive fitness*. Parents and offspring have some genes in common; but so do sisters and brothers, and in some circumstances it can profit an individual to promote the survival of a proportion of its genes in its siblings or cousins (by helping them to survive) instead of in its own progeny[89,280].

There remains a further stumbling-block, the concern of pragmatic ecologists and ethologists rather than of evolutionary theorists. Why do some species have complex societies structured around helping behaviour when others do not? In what ecological and social conditions is helping liable to evolve? The nearly 200 species of birds having helpers at the nest are so varied—from warblers and geese to kingfishers and ostriches—that they have almost nothing else in common, unless it is living in parts of the world lacking harsh extremes of climate*. Bee-eaters, morphologically and ecologically uniform as they are, exemplify the difficulty: for some species never have helpers, others have them occasionally, and one always has numerous helpers. I shall return to discussion of this problem in the next chapter.

NIDIFICATION

In most ways bee-eaters are ideal subjects for biological field research, but their hole-nesting habit makes for some difficulties. To observe the contents of the nest chamber a 'riparioscope' or tubular arrangement of mirrors has sufficed for some species with short, straight burrows[158], and for curved ones I have used a one-metre long industrial endoscope with great effect, its optical-fibre bundles 'bending' the image over the hump in Red-throated Bee-eaters' tunnels. With cliff-nesters easily the best system, although a laborious one, is to dig a large pit behind the top of the cliff and whittle away that side toward the cliff-face until nest chambers are just broken into. Every breach is repaired with a window, and the observer can sit in his trench, close its lid, and from the dark spy at leisure into a score of tenements dimly illuminated by daylight entering through the tunnels[230].

It has even proved possible to monitor the growing nestlings' weights continuously and to weigh every one of the hundreds of food items entering the chamber—even to measure the nestlings' evaporative loss of water—by replacing a nest chamber together with a short length of tunnel with an artificial chamber[248]. Disposable urine flasks made commercially for male hospital patients are ideal, we found, with a removable perspex window let into the back. Choosing a moment when the parents were away we transferred the clutch of eggs and installed the assembly onto a precision balance such that the 'tunnel' of the flask fitted against (but did not quite touch) the cut-away inner end of the natural tunnel. If the adult bird on its return was dismayed at the small gap which ringed its tunnel or, when it crossed that gap, by a sinking feeling as the artificial chamber sank 3 mm onto the balance pan, it did not show it but resumed incubating as if nothing had happened.

Another gadget which has been used with great success weighs wild adult bee-eaters with speed and accuracy. A bird lands on a short wooden rod projecting from its nesting cliff face, and the rod pressures a load-cell

---

* Mainly the tropics[230]. Co-operative-breeding species presently comprise some 2–2½% of the world's avifauna, but with demographic studies of tropical birds on the increase I would expect the proportion to rise ultimately to 5–7%.

which transmits a current to an instrument in a distant observation hide giving a digital display of damped weight, accurate to 0.1 g[248]. Using four weigh-heads on the cliff and visually identifying the birds which land on them, we have been able to obtain thousands of weights of most of the Red-throated Bee-eaters in a colony, at all times of the day and year, and thereby to follow their fortunes—the changing weights of mothers or fathers or helpers reflecting shifts in the energetic balance between feeding and exercising.

The clutch

All bee-eaters' eggs are pure white, smooth and glossy, oval or nearly spherical[124]. Clutch size obeys the rule in being low at low latitudes and quite high at mid latitudes, with a range in specific modes from two eggs near the Equator (Blue-headed, Black, Cinnamon-chested and Rosy Bee-eaters) to six in the Palaearctic, South Africa and Australia. Some tropical clutches are complete at a single egg[176], while temperate-zone ones of ten eggs are on record.

They seem to be laid at 1–2 day intervals by all bee-eaters—never less than 24 hours I believe. Little is known about what is, after all, an important attribute, for incubation begins with the first or second eggs laid, which are accordingly the first to hatch. So the laying timetable determines the hatching schedule, which affects the average size difference between successive chicks in the brood—and that in turn will greatly influence the survival of its younger members. Since each egg is about a sixth of the mother's pre-breeding body weight (a ninth in larger bee-eaters) it is not surprising that she needs at least 24 hours to form one, even with the considerable benefit of her mate's 'courtship feeding'. Calcium may be the limiting factor—laying bee-eaters are clearly in great need of it, judging from their readiness to eat bits of mollusc shell, birds' and snakes' egg shells and other chalky material at the time[342,344].

Red-throats have a high degree of egg-laying synchrony at a colony, with 90% laid within 8–10 days, but the synchronization must be achieved by social means rather than by outside factors like food supply or weather since another colony nearby, although synchronized within itself, can differ in mean laying date by up to a fortnight. I once investigated separate colonies nesting in opposite sides of a cliffy headland eroded into a promontory only five metres wide, where all eggs appeared in one colony in the first half of February and nearly all in the other in the second half, averaging 12 days later.

Hatching schedules have been studied by Michael Dyer. He found that the first and second eggs in a Little Bee-eater's clutch hatch only two or three hours apart, with the remaining eggs at successive 20–24 hour intervals. Red-throats have a significantly shorter interval between the eggs in clutches of two (about 17 hours) than in clutches of four (successive intervals of 19, 26 and 26 hours), with clutches of three intermediate; and in a small sample of Carmine Bee-eater nests he found an interval of about 48 hours in clutches of two and of three eggs. Because of their effect on nestling sizes within the brood I would expect hatching times, hence the laying schedule, to be under strong selection pressure by way of incubation regimes; but this aspect of bee-eater biology has been poorly documented.

Nestlings

The inevitable result of hatching asynchrony is an often striking difference between the oldest and youngest nestlings. In larger broods the youngest one or two chicks are often ill-fed, grow slowly and die after about a week. In a brood of seven White-throated Bee-eater nestlings (which would weigh about 30 g before fledging) there was a difference of 19 g between the oldest and youngest[179]—the former well-feathered, alert and mobile and the latter naked, blind and doomed.

Nearly all animals grow slowly at first, the rate accelerating and then slowing to the plateau of maturity: typically the growth curve is ∫-shaped (usually described as sigmoid or S-shaped, which it is not). Up to their third week, or just into the fourth, healthily growing bee-eaters follow the typical pattern but exceed the average adult weight, usually by about 20% and rarely by almost 50%. Then during their last few days in the nest their weights fall until they fledge about 5–10% heavier than their parents. Probably the heavy nestlings are fat (it has not been investigated) to tide them over a day or two of insect shortage, an adaptation found in some other birds which feed on flying insects[444].

Because of the time it takes a clutch to hatch, incubation and nestling periods of bee-eaters are difficult to measure accurately. The shortest known incubation period is 20 days (Red-throated Bee-eater) and the longest 24–26 days (Blue-cheeked), and nestling periods vary from 23–24 days (Little) to 30–31 days (European): smaller variations than size and geographical differences might lead one to expect.

Nestling growth and development have been detailed in the species account for the European Bee-eater, and other species are very similar[178,347], so I shall elaborate here no further than to explain the seemingly wasteful deaths of so many younger members of broods.

Why lay four eggs, if as often as not the last-hatched nestling fails to fledge? Michael Dyer's researches in Nigeria[176,178] have shown unequivocally that it is, in adaptive terms, a simple failsafe mechanism. When suitably fed all nestlings survive to fledging but, in the event of adverse weather reducing the abundance of flying insects for even a few days, the oldest nestlings get all of the feeds and the youngest none. Some die that others might live, and according to the severity of food shortage, the cut-off point between the haves and the have-nots is adjusted with the effect that among the survivors there are no weaklings but all are robust and vigorous.

With one exception all bee-eaters are wet-season or summer breeders, rearing their young in those few months when flying insects are most abundant[244]. At latitudes in West Africa where the annual rains are ephemeral the various species of bee-eater all nest about the same time, but at places where the rains last for months their breeding seasons are staggered, evidently to reduce mutual competition for food[231]. The exception is the Red-throated/White-fronted Bee-eater superspecies which, as the earliest of all, has been effectively squeezed out of the wet into the preceding dry season—although the young do fledge at a time near the first rains when insects have become numerous.

For wet season breeders a common hazard is prolonged rain keeping both bee-eaters and their insect prey from flying—even a short sharp rainstorm can depress adults' and nestlings' weights severely[222]. For Red-throats, at least as great a peril in the dry season—often fatal for their nestlings—is 'harmattan' weather. The harmattan is an episodic light north wind so laden with Saharan dust that, over the whole of inland West Africa at any time from December to March, the visibility can be reduced to a hundred metres and the sun blotted out for days on end. There is a great drop in temperature (and in humidity) and as soon as the harmattan arrives at a locality flying insects become scarce and bee-eater nestlings' weights fall dramatically. Parental provision of food favours the older members of the brood, and younger ones whose weights fall below a certain threshold fail to recover with the return of sunny weather and they die.

It is at such critical times that the helper's invaluable rôle is most apparent, for the extra nutriment that it provides tips the balance from brood deaths by starvation to survival.

How helpers benefit nestlings

The influence of helpers upon growth rates and survival of the young has been demonstrated nicely by Michael Dyer in his studies of Red-throated Bee-eaters in Nigeria[178]. He made daily weighings of 50 broods of two or three nestlings reared by pairs with and without a helper, and also of a few broods variously with up to three helpers and four young. Unassisted pairs often have no difficulty in rearing broods of two. But sometimes the younger one fares badly after its eighth day, when its elder sibling has become sufficiently mobile to help itself to the lion's share of incoming provisions[231], and in one-third of cases it dies[176]. In broods of three, growth of the middle nestling similarly starts to lag a little at its 8th day but that of the youngest slows at about its 4th day, and either it makes a slow recovery to fledge just lighter than its senior siblings, or else it goes under. Of 30 unassisted broods of three the junior nestling in 18 broods died, and in one more both middle and junior ones died. Unassisted parents cannot rear broods of four; the fourth nestling always dies and the third may do poorly too.

By contrast a trio of adults (pair with their helper) can feed a brood of two so well that they grow faster than unassisted broods of two, and with broods of three the youngest nestling grows barely less fast than its seniors. When there are two or three helpers, all members of broods of three grow rapidly and robustly and in broods of four the most junior member has a struggle at first but then it catches up and fledges at the same healthy weight as the others. Overall, Dyer found that unassisted pairs fledge 78% of their young but with helpers there is 95% success.

How helpers benefit parents

Humphrey Crick, also working with Nigerian Red-throated Bee-eaters, has been monitoring the weights of adult birds using the novel weigh-heads mentioned earlier. The general pattern is that all adult birds are quite light at the end of the rains in September when they are spending much energy in digging burrows; then they increase in weight to a pre-breeding high, fall rapidly during the first four or five weeks of nesting, level off towards the end of the nestling period and start a slow recovery into the new rainy season.

Computer analysis of the hundreds of weighings he has obtained over the course of the season for each of numerous helpers and breeding males and females shows unequivocally that at all times females of assisted pairs are significantly heavier—by nearly 10%—than females of unassisted pairs; it probably stems from helpers 'courtship'-feeding them during incubation as well as helping with the provision of food for the young. Assisted and unassisted males do not differ appreciably from each other in weight, except in the incubation period and the beginning of the nestling period. The female does most of the incubating, but the energy cost is shared by her mate who supplies her with a substantial part of her food by way of courtship feeds. However, helped males do not lose weight at that time as rapidly as unhelped ones, and that is surely because the helper contributes a proportion of the courtship feeds. (Most helpers are male; whether female helpers give courtship feeds I am unsure.)

blue-brown

blue

pink

pale blue

black & blue

red-brown

pink-brown

very pale blue

pale blue

brown

7: Evolving specific differences

LIVERY

Green bee-eaters with buffy underparts can be quite hard to see in some circumstances, and the way in which they fly to leafy trees and keep still when they spot a distant hawk suggests that their plumage may have some concealing value. Other bee-eaters, with their bright overall colours, are anything but cryptic and, except that forest species are on the whole blackish or dark plumaged (which is usually thought of as being somehow adaptive to humid environments: Gloger's Rule), I see little evidence that in evolving plumage distinctions they have responded to any of the classical selection pressures stemming from predators, food or the physical environment. Instead the pressures have been purely social and the dominating greens, blues, ochres or pinks, so different between the species, are the ultimate product of the dual requirements for distinction and conformity.

Consider two closely allied kinds of bee-eater, recently allospecies but now, having chanced to evolve a degree of ecological difference, beginning to penetrate one another's ranges; they are still rather similar in all respects including appearances and they are reproductively compatible. Their incipient behavioural differences will be insufficient to prevent hybridization*, unless they are reinforced by visual *distinction* (visual, because that is birds' principal sensory modality). So any small nonadaptive differences in appearance which happened to arise while the two birds were still allopatric will suddenly assume significance, serving to discri-

---

* A. Prigogine has demonstrated over 20 tropical African examples of hybridization where two nascent species (or paraspecies) of birds meet[470].

minate each kind and helping to isolate it reproductively. Facial markings are particularly important, for like us bee-eaters interact face-to-face, and at low taxonomic level they tend to differ especially in hue and contrast of frontal features, which the dark gorget serves to delimit and accentuate. But greater than a population's need to look distinct is the individual's need for *conformity* with its own kind, since its mating and procreation depend upon it. The result is that each species evolves specific recognition marks like football clubs' liveries: initial selection of colour and pattern is arbitrary, but what is of critical importance is that one team shall look all alike and shall differ—preferably distinctively—from the competing team.

Comparison of closely allied taxa shows instructively which parts of the plumage bee-eaters are most prone to employ in sporting their colours. The two species of *Nyctyornis* (Plate 1) differ startlingly in forecrown and 'beard' colour, and conspicuously too in the appearance of the tail as seen from the front (its underside). But—suggestively parapatric as their geographical distributions may be—I doubt whether they are of immediate common descent. Confining myself to taxa of *Merops* whose close affinities I am quite confident about*, I find that the parts of the plumage the most significant for specific insignia are the forehead, eyebrow, cheeks and chin (different respectively in 8, 8, 8 and 7 comparisons) and then the gorget, throat, tail upperside and crown (respectively 5, 5, 5 and 3). Other colour characters—of the breast, back, wings or tail underside—hardly score at all.

Hybrids sometimes suggest interesting things about plumage evolution: the only bee-eater hybrid I know of was between a female *M. apiaster* and a male *M. nubicus nubicus*, bred in captivity by E. Callegari[107] (pc). Colour photographs of the living bird in my possession show that overall it resembled the Carmine better than the European but differed from both parents in four features, all facial and frontal (see chapter head). There are (1) a discrete blue supercilium, (2) discrete blue cheeks, paling to white posteriorly as in *M. variegatus*, (3) a very narrow black gorget with blue lower edge, like *M. ornatus*, and (4) *pink* chin and throat—neither the yellow of one parent nor the blue of the other. The inescapable inference is that in *Merops* phenotypic expression of a new combination of facial and frontal livery is, genetically, a simple matter.

Besides livery, bee-eaters show their allegiance also by means of their silhouette, using the tail. Elongated central feathers or streamers, or outer

---

* 23 comparisons: Plate 2—*M. g. gularis* cf *australis*, *M. m. muelleri* cf *mentalis*; Plate 3—*M. hirundineus* cf *M. pusillus* cf *M. variegatus* cf *M. oreobates*, and *M. h. hirundineus* cf *chrysolaimus*, *M. p. pusillus* cf *cyanostictus* cf *meridionalis*, *M. v. variegatus* cf *bangweoloensis* cf *lafresnayii*; Plate 4—*M. bullockoides* cf *M. bullocki*, and *M. b. bullocki* cf *frenatus*; Plate 5—*M. o. viridissimus* cf *flavoviridis* cf *cyanophrys* cf *beludschicus* cf *ferrugeiceps*; Plate 6—*M. persicus* cf *M. superciliosus*, and *M. s. superciliosus* cf *alternans* cf *philippinus*; Plate 7—*M. v. viridis* cf *americanus* and *M. l. leschenaulti* cf *andamanensis* cf *quinticolor*; Plate 8—*M. n. nubicus* cf *nubicoides*.

feathers in the case of Swallow-tailed Bee-eaters, lend each species a subtly distinctive outline even at considerable distance, and again this tends to be among the first characters to change in a differentiating population. One race of Blue-headed Bee-eater is streamered, another not; races of Little Green Bee-eaters vary greatly in streamer length; and the Swallow-tailed is a near ally of the square-tailed Little Bee-eater. The reason for modification of this particular part for recognition purposes is that all perched bee-eaters wag their tails back and forth (originally for balance I suspect, now ritualized) and because it wags, exaggerating its length makes it more eye-catching. Red-throated Bee-eaters calling youngsters out of the nest perch prominently and tail-wag vigorously; and immediately after leaving the nest for the first time young birds tail-wag too (H. Crick pc). Given time, some bee-eaters will surely acquire a blob at the end and become racquet-tailed and even more conspicuous, like certain motmots and drongos.

Red-throated and White-fronted Bee-eaters (together a superspecies) are the only ones in the entire Family which habitually nest in cliffs and never in flat ground. In season every bird spends much time clinging to the cliff by its hole entrance, supporting itself with the spread tail pressed against the soil (miniature bird in Plate 4), and in this posture it looks over its shoulder and calls vociferously in greeting a mate or threatening a neighbour; moreover there is a common behaviour obviously of some social significance in which the bird flutters momentarily into the air and resumes its hear-me-and-see-my-tail position under its nest hole. Significantly, each bee-eater has colour signals which relate with the posture: in White-fronts a blue rump contrasting with the all-green spread tail, and in Red-throats a concolorous green rump but a spread tail conspicuously patterned in green and ochre. Although serving the same social end, the signal colours of the two species differ markedly, and were the birds ever to meet and nest close by each other their tails would serve further to identify not only the home team but also the opposition.

Sexual dimorphism

Another category of species difference in the genus *Merops* stems from the varying degree of sexual dimorphism in plumage. In nearly all, male and female are exactly alike (except that in streamered ones males have slightly longer streamers, on average), but the Rainbowbird sexes are strongly dimorphic in streamer length and shape and perhaps in gorget colour, and the female European Bee-eater is greener above—less chestnut-and-gold—than her consort. An explanation has been suggested by J. Watson in discussing the world's 14 kestrels[589], of which nine are tropical and sedentary with male and female looking alike, and the five temperate-zone breeders, necessarily migratory, are in varying degree dimorphic in plumage. Dimorphism is a product of sexual selection which, he argues, is likely to be more intense in birds which have to establish or re-establish pair-bonds every year, synchronously (hence competitively). Such conditions are more likely to occur in migratory, high-latitude species with a curtailed breeding season than in sedentary tropical ones in which male and female may remain in their home territory from one year to the next.

European Bee-eaters and Rainbowbirds, with Blue-cheeked, are the highest-latitude and most migratory members of their Family. There are insufficient data to tell whether they really do differ from tropical forms in permanence of the pair bond, nor do they have a notably shorter or more synchronized breeding activity. But then sexual dimorphism is much less marked than in kestrels and at best only incipient (none has yet been described in Blue-cheeked Bee-eaters), and Watson's explanation stands.

Other bee-eaters are indistinguishable not only morphologically but also behaviourally. Such indistinguishability is a feature of many other colonial, monogamous birds and has been interpreted in terms of high degrees of sexual competition[98], not unlike Watson's explanation.

The mask

Incidental mention may be made here about another peculiarity of bee-eater plumage—the mask—even though it does not vary among the species (except that *Nyctyornis* is not masked and that two races of *Merops leschenaulti* have rufous, not black, masks). Black highwayman's masks occur widely among birds, but all-inclusively in very few large genera other than *Merops*. What purposes they may serve are unknown although their distribution among species is a pointer. Some water birds are masked (ringed plovers, in which the mask is disruptive of outline; terns, ducks), and a number of non-passerine land birds (barbets, woodpeckers, *Halcyon* kingfishers). They are more prevalent among passerines and well-developed masks—lores, eyes and ear-coverts, with or without the forehead—seem to be the most widespread in insectivorous songbirds (wheatears, robin-chats, cuckoo-shrikes, shrike-tits, Australian babblers, American warblers) and particularly in shrikes and shrike-like predators of strong, vigorous insects. At least a dozen genera of laniid and malaconotine shrikes and tyrant-flycatchers each have several masked species and, with bee-eaters, it suggests an adaptive correlate of masks with spirited 'fly-catching' (although exactly what advantage they might confer is hard to understand). Eye 'obliteration' is an unlikely function— bee-eaters' red eyes being in stark and obvious contrast—but improving visual acuity by diminishing light scatter and dazzle is a possibility— particularly considering that many masked birds live in bright and sunny places.

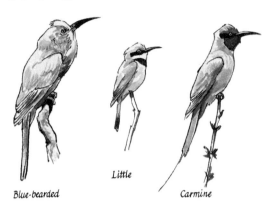

Little

Blue-bearded   Carmine

Size

Weight is the best measure of size, and *Merops* bee-eaters vary in weight by a factor of four, from the 13–15 g Little and Somali to the 54–64 g Carmine Bee-eaters (*Nyctyornis* species are somewhat heavier). An individual animal faces the greatest competition for food, space and other resources from its own kind, and next from its species' closest relatives. Congeners living sympatrically can reduce mutual competition by several means, a common—and obvious—expedient being to eat different-sized foods and to evolve different body sizes accordingly. A body weight ratio around 2.0 is often found in co-existing birds[199]: for example, four *Chloroceryle* kingfishers and the related Ringed Kingfisher which I captured at an Amazon locality had mean weights in the proportions 1 : 2.6 : 4.1 : 9.2 : 24, which differ successively by factors of 2.6, 1.6, 2.2 and 2.6[237]. (There are numerous other instances in nature of this size-doubling rule which, mysteriously, also applies to sets of artefacts like wind- and string-instruments and kitchen skillets[305].)

Bee-eaters recognize the rule without obeying it to the letter. Their subspecies vary in size and so do allospecies: for instance *M. nubicus nubicoides* is 1.3 or 1.4 times the weight of *M. nubicus nubicus*, and *M. bullockoides* is heavier than *M. bullocki* in the same ratio. Of all bee-eaters, the co-existing pair of species which look the most alike and probably compete the most severely is the Blue-breasted and Little, and the former weighs 1.5 times the latter. Throughout Africa Little Bee-eaters often nest in the same cliffs (and at about the same time) as Red-throats/White-fronts and Carmines, whose specific weights all differ by factors of at least 1.7. In some places in southeast Asia, Bay-headed, Blue-throated and Blue-tailed Bee-eaters nest together, but their average weights differ respectively by factors of only 1.25 and 1.05. They must reduce competition in other ways and significantly one of them, the Blue-tailed Bee-eater, has a qualitatively different diet (dragonflies).

Wing shape

Aside from tail shape, the most obvious structural variation within the Family is in the wing—indeed wing and tail characters alone were used to diagnose the formerly-recognized genera *Melittophagus, Dicrocercus* and *Aerops* and to distinguish them from *Merops*. With the addition of another feature, the beard, the same can be said of the genera *Bombylonax, Meropogon* and *Nyctyornis*.

My own view about genera is that if all characteristics of each bee-eater are taken into account, behavioural as well as morphological ones, there results a mosaic distribution of characters permitting the recognition of only three genera: *Nyctyornis, Meropogon* and the large genus *Merops* with 21 species[226]. Certainly tail shape, whether streamered, square or fish-tailed, is a useless criterion; but I do have to admit that with respect solely to wing morphology a case can still be made for splitting *Merops* into two—*Melittophagus*, and *Merops* in the strict sense. Indeed the whole Family falls into two groups along the same lines.

Nine species—*Merops sens. str.*—have a minute, pointed outermost primary (the 10th) never over 15 mm long, and rather a long, pointed wing. In sequence of increasing wing length they are: Little Green, Bay-headed, Rainbow, Blue-throated, Blue-tailed, Rosy, European, Carmine and Blue-cheeked Bee-eaters. The longest primary is the 9th in all except the first three in which the 8th is equal or just longer.

All of the other 15 species are comparatively round-winged, with the outermost primary round-ended and quite long, from 27 mm in the smallest to over 40 mm in larger members of '*Melittophagus*' and to 55 mm in the Blue-bearded *Nyctyornis athertoni*. The 9th primary, although much longer than the 10th, falls well short of the wing point, which is formed by the 8th or even the 7th primary. Further, there is a substantial difference between the two groups of birds in aspect ratio, or the proportion of wingspan to breadth (chord). Using the longest primary as a measure of wing length and the outermost secondary as one of wing breadth, I find length/breadth ratios are almost exclusively different, from 1.25 to 1.58 in the 15 round-winged bee-eaters (average 1.41) and from 1.56 to 2.20 in the nine pointed-winged forms (average 1.78).

Within each group there is quite a good correlation of wing length with body weight, as one would expect (only the Blue-cheeked Bee-eater is markedly out of step, being very long-winged but rather light). Hand skeleton length also correlates well, rising in the 15 round-winged bee-eaters from 21 to 39 mm as their wing length (wrist to wing tip) increases from 75 to 140 mm, and in the nine pointed-winged birds rising from 27 to 46 mm with a wing length increase from 90 to 155 mm—hand length is proportionately greater in the latter group and particularly in its longest-winged members like the European and Carmine Bee-eaters.

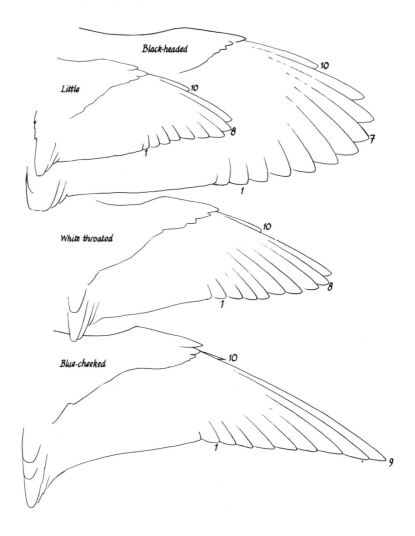

It is well known that migratory birds have longer, more pointed wings than sedentary ones, and the rule holds fairly well among bee-eaters. In the pointed-winged series the least migratory are the Little Green and Bay-headed, which have the shortest wings and (with the Rainbowbird) the least pointed, and the others are all mid- or long-distance migrants with long wings. Perhaps Rainbowbirds, being inter-continental migrants, 'ought' to have longer wings with the 9th primary at the tip, and Carmines and Rosies, neither migrating inter-continentally, 'ought' to have shorter wings. In the round-winged series, by-and-large sedentary birds, there is no relationship at all of migratory propensity with wing *length* but there is an evident one with wing *pointedness*: the least round-winged are White-throated Bee-eaters and Swallowtails, which is the very pair that migrates any distance.

Far more important a determinant of bee-eaters' wing shapes than migration, which occupies them for only a few weeks a year, is surely aerial foraging, which occupies practically their every waking hour. Aerodynamic considerations dictate that short-sallying birds hunting in confined airspace (Red-bearded and Blue-headed Bee-eaters, for instance) should have much shorter and rounder wings than far-hawking and continuous-flight feeding ones in unrestricted airspace. In the group of nine pointed-winged species (*Merops sens. str.*) it is broadly true that those with the highest aspect ratio (longer, narrower wings), like the Blue-cheeked Bee-eater, are the ones spending most time hawking aloft and those with the lowest (eg Little Green) are 'flycatchers' sallying amongst vegetation. Also, comparing the two series, the 15 round-wings forage in more restricted airspace, within bushy woodland or forest, and (with the signal exception of the White-throated Bee-eater) seldom or never feed in continuous flight on high. But unfortunately, within the round-winged group no correlation between wing shape and foraging habitat is evident at all, other than a not-very-convincing one by the White-throat: neither large nor small forest dwellers (Red-bearded, Blue-headed) differ

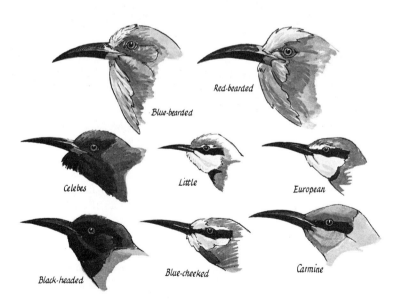

meaningfully in wing shape from small or large open savanna species (Somali, White-fronted).

Maybe the adaptive characteristics of wing shape, and the significance of the form of the 10th primary, will be better understood when, instead of relying on subjective assessment of foraging techniques and airspace restriction, such parameters are researched in depth.

Beak shape

There is not much variation within *Merops*, where Little and Blue-cheeked have the slenderest beaks and Black-headed and Carmine the stoutest. *Meropogon*, the Celebes Bee-eater, is slender-billed, and in *Nyctyornis* the Red-bearded has a very stout beak and Blue-bearded a relatively lightly-built one. As we would expect, it suggests some adaptive correlate with the size and strength of the preferred prey.

ECOLOGICAL VARIATION

Although there are specific differences in habitat and some subtler ones in diet, I have always been impressed by the Family's ecological uniformity. For a large genus, *Merops* does not exhibit the degree of resource partitioning that one might expect; other birds—falcons, for example, or tits or finches—carve up space and season and prey to a much more evident extent.

For geographical range, warmth is a key factor and no bee-eater can tolerate day temperatures below 21°C for any sustained period. The Family is rooted firmly in the tropics and only seven species extend distantly therefrom: Blue-bearded, Little Green, Bay-headed and Blue-throated Bee-eaters to about 30° of latitude, Rainbowbirds to 40°, Blue-cheeked to 45° and European to 55°. Only the last-named has managed to become a truly temperate-zone bee-eater, with a breeding range entirely outside the tropics. For the same reason of temperature limitation all but one are lowland birds, with breeding ceilings at about 2,000 m. European Bee-eaters sometimes nest higher, but only the Cinnamon-chested can be considered a montane bird, breeding as high as 3,000 m.

Three Asian and three African species are confined to the tropical rainforest zone and they inhabit variously the understorey, mid-storey, canopy and edges of tall, dank forest where they are all sedentary. The remaining three-quarters of the Family are birds essentially of open habitats, occupying between them the whole range of tropical wooded and grassy savannas, and at higher latitudes farm-land and desert steppe. In most instances specific habitat preferences are discernibly different; in West Africa (where there is a rather simple geographical arrangement of

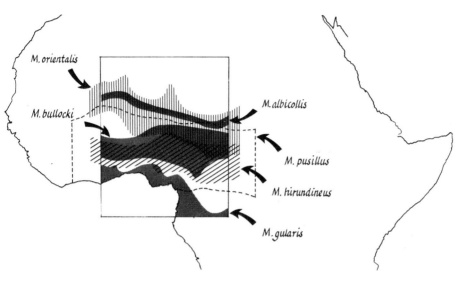

Breeding ranges, slightly simplified, of six bee-eaters in a part of West Africa where biomes are neatly zoned from rainforest in the south, via savannas, to desert in the north. Differing latitudinal positions and amplitudes of their ranges demonstrate specific ecological preferences and tolerances.

progressively drier types of vegetation with distance from the coastal rainforest to Saharan steppe) it results in an obvious stratification of specific ranges. The map shows that Black (and Blue-headed) Bee-eaters are confined to rainforest, with Swallow-tailed, Red-throated, Little Green, and White-throated Bee-eaters breeding successively further north toward the desert. Little Bee-eaters are latitudinally widespread; Carmine and Rosy Bee-eaters are not shown. In some cases it is hard to see any habitat differences between overlapping species. Where species with like habitats are allopatric any differences that *can* be found—between diverging allospecies like Red-throated and White-fronted Bee-eaters for instance—will give valuable insight into the evolution of new habitat preference; where they are sympatric and no other ecological distinctions are evident, the species seem to challenge the universality of the principle of competitive exclusion and so beg for investigation: Little and Blue-breasted Bee-eaters are an example.

Perhaps because specialization has enabled the Family to corner the market in the exploitation of venomous Hymenoptera in general and honeybee eating in particular, specific dietaries are very much the same, both qualitatively and quantitatively. The few exceptions, given on p. 217, suggest an incipient adaptive radiation based on the exploitation of other sorts of flying insects *as well as* wasps and bees, and not (yet) instead of them.

Of course to some extent different diets will result from different habitats. For example dragonflies are more frequent in wet than in dry places and in steppe or savanna than in rainforest, and bee-eaters eat them in greater or lesser quantity accordingly. Presumably, too, there are substantial qualitative differences between the flying insect faunas at, say 1, 10 and 100 metres above ground level, which ought to reflect themselves in diets of birds tending to forage about each level. It makes bee-eaters' dietary uniformity all the more remarkable.

Migration

Three bee-eaters are great migrants, the European, Blue-cheeked and Rainbowbird, on some routes travelling thousands of kilometres inter-continentally. Why they have to migrate so far is obvious: they are simply the highest-latitude breeding species and a winter dearth of insects compels them to move to the tropics. Extra-tropical populations of other species are migratory too, in whole or part, but much less spectacularly so, from south China, the Himalayan foothills and northern India, the lower Nile and Cape Province, all for varying distances towards the Equator and presumably for the same reason of winter food shortage. But of the purely tropical species, some are migrant while others are quite sedentary, and at the present state of knowledge about tropical environments it is impossible to say why. Rosy Bee-eaters may have to migrate because river sand-bars are available for nesting only at seasonal low-water levels and because after breeding in huge concentrations local food stocks are exhausted. But that argument cannot apply to Carmines nor explain why Southern Carmine Bee-eaters have a three-stage migration with pre-breeding southward, post-breeding southward, and wintering northward movements. And why should White-throated Bee-eaters so conspicuously vacate their Saharan-edge nesting grounds, when Little Greens stay put?

One further aspect of the environment is the sum of all those factors influencing survival—the field of predators, the unpredictable incidence of bad weather, hazardous nest sites, and the seasonal occurrence of climatic adversity. They affect each species' demographic structure differently and thereby, I believe, they help to shape one of the more perplexing distinctions between the species: the degree of co-operative breeding.

SOCIAL AND BEHAVIOURAL VARIATION

If bee-eaters are rather uniform morphologically and ecologically, they are certainly not so socially: great is the contrast between a vast congregation of breeding Rosy Bee-eaters and a pair of Little Bee-eaters quietly attending their solitary nest nearby, or between the compact White-fronted Bee-eater colony with its complex society but wretched nesting failures and the half-dozen White-throated Bee-eaters successfully rearing a large brood at each nest.

Coloniality

Why do some birds breed solitarily, others in great colonies? David Lack was able to demonstrate some broad ecological correlates, particularly the important influence of diet on nesting dispersion[361]. If food is evenly distributed in time and space, birds will ensure a constant supply by defending a feeding territory; each pair nests in its territory and hence the species breeds solitarily. Birds whose food is less predictable in occurrence often have to forage distantly and their food supply is indefensible, and if the advantages of solitary nesting (being hidden from predators, for instance) are outweighed by benefits of coloniality, they will become gregarious. Some such benefits are that many eyes are more likely to detect potential predators; that the colony may act as an information-exchange enabling all of its members to exploit any new-found source of food; and that the birds are 'socially facilitated' to synchronize their breeding so that all of the young fledge at the same time and 'swamp' their predators.

Strong-flying species tend to become colonial because they do not require to nest close to their food supply and it may be more important for them to find a safe site, even if distant. Insectivorous birds that forage aerially are all strong fliers, and the large majority of them breed gregariously in relatively safe places—swallows, wood-swallows (Artamidae), swifts, pratincoles, Red-footed Falcons' and, of course, bee-eaters.

Six kinds of bee-eaters always nest solitarily (Red-bearded, Blue-bearded, Celebes, Blue-headed, Little, Blue-breasted). Seven poorly-known ones seem sometimes to breed solitarily, sometimes in small loose colonies (Black-headed, Black, Swallow-tailed, Somali, Boehm's) or large loose colonies (White-throated, Little Green). Two always form loose colonies (Cinnamon-chested, Rainbowbird). Five each vary from loose to dense colonies and from a few nests to many hundreds (Bay-headed and European more loosely, Blue-throated, Blue-cheeked and Madagascar/Blue-tailed more densely). Last, four species always breed in tight colonies, of tens of nests in the Red-throated and White-fronted, hundreds in the Carmine, and thousands in the Rosy Bee-eater. Evidently some species are quite variable; Little Greens, for instance, are mainly solitary or loosely colonial in Africa but can nest in quite dense colonies in India. Notwithstanding such variation, nor ignorance about the foraging biology of most species, some correlates are readily apparent.

First, habitat. Of the six solitary species four inhabit primary forest; two further birds of secondary forest and forest-edge habitats (Black-headed and Black Bee-eaters) are solitary or form small, loose colonies. So the rule is that forest bee-eaters are solitary, and I think the reason is that insect food there is evenly distributed and constantly replenishing itself. Good nesting sites are rare (forest bee-eaters seem to use man-made sites like sawyers' pits, earth heaps, and banks by paths much more frequently than natural sites), which might promote common use of them, but predators are legion, probably discouraging gregariousness. I would expect these birds to be territorial.

Second, foraging technique. Among the open-country bee-eaters the smaller species in general hunt by making short flycatcher-like sallies low down in bushy habitats, within a few hundred metres of their nests; and the larger ones tend to make long hawking forays in uncluttered airspace well above the vegetation, hunting widely several kilometres away. The smallest six, with mean specific weight from 13 to 23 g, are solitary or form small loose colonies (except that the Little Green can be more highly aggregated); Little and Blue-breasted Bee-eaters are always solitary and I suspect that they may be better able to defend an all-purpose territory in their grassland habits than can the somewhat less solitary Boehm's, Swallow-tailed and perhaps Somali Bee-eaters in woodland. Three mid-sized species, of 27 to 29 g, nest in small but quite dense colonies (Cinnamon-chested, Rainbow, Bay-headed). Blue-throated and Blue-tailed Bee-eaters, 35 and 37 g, breed in large loose or quite dense colonies; and Rosies and Carmines, 43 and 61 g, form huge compact colonies. Neither Blue-cheeked nor European Bee-eaters are quite as densely colonial as their large sizes, 45 and 55 g, might lead one to expect: but being temperate-zone birds their foraging energetics may differ substantively from similar sized tropical kinds.

It all accords quite well with the theory of breeding dispersion being determined by feeding-ground defensibility[362]. Presumably the Little Bee-eater's seasonal nesting territory, for instance, is large enough to ensure a regular supply of small insects hatching in and flying around the herbage, but not so large that the pair cannot defend it; at the other extreme the Carmine Bee-eater's feeding seems to be much less predictable—a bird has to travel far and wide to find a hatch of large bugs or an antelope or bush fire to exploit, and in between times it relies mainly on such transient insects as it can find high in the air. But I did not mention three bee-eaters in the previous paragraph because they do not fit so neatly into the weight/coloniality scheme. They are the White-throated, Red-throated and White-fronted, and they are exceptional in interesting ways.

The White-throated Bee-eater *Merops albicollis* is the most desert-dwelling of all, more so even than the Blue-cheeked. Although at 24 g a small species, it nests in loose but often quite large colonies, probably because its barren-looking habitat obliges it to forage over a wide area—for the occasional lizard as well as for insects. This makes it probably the most far-ranging of the round-winged bee-eaters, and appropriately it has the least rounded wings of all birds in that series. After breeding in the ephemeral rains it has to quit the worsening desert; on migration and all winter it keeps in large flocks feeding from high tree tops and making use of its good flying ability by ranging widely to exploit hatches of winged ants. Two other feeding peculiarities may be connected with adaptation to desert life: on their forested wintering grounds they are immobilized by rain, so on wet days may lose up to a fifth of their weight (although resident Black Bee-eaters go on feeding without hindrance)[558]; and they are versatile feeders, as shown by their ability to catch bits of fruit dropped by squirrels.

For a small bee-eater the Red-throated *M. bullocki*, 24 g, is highly gregarious, with its 50 nests aggregated into a dense cliff-face colony, and so is its close relative the White-fronted *M. bullockoides* even if at 34 g it is a lot larger. Furthermore the superspecies is remarkable for being at once markedly colonial and strongly territorial. The explanation, I conjecture, is as follows. As the only dry-season-breeding bee-eaters, food has been less reliable for them than for their congeners nesting a few weeks later in the rains. Feeding grounds may be quite distant and cannot be defended by a nesting pair, which has promoted a degree of coloniality, as has their refusal to nest in flat ground and their total dependence on cliffs (often scarce). Having become colonial, and nearly all spending their lives within 3 km of their birthplace, they were able to evolve a complex society of clan groups. Each clan repairs daily to forage in one particular area which it is able to defend corporately, so that every individual's food supply is protected for it even when it is away taking food to its nest. This successful stratagem surely has promoted a greater degree of coloniality, up to the limit of the most clans that can fit themselves into a circle whose radius is the maximum economic foraging distance from the colony.

Co-operative breeding

Because of plumage uniformity, helpers are not very easy to detect, and for most bee-eaters little or no information about the incidence of helpers has yet been obtained. No solitary-breeding species, and only the Black-headed Bee-eater among nearly-solitary ones, has been reported so far to have a helper. But the phenomenon is quite prevalent in colonial forms: Europeans have a helper at 20%, of nests, Red-throats have 1–3 helpers at 30%, White fronts 1–5 at 60% and White-throats 1–3 (or −5?) at 90%. In addition Rainbowbirds certainly have a number of helpers at some nests, and a few Carmine Bee-eater nests have a helper; also

Swallow-tailed and Cinnamon-chested Bee-eaters. Other species have not been studied; but, woefully incomplete as the evidence is, it does suggest that coloniality is one predisposing factor in the evolution of this type of society—at least among bee-eaters. But that is not the case with birds in general, for bee-eaters are the *only* co-operative breeding birds, other than the Social Weaver, which are densely colonial (a few others are loosely colonial[90], like Piñon Jays and Pied Kingfishers).

Field studies of co-operative breeding in other birds have given rise to a large body of theoretical speculation about the routes along which it has evolved, but no single unifying principle has emerged. Doubtless, in fact, there are multiple causes for the behaviour and they never operate in quite the same combination in any two species, especially if distantly related.

Systematically and ecologically the birds concerned are amazingly diverse, embracing wrens and ostriches, jays, gallinules, honey-eaters, buzzards, babblers, Acorn Woodpeckers and others exploiting most classes of foods in all major biomes[90,230,234]. Hardly surprisingly, it makes ecological common denominators difficult to discern, and the only obvious one is that the great majority of known co-operative breeding land birds are found in the tropics and sub-tropics, in regions with climates sufficiently benign not to have generated much migration—most co-operative breeding birds are sedentary—but where there are episodic, unpredictable periods of some hardship.

Almost any social (or ecological) factor militating against sexually mature individuals obtaining a mate (or an ensured supply of food) can, it seems, promote co-operative breeding, and on the present evidence we can identify the following predisposing elements applicable to birds in general and to bee-eaters in particular. Helping-at-the-nest will evolve when:

—survival is good. Survival curves, and hence the shape of the 'population pyramid', are seldom identical in different species; if in some, productivity of fledglings and survival for the first 12 months are high, it will be harder for yearlings to break into the breeding community than it will be in other species with low breeding success and first-year survival[181]. That would be particularly the case should it ever prove that a yearling prefers to mate with an experienced older bird than with an inexperienced one of its own age (which is entirely speculative—but is quite likely to happen since a naïve bird would be at a considerable advantage in having an experienced mate). In any event, a non-breeding yearling is available to become a helper. Many small tropical land birds survive excellently at least when adult, and a part of their populations is often remarkably long-lived; such species are frequently co-operative breeders[236]. Survivorship may provide the one unitary clue to the problem of co-operative breeding, and it needs much more study[491A].

—there is an unbalanced sex ratio, preventing the surplus of one sex from finding mates. Young females of European Bee-eaters, and probably other species, tend to disperse more widely than young males, exposing themselves to new dangers and evidently surviving less well as a result—for in many kinds there are far fewer females than males in the adult population. The sexes are at parity in Little, Blue-breasted and Blue-bearded Bee-eaters, which are all solitary; but there are 1.5 times as many males as females in the Red-throated, European and Carmine, which all have helpers, and nearly twice as many in the White-fronted and White-throated in which helping behaviour is the most strongly developed of all[230].

—young birds remain with their parents as a family unit. That *has* to happen in bee-eaters to the extent that their feeding is so specialized that the young bird must have a protracted weaning period before its bee handling skills are perfected. Helping behaviour is particularly prone to originate when the social units are what may be termed *extended*-family parties[191].

—social structure is inclusive rather than exclusive, ie there is little or no breeding territoriality and nesting is colonial rather than widely dispersed. (This is not to say that territorial species cannot evolve co-operative breeding; in fact most co-operative breeding birds are highly territorial.)

—yearling birds do not disperse very far but remain within the local population of individuals well-known to them. It helps if the population is highly sedentary. (Although I do not believe that having to migrate frays the social fabric to any significant extent. The indications are few, but they add up the probability that migrants, even night and inter-continental ones like warblers, supposed to move on a broad front, actually travel and winter together in undisrupted social units.)

—a high population density saturates the foraging habitat. With no good-quality and hardly any marginal-quality habitat left unoccupied, some prospective first-time breeders will be denied adequate feeding territory and hence nesting opportunity[349]. Moreover, in regions where the climate is irregular and habitat quality fluctuates erratically—as with Kenyan White-fronted Bee-eaters—a given density of birds can have enough food to breed on one occasion but insufficient to go round on another. In the latter situation the 'cost' of attempting to breed is too high for many young and old birds, and they abandon the attempt in favour of helping at a clansman's nest[191].

When, for any of the above reasons, helping behaviour is incipient, kin selection will operate to establish it in a community even if the helpers 'lose out', on balance, by having their own lifetime's production of offspring curtailed. But if *all* social classes, including the helpers, profit from the arrangement, the contentious issue of kin selection need not be invoked and the maintenance and further evolution of co-operative breeding is simply explicable in straightforward Darwinian terms. In Chapter 6 I showed that bee-eater nestlings and also their parents benefit greatly from the presence of helpers; and evidence is now mounting that the helpers do in fact profit from their own behaviour as well[193A]. If inexperienced, their apprenticeship in the art of rearing young may serve to improve their own reproductive performance in succeeding years— moreover there is the subtle added advantage that the nestlings, forming close bonds with their helper, are likely to remain tied and to help *it* when it breeds the following year. If the helper is an experienced past-breeder (prevented from breeding this year by some calamity) it is advantageous to help because one of the breeding pair which it is helping may reciprocate in a later year.

Because *Merops* is a large genus, uniform ecologically and in other respects yet so variable in its development of co-operative breeding, better knowledge about all of its species, the unhelped as well as the helped, will give really valuable insight into the evolutionary origin of helping behaviour among animals as a whole. Savouring the fruits of such researches will fall to the lucky few for many years to come. But those ornithologists whose contact with bee-eaters is necessarily more fleeting, will have found numerous other excuses in this book, I dare to hope, for taking a closer look at the lives of any one of the twenty-four kinds and augmenting, with the rewards of discovery, the pleasure of watching these altogether delightful birds.

Glossary of evolutionary and other terms

Allele Gene derived from one parent, contrasted with homologous but not necessarily identical gene derived from the other.

Allopatric Of two or more populations or subspecies or species, having geographically exclusive breeding ranges.

Allospecies Two or more species (together comprising a superspecies), of immediate common descent and with geographically exclusive breeding ranges.

Cline Geographical change in characteristic(s) of a species, too gradual for subspecific boundaries to be located.

Competitive exclusion, principle of No two species having identical ecological requirements can co-exist indefinitely; one must eventually exclude the other.

Congeneric Belonging to the same genus.

Convergence Distantly related animals evolving similar attributes in response to similar selection pressures.

Coraciiform Pertaining to Order Coraciiformes (bee-eaters, kingfishers etc).

Dipterocarp Member of Family Dipterocarpaceae, mainly tropical trees.

Drone Fertile male bee or other social insect.

Electrophoresis Electrical separation of protein and other molecules in solution.

Eutaxic Not lacking the fifth secondary remex.

Exogamy Outbreeding.

Gastrolith Abrasive material such as grit ingested by bird and lodging in its gizzard.

Gene flow Tendency for a new gene to migrate geographically with accumulating dispersive movements of animals over many generations.

Gloger's Rule Birds and mammals of warm, humid climates tend to have dark plumage and pellage.

Inclusive fitness A measure of survival of an individual's genes not only in its progeny but in other close relatives.

Introgression, -ive Mixing of genes by hybridization.

Kin selection Natural selection operating upon genomes shared partly by individuals of close kinship.

Monotypic Of a taxon, having only one member.

Nidicolous Being reared in the nest (cf nidifugous—chicks leaving nest soon after hatching).

Palaearctic   Zoogeographical region embracing North Africa, Europe, and non-tropical Asia.

Parapatric (cf *Allopatric*)   Having geographically exclusive but bordering ranges.

Phenotype, -ic   The characteristics manifested by an animal as the expression of its genes (cf *genotype*, the genes themselves).

Philopatry   Remaining in or migrating back to place of birth.

Piciform   Pertaining to Order Piciformes (woodpeckers, honeyguides etc).

Pleistocene   Geological period usually dated from 3 million years ago, ending 11 thousand years ago.

Polytypic   Of a taxon, having more than one member.

Prognathous   With the jaw ('lower mandible' of birds) projecting forward of the premaxilla ('upper mandible').

Rectrices (sing. *rectrix*)   Flight feathers of the tail.

Remiges (sing. *remex*)   Flight feathers of the wing.

Sclerite   Any hard part of an insect's exoskeleton.

Species-group   Closely-allied species, of recent common descent but no longer allopatric—now sympatric.

Superspecies   See *Allospecies*.

Sympatric (cf *Allopatric*)   Having overlapping breeding ranges.

Systematics, -ist   Study of evolutionary relationships.

Taxa (sing. *taxon*)   Any of the hierarchical categories used in classification.

Taxonomy, -ist   Often used as synonym for systematics (qv) but, strictly, the science of classification.

Worker (cf *Drone*)   Sterile female bee or other social insect.

APPENDIX 2

Systematic names of birds (other than bee-eaters) and wild mammal species mentioned in text

Bustard, Kori *Otis kori*
  Sudan *O. arabs*
Buzzard, Grasshopper *Butastur rufipennis*
  Honey *Pernis apivorus*
Crane, Crowned *Balearica pavonina*
  European *Grus grus*
Drongo *Dicrurus adsimilis*
Egret, Cattle *Bubulcus ibis*
Falcon, Eleonora's *Falco eleonorae*
  Red-footed *F. vespertinus*
  Sooty *F. concolor*
Flycatcher, Spotted *Muscicapa striata*
  Verditer *M. thalassina*
Guinea-Fowl *Numida meleagris*

Harrier-Hawk *Polyboroides radiatus*
Heron, Black-headed *Ardea melanocephala*
Honeyguide, Greater *Indicator indicator*
  Lesser *I. minor*
Ibis, Sacred *Threskiornis aethiopica*
Jacamar, Paradise *Galbula dea*
  Rufous-tailed *G. ruficauda*
Jay *Garrulus glandarius*
  Piñon *Gymnorhinus cyanocephalus*
Kingfisher, Pied *Ceryle rudis*
  Ringed *Megaceryle torquata*
  Striped *Halcyon chelicuti*
  White-breasted *H. smyrnensis*
Kite, Black *Milvus megrans*

Kookaburra *Dacelo gigas*
Ostrich *Struthio camelus*
Sand-Martin *Riparia riparia*
Secretary Bird *Sagittarius serpentarius*
Shrike, Red-backed *Lanius collurio*
Sparrow, Rock *Petronia petroni :*
Starling *Sturnus vulgaris*
Stork, Abdim's *Ciconia abdimii*
  Marabou *Leptoptilos crumeniferus*
  Openbill *Anastomus lamelligerus*
  Saddle-billed *Ephippiorhynchus senegalensis*
  White *Ciconia ciconia*

Swallow, White-backed *Cheramoeca leucosterna*
Swift, Alpine *Apus melba*
  Horus *A. horus*
  Philippine Spine-tailed *Chaetura dubia*
Tit, Great *Parus major*
Vulture, Palm-nut *Gypohierax angolensis*
Weaver, Social *Philetairus socius*
Wheatear, Black *Oenanthe leucura*
Woodpecker, Acorn *Melanerpes formicivorus*
Wren, Cactus *Campylorhynchus brunneicapillum*

Aardvaark *Orycteropus afer*
Babirusa *Babyrousa babyrussa*
Beisa Oryx *Oryx beisa*
Black Ape *Cynopithecus niger*
Fox *Vulpes vulpes*
Gerenuk *Litocranius walleri*

Grant's Gazelle *Gazella granti*
Soemmering's Gazelle *G. soemmeringi*
Susliks *Citellus citellus* and *C. pygmaeus*
Topi *Damaliscus korrigum*
Wart Hog *Phachochoerus aethiopicus*
Zebra *Equus burchelli*

APPENDIX 3

European Bee-eater breeding localities in southern Africa (with years)

Namaqualand to Cape Town
Silverfontein, Namaqualand (29°55′S 18°05′E) (1962)
Lambert's Bay (32°05′S 18°17′E) (1917)
Aurora Road, Veldriff (1960)
Kersefontein, Hopefield District (1974)
Hazenkraal, Hopefield (1928)
Bergriver Road, Hopefield (1969)
Saldanha Bay (1961)
Klipolei, Saldanha Bay (1926)
Langebaan (1926)
Langebaan Lagoon, Seeburg (1978)
Churchaven (1969, 1971)
Geelbek Road, Darling (1956)
Between Darling and Paternoster (12 sites, 1976)
Ysterfontein (1953)
Mud River, Darling (1961)
Blouberg, Belleville (1926)

Other regions

Meirings Poort, Oudtshoorn (33°35'S 22°14'E) (year?)

Van Wyks Vlei, Karoo[605] (1886)

Kendrew (32°30'S 24°30'E) (year?)

Graaff-Reinet (32°13'S 24°35'E) (1956)

Port Elizabeth (1934, 1943,[198] 1947, 1959)

Thorngrove, Bedford District (33°19'S 26°31'E) (1957)

Katkop, Great Fish River (1961)[134A]

Bell Rock, Colesberg (30°45'S 25°05'E) (1940)

Naval Hill, Bloemfontein (29°06'S 26°14'E) (1956)

Vierfontein (27°03'S 26°46'E) (1951)

Wagenhoutskop, Zwartruggens District (25°39'S 26°42'E) (cliffs of Elands River) (1955, 1956)

Voigtsgrund, Mariental District (24°40'S 17°30'E) (1976)

Hardap Dam, Mariental District (24°30'S 18°00'E) (1976)

Loẅen River, Keetmanshoop District (a colony probably of this sp.) (26°35'S 18°00'E) (1977)

Aansluit, confluence of Mashewing and Kuruman Rivers (26°25'S 22°50'E) (1977)

Data from Charles Clinning, Len Gillard, and the South African Ornithological Society nest record scheme courtesy of Philip Hockey (observers: R.K. Batham, J. Bell, J. Blignaut, G.J. & M.H. Broekhuysen, R.M. Cary, R.W. Douglass, Van Ee, C. Hopkins, G.K. Lestrange, T.D. Longrigg, A. Moore, J. Munro, L.S. Naylor, C. Niven, E.O. Pike, J.A. Pringle, V.L. Pringle, A. Roberts, M.K. Rowan, R.E. Shannon, S.G. Stander, G.D. Underhill, C.J. Vernon, M. Waltner, G.H. Wilson, C. Wyndham). Some SAOS cards referring to European Bee-eater nests in Rhodesia in the 1920s and 1950s are surely misidentifications, probably of Madagascar Bee-eaters.

APPENDIX 4

Carmine Bee-eater breeding colony localities

A nesting colony may occupy exactly the same site for many years, if it is not disturbed. Birds may also change site locally, moving a few kilometres along a river bank; or they can arrive in a new area, breed there for a year or two and then disappear again. Years of occupation of a site are not shown in this list, and some nearby alternative sites are excluded (for instance, the Beatrice colony in Zimbabwe nests in some years at Alsace, Inyondo and Dunotar, up to 20 km apart). The localities give a broad indication as to the area in which nesting Carmine Bee-eaters can be found in the appropriate season.

NORTHERN CARMINE BEE-EATERS *Merops nubicus nubicus*

	°	'N	°	'W	Source
Senegal/Mauritania					
R. Senegal, Matam	15	34	13	17	425
Bakel	14	56	12	20	425
Podor	16	28	15	00	G.J. Morel pc
R. Gambia	13	01	13	13	175
R. Niokolo	13	01	13	19	175
Mali					
R. Niger, Bamako	12	34	07	55	363
Timbuktu	16	50	03	00	382
All inundation zone between Bamako and Timbuktu 363					
s of Ansonogo	14	50	00	35E	342
Ghana					
R. Black Volta, Buipe	08	45	01	25W	544
Niger/Benin		°		'E	
R. Mekrou	12	00	02	20	S.H. Koster & J.F. Grettenberger pc
Nigeria					
R. Niger, Yelwa	11	56	04	43	509
Shagunu	10	20	04	39	590
Kainji	09	58	04	35	585
Pateggi	08	43	05	51	311 and pers. obs.
Pateggi/Eggan	08	48	05	55	pers. obs.
Eggan	08	48	06	00	91
Katcha	08	44	06	15	pers. obs.
R. Kaduna, Wushishi	09	44	06	05	311
Dokomba	08	50	05	45	pers. obs.
R. Benue, Lokoja/Loko c	08	00	07	15	91
Loko	07	58	07	53	29
Ibi	08	14	09	46	M. & M. Dyer, pc
R. Galma, Zaria	11	06	07	49	M. Dyer and pers. obs.
R. Yashi, Mainamaji	09	45	10	15	} pers. obs.
R. Yobe, Gashegar	13	22	12	46	
Geidam	12	54	11	52	

	°	'N	°	'E	Source
R. Ngadda, Maiduguri	11	52	13	13	pers. obs., M. Dyer (2 sites)
Near Yalo	09	50	10	57	H. Crick, pc
Cameroun					
Galim	06	58	12	40	265
Tchad					
Breeds R. Chari and perhaps R. Logone					171
R. Chari, Dougia	12	22	14	52	170
R. Ouandgia, Lake Gata*					170
Zaire					
R. Garamba	03	55	29	20	
R. Dungu	03	45	29	21	
Aka	03	55	29	18	580
Kibali (probable)	03	30	29	25	
Mogbwarnu (probable)	04	20	29	30	
Sudan					
Breeds Setit, Atbara and Blue Nile Rivers 102					
Abundant and widely distributed s of 12°–15°N 102					
R. Lol, near Gassinga	08	50	26	10	G. Nikolaus, pc
Ethiopia					
R. Tacazze, Om Hagar	14	25	36	45	530
	c 11	45	40	15	
R. Awash	c 11	35	41	15	
	c 10	25	40	15	
	c 09	15	40	10	
	c 08	50	40	10	J.S. Ash, pc
R. Baro	c 08	30	33	45	
	c 08	30	34	15	
	c 08	30	34	45	
R. Ganale Dorya	c 04	15	42	15	
R. Omo	05	05	36	04	M. Jaeger, pc
Somalia					
Bulhar (probable colony)	10	23	44	25	
R. Dolo	04	10	42	05	
Afgoi	02	06	45	12	J.S. Ash, pc
Mogadishu	02	00	45	17	
Gezira	01	56	45	08	
R. Juba, Ionte	00	08S	42	36	9
Kenya					
Lake Turkana basin,					
Ileret	04	19N	36	14	539
Audache	03	28	35	56	304
Lokichokio	04	12	34	21	79

SOUTHERN CARMINE BEE-EATER *M. nubicus nubicoides*

	°	'S	°	'E	Source
Zambia					
Lake Bangweulu					
(probable breeding)	c 11	00	30	00	R.J. Dowsett, pc
R. Luangwa and valley,					
Mpika	c 12	15	32	00	59
Munyamadzi					
confluence	c 12	30	30	15	59
Old Chibembe	12	32	32	10	} R.J. Dowsett, pc
R. Mupamadzi	c 12	45	32	10	
Lion Camp	12	53	31	57	D. Aspinwall, pc
R. Mfuwe	13	03	31	47	D. Aspinwall and P. Watson, pc
Chinzombo	13	31	31	47	} R.J. Dowsett, pc
Chilongozi Camp	13	31	31	15	
Two colonies between 12°30'S and 13°30'S					59
Luangwa/Zambezi					
confluence, Feira	15	36	30	23	59
R. Lungwebungu					
(Lungevungu)	13	35	22	13	77
R. Luansemfwa, Chembe	14	53	29	24	R.J. Hayward, pc
R. Zambezi	14	42	23	05	R.A. Conant, pc
Lealui	15	10	23	02	601; P. Watson, pc
Mongu	15	16	23	12	603
Senanga	16	02	23	14	601
Sesheke	17	29	24	56	601
Ngwemanzi confluence	17	59	26	32	J.D. Huckabay, pc
R. Kafue, Itezhi-tezhi	15	46	26	01	D. Aspinwall, pc
Malaŵi					
R. Shire, Chikwawa	16	03	34	48	56
R. Ruo, Chiromo	16	33	35	08	56
Zimbabwe					
R. Zambezi	17	29	26	32	Zimbabwean information was given
Bumi Gorge (R. Ume)	16	59	28	25	to me independently and with much
R. Nyanyana	16	36	29	02	overlap by R.K. Brooke, R.M.
R. Naodza	16	35	29	05	Harwin and D.V. Rockingham-Gill,
R. Sharu	16	17	28	53	and by Pat Lorber who put out a
Zambezi, Chirundu	16	02	28	51	questionnaire to which B.G.
near Nyakasanga					Donnelly, O. Fitzgerald, C.W.
confluence	15	53	29	06	Hustler, R.L. Murray, E.W. Ostrosky,
R. Rukomechi	c 15	51	29	12	C. Pollard, I.C. Riddell and
Vundu Camp					E.W. Thomson helpfully responded.
(3 colonies)	15	46	29	16	Additional localities are
Mana Pools/Chiruwe					from P. Ginn and H. Nicolle,
confl. (4 colonies)	15	42	29	22	Zimbabwe Orn. Soc. nest records,
Sapi confluence					and references 413 and 600.
(2 colonies)	15	40	29	33	Localities have been pinpointed
near Mwanja confluence	15	39	29	58	on "Rhodesia 1 : 1,000,000 7th
Mupata Gorge	15	38	30	05	edn. 1973 Relief" map, to which
Maura/Angwa confluence	16	13	30	06	I have referred for spelling. My

	°	'S	°	'E
R. Angwa	16	07	30	15
R. Hunyani, Mushumbi Pools	16	07	30	35
Zambezi Escarpment, R. Kadzi	16	32	30	46
R. Dande	16	15	30	33
R. Musengezi tributary* R. Hoya	16	25	31	30
R. Lower Mazoe*				
R. Gwaai, Wankie*				
R. Busi	17	57	27	57
R. Lutope	18	11	28	08
9 km s Sengwa Gorge	18	12	28	14
R. Sengwa (2 colonies)	18	04	28	12
R. Sengwa	18	00	28	12
Chewonde	17	56	28	11
R. Sengwa	17	52	28	11
R. Pohwe	17	59	28	28
R. Gadzi	17	44	28	26
Sessami/Pohwe confluence	17	45	28	34
Sessami/Tari confluence				
Sessami/Swiswi confluence (2 colonies)	18	03	28	48
Sessami/Kanyati (=Bay) confluence	18	05	28	50
R. Ume	17	56	28	54
R. Gwelo*				
R. Chowe	17	30	29	42
Near R. Washanje*				
Near R. Mukwadzi*				
R. Hunyani, Swandale	17	50	30	39
R. Chinyika	17	48	31	28
Near Gwazana*				
R. Ngezi	c 18	37	30	45
R. Umfuli, Beatrice	18	16	30	54
R. Nyatsime*				
Near Wedza	c 18	39	31	35
Rhodes Nyanga National Park, near Mare Dam	18	15	32	45
R. Umguza, Sawmills	19	36	28	02
Near Nyamandhlovu*				
R. Umguzu, Bonisa	19	59	28	32
R. Popoteke tributary	19	45	30	57
R. Nyabisi, Zaka	20	20	31	28
R. Nyatari, Ndanga	20	11	31	20
Near R. Tugwe*				
R. Sabi	20	21	32	18
Near R. Mtilikwe*				

Source
guess is that these 56 known localities represent considerably less than half the true number in Zimbabwe.

	°	'S	°	'E	Source
R. Chiredzi, Mbubelani	21	00	31	44	
R. Lundi, Chilojo cliffs	21	26	32	04	
R. Nuanetsi	21	50	31	28	
Buffalo Bend	21	56	31	29	

Botswana

		°	'S	°	'E	Source
Lianshulu	c	18	20	23	15	C.F. Clinning, pc
R. Chobe		17	50	24	45	A. Kemp, pc
Kasane		18	15	23	47	R.K. Brooke, pc
breeds commonly east of 24°E						315
R. Kwando, Kangolo		18	00	23	15	
R. Okavango, Kangongo		17	57	21	02	C.F. Clinning, pc
breeds in several parts						130, 534

Mozambique

		°	'S	°	'E	Source
R. Ruenya, Changara		16	50	33	16	87
R. Pungwe	c	19	30	34	30	88, 124

* Precise locality unknown.

SPECIFIC DIETS—APPENDICES 5-8

Analysis of thousands of pellets has provided the author with a good deal of information on the dietaries of most African and some other bee-eaters. How similar are the diets of most species, both qualitatively and quantitatively, is shown by the summarizing accounts in Chapter 2; so hitherto unpublished details are given below for only two species. In addition there are appended previously published information on the food of Little and European Bee-eaters.

APPENDIX 5

Diet of the Little Bee-eater

160 pellets or gizzards from nine localities in Nigeria, Zambia, Malaŵi, Zimbabwe and Botswana[167] yielded the following 117 taxa (and an unidentified 27 taxa, not listed).

ODONATA (8% of prey items)
Zygoptera: Coenagrionidae (*Ceriagrion, Enallagma angolicum, Agriocnemis*)
Anisoptera: Libellulidae (*Orthetrum, Hemistigma albipuncta, Diplacodes okavangoensis, Trithemis stictica, T. hecate, T. monardii, Urothemis edwardsi, Aerthriamanta rezia*).

ORTHOPTERA (1%)
Tridactylidae (*Tridactylus*); Gryllidae.

HEMIPTERA (5%)
Homoptera: Jassidae; Typhlocybinae; Psyllidae. Heteroptera: Reduviidae;
Lygaeidae; Coreidae; Pentatomidae; Cydnidae.

NEUROPTERA (trace)
Myrmeleontidae.

EPHEMEROPTERA (3%)

LEPIDOPTERA (1%)
Pyralidae: Crambinae.

DIPTERA (10%)
Trichoceridae; Macroceridae; Ceratopogonidae; Stratiomyiidae, Beriinae; Tabanidae (*Haematopota, Tabanus*); Asilidae; Therevidae; Empididae; Dolichopodidae;
Syrphidae; Pyrgotidae; Ephydridae; Calliphoridae (*Chrysomya*), Rhiniinae; Muscidae (*Musca, Stomoxys, Glossina morsitans*), Anthomyidae; Tachinidae.

HYMENOPTERA (57%)
Ichneumonoidea (2%): Ichneumonidae (*Metopius, Ictoplectis, Oneilella, Anomalon*);
Evanioidea (trace): Gasteruptiidae (*Gasteruption*); Chalcidoidea (2%): Chalcidi-
dae (*Rhynchochalcis*); Eucharitidae; Bethylidae (*Epyris, Plutobethylus*); Chrysidoidea
(1%): Chrysididae (*Acrotoma*); Scolioidea (5%): Scoliidae (*Campsomeris*);
Tiphiidae (*Tiphia, Elis, Mesa, Meria, Myzine*); Mutillidae (*Mutilla*); Formicoidea
(7%): Myrmicinae (*Pheidole, Camponotus, Dorylus*); Pompiloidea (1%): Pompilidae
(*Batozonellus, Homonotus*); Vespoidea (< 1%): Vespidae (*Ropalidia, Odontodynerus*);
Sphecoidea (6%): Sphecidae (*Dolichurus, Astata, Liris, Prosopigastra, Tachytes, Psen,
Sphex, Bembex, Stizus, Philanthus, Cerceris, Oxybelus*); Apoidea (33%): Halicitidae
(*Nomia, Halictus, Thrincostoma, Sphecodes, Pseudapis, Lassioglossum*); Megachilidae
(*Megachile*); Apidae (*Apis mellifera, Trigona, Ceratina*); Anthophoridae (*Anthophora,
Thyreus*).

COLEOPTERA (15%)
Histeridae; Staphylinidae (*Acylophorus*); Scarabaeidae, Cetoniinae, Coprinae
(*Sisyphus, Phalops, Oniticellus, Onthophagus*), Melolonthinae (*Trochalus*), Aphodiinae
(*Aphodius*); Buprestidae (*Agrilus, Meliboeus*); Dermestidae; Bostrychidae
(*Xyloperthella*); Tenebrionidae (*Alphitobius*); Cerambycidae; Bruchidae (*Bruchidius,
Spermophagus*); Chrysomelidae (*Scelodonta*); Eumolpinae; Curculionidae (*Doliopy-
gus, Menemachus*); Rhipiphoridae (*Rhipiphorus*).

APPENDIX 6

Diet of the Red-throated Bee-eater

The data are all from one locality, Zaria, 11°08'N, 07°37'E, in northern Nigeria, where pellet samples were collected weekly during the breeding season in February and March and every third week during the rest of the year—200 pellets in all. With the contents of several gizzards, nearly 4,000 insects eaten by adult birds were identified altogether, comprising 158 taxa (below) and about 210 more, identified to Family only (not listed). Beetles and flying ants were the most important prey in the rainy season (July, August and September), and a large variety of hymenopterans in the dry—with honeybees predominating from about February until the beginning of the rains in April–May[231]

ODONATA (1% of prey items)
Libellulidae.

ORTHOPTERA (<1%)
Acrididae; Gryllidae; Tettigonidae.

ISOPTERA (trace)
Termitidae (*Odontotermes*).

HEMIPTERA (4%)
Homoptera: Cicadidae (*Platypleura*); Membracidae; Jassidae; Issidae Heteroptera: Reduviidae; Lygaeidae; Coreidae (*Riptortus, Anoplocnemus, Cletus, Acanthomyia, Homoeocerus*); Pentatomidae (*Euryaspis, Aspavia, Callidea, Sphaerocoris, Atelocera*, Diploxys, Acrosternum**); Cydnidae (*Cydnus*); Mononychidae (*Nerthra*); Naucoridae (*Macrocoris*); Nepidae (*Nepa, Ranatra*).

LEPIDOPTERA (<1%)
Microlepidoptera; Pieridae (*Graphium*).

DIPTERA (1%)
Tabanidae (*Chrysops**); Asilidae; Muscidae; Calliphoridae.

HYMENOPTERA (79%)
Ichneumonoidea (2%): Ichneumonidae (*Ichneumon, Oneilella, Ctenochares*, Delaulax, Metopius, Syzeuctus, Ictoplectis*, Larpelites*, Afrocoelichneumon**); Evanioidea (trace); Chalcidoidea (2%): Chalcididae (*Eucepsis, Dirhinoides, Hockeria*, Peltochalcidia*, Asparagobius*, Stilbulaspis*, Brachymeria**); Eucharitidae; Perilampidae (*Perilampus*); Pteromalidae (*Dinarmus**); Bethyloidea (<1%): Bethylidae (*Epyris, Holepyris**); Chrysididae (*Holochrysis*, Chrysis, Tetrachrysis**); Scolioidea (4%): Scoliidae (*Campsomeris*); Mutillidae (*Mutilla, Agama*, Apterogyna*); Tiphiidae (*Elis, Mesa, Tiphia, Myzine*); Formicoidea (12%): Formicidae (*Camponotus, Odontomachus, Paltothyreus*, Messor**); Pompiloidea (2%): Pompilidae (*Ceropales, Platyderes, Homonotus, Batozonellus, Pseudagenia, Hemipepsis*, Cryptocheilus*, Paracyphononyx**),

Vespoidea (4%): Vespidae (*Synagris, Pseudopipona, Odynerus, Odontodynerus, Polistes, Rygchium, Celonites, Ropalidia, Raphiglossa, Pseudonortonia, Ancistrocerus, Labus, Eumenes, Discoelius, Belonogaster*); Sphecoidea (3%): Sphecidae (*Dolichurus, Astata, Palarus, Liris, Piagetia, Atelosphex, Tachysphex, Gastrosericus, Pison, Trypoxylon, Psenulus, Passaloecus, Sphex, Chalybion*, Sceliphron, Styzus, Philanthus, Cerceris, Oxybelus, Dasyproctus**); Apoidea (50%); Colletidae (*Prosopis*); Halictidae (*Halictus, Thrincostoma, Sphecodes, Nomia*); Megachilidae (*Megachile, Heriades, Euaspis, Tetralonia, Anthidium*); Apidae (*Apis mellifera, Trigona, Anthophora, Ceratina*).

COLEOPTERA (14%)
Histeridae; Staphylinidae; Scarabaeidae (*Trochalus, Pseudotrochalus, Heteronychus*, Camenta, Plagiochilus*, Oniticellus, Onthophagus, Sisyphus, Drepanocerus, Gymnopleurus, Aphodius*); Buprestidae (*Sphenoptera, Agrilus, Meliborus*); Elateridae; Dermestidae (*Dermestes*); Bostrychidae (*Xyloperthella*); Tenebrionidae; Rhipiphoridae (*Rhipiphorus, Macrosiagon*); Bruchidae (*Bruchidius, Spermophagus*); Chrysomelidae (*Scelodonta, Menius*); Curculinoidae (*Dereodus, Doliopygus*): Chironidae (*Chiron*).

* Or near ally.

APPENDIX 7

Diet of the White-throated Bee-eater

In their winter quarters they commonly eat epicarp strips of oil-palm fruits dropped by squirrels and on their breeding grounds they sometimes take small lizards and flightless arthropods (see p. 218). 105 pellets or gizzards obtained in nearly equal proportions from migrants in central Nigeria and breeding and wintering birds in the north and south of that country, contained the following 138 taxa—imagos or flying adult insects unless otherwise stated—and a further 125 unidentified taxa (including 22 myrmecine and formicine ants, unlisted).

ODONATA (0.05% of prey items)
Zygoptera; Anisoptera.

ORTHOPTERA (3%)
Acrididae; Tettigonidae.

ISOPTERA (trace)
Termitidae (*Odontotermes, Anoplotermes*).

HEMIPTERA (5%)
Homoptera: Membracidae.
Heteroptera: Reduviidae; Miridae; Lygaeidae; Coreidae (*Riptortus, Acanthomyia, Homoeocerus*); Pentatomidae (*Afrius, Hotea*).

NEUROPTERA (trace)
Myrmeleontidae (*Palpares*, and an 'ant-lion' larva).

LEPIDOPTERA (1%)
Pieridae (*Catopsilia*); Noctuidae—larvae.

DIPTERA (3%)
Tabanidae; Asilidae (*Neolapanus**); Mydaeidae*; Muscidae; Sarcophagidae.

HYMENTOPERA (69%)
Ichneumonoidea (trace); Ichneumonidae (*Oneilella, Afrocoelichneumon*, Brachymeria*, Orientostenaraeus, Campsophorus*); Chalcidoidea (trace): Chalcididae (*Hockeria* Dirhinoides, Peltochalcidia**); Bethyloidea (trace): Bethylidae (*Epyris*); Chrysididae (*Chrysis*, Acrotoma*); Scolioidea (2%): Scoliidae (*Campsomeris*); Tiphiidae (*Elis, Tiphia, Mesa, Iswara**); Mutillidae (*Mutilla, Apterogyna**); Formicoidea (56%): Formicidae (Ponerinae: *Camponotus, Anochetus, Paltothyreus*, Oecophylla, Dorylus*, Messor*; and 22 forms of Myrmicinae and Formicinae); Pompiloidea (trace); Pompilidae (*Pseudagenia*, Hemipepsis*, Platyderes**); Vespoidea (1%); Vespidae (*Rygchium, Odynerus, Odontodynerus, Polistes, Labus, Eumenes, Ropalidia*); Sphecoidea (2%): Sphecidae (*Tachytes, Tachysphex, Parapiagetia*, Piagetia*, Sphex, Chlorion xanthocerus, Chalybion, Sceliphron*, Arpactus, Bembex, Philanthus, Cerceris, Oxybelus, Dasyproctus**); Apoidea (6%): Halictidae (*Nomia*); Megachilidae (*Sphecodes*, Megachile*); Apidae (*Apis mellifera, Trigona, Xylocopa, Ceratina*).

COLEOPTERA (17%)
Cincindelidae (*Cicindela*); Carabidae; Dytiscidae; Histeridae (*Saprinus*); Staphylinidae; Scarabaeidae, Coprinae (*Oniticellus, Onthophagus, Gymnopleurus*), Cetoniinae (*Plagiochilus, Clastocnemus**), Rutelinae (*Heteronychus, Trochalus, Adoretus*), Aphodiinae (*Aphodius*); Buprestidae (*Sphenoptera, Agrilus, Cardiophorus**); Elateridae (*Melanoxanthus*, Propsephus**); Dermestidae (*Dermestes*); Bostrychidae (*Xyloperthella*); Melyridae; Tenebrionidae (*Pimelia*—flightless imago); Rhipiphoridae (*Macrosiagon*); Meloidae; Cerambycidae (*Graciella*); Bruchidae (*Bruchidius, Spermophagus*); Chrysomelidae (*Corymodes, Aspecesta, Lema, Aulacophora*); Anthribidae; Curculionidae (*Parapoderus, Doliopygus, Tetragonothorax*).

* Or near ally.

APPENDIX 8

Diet of the European Bee-eater

The following comprehensive list of over 300 kinds of insects known to have been eaten by *M. apiaster* has been compiled from several West European sources[36,43,208,222,293A,298,352,366,498,546,574] but mainly from detailed economic studies in USSR[50,321,351,448,457,461,609]: altogether they encompass 26,000 insects from 1,550 pellets and 750 gizzards (nearly all of adult birds). For the occasional food items other than volant insects, and for some quantitative information see species account and Chapter 4.

EPHEMEROPTERA (Mayflies)

ODONATA (Dragonflies, damselflies)
Zygoptera: Coenagriidae; Lestidae (*Lestes*); Agriidae (*Calopteryx [Agrion] splendens, C. virgo*).
Anisoptera: Aeshnidae (*Anax parthenope, A. imperator, Aeshna grandis, A. mixta, A. affinis, A. coerulea, A. viridis, A. isosceles, Brachytron pratense*); Gomphidae (*Gomphus flavipes*); Libellulidae (*Sympetrum vulgatum, S. meridionale, S. sanguineum, S. flaveolum, S. depressiusculum, S. striolatum, Libellula depressa, L. quadrimaculata, Orthetrum cancellatum*).

PLECOPTERA (Stoneflies)

ORTHOPTERA (Grasshoppers etc)
Tettigoniidae (bush-crickets) (*Decticus, Metrioptera, Conocephalus fuscus, C. dorsalis, Tettigonia viridissima*); Gryllidae (crickets) (*Oecanthus pellucens*); Gryllotalpidae (mole crickets) (*Gryllotalpa gryllotalpa*); Acrididae (grasshoppers) (*Calliptamus italicus, Euchorthippus declivus, Chorthippus albomarginatus, Oedaleus decorus, Oedipoda miniata*); Tetrigidae (*Acrydium subulatum*).

DERMAPTERA (Earwigs)
Forficulidae (*Forficula*).

DYCTYOPTERA (Mantises etc)
Mantodea: Mantidae (*Mantis religiosa*).

ISOPTERA (Termites)
Termitidae (*Odontotermes*, Cubitermes**).

HEMIPTERA (Bugs)
Homoptera: Cercopidae (cuckoo-spit insects) (*Cercopis*); Cicadidae (cicadas) (*Cicadetta, Tibicen haematodes*).
Heteroptera: Miridae; Reduviidae (assassin bugs); Lygaeidae; Coreidae (*Camptopus lateralis, Cletus, Riptortus, Mesocerus marginatus*); Pyrrhocoridae (*Pyrrhocoris*

apterus); Pentatomidae (shieldbugs) (*Graphosoma italicum, Eurygaster maura, E. austriaca, E. integriceps, Palomena prasina, Aelia acuminata, Carpocoris fuscispinus, Odontotarsus, Aspavia*); Cydnidae (*Microporus nigrita*); Naucoridae (saucerbugs) (*Naucoris cimicoides*); Nepidae (water scorpions and water stick insects) (*Nepa cinerea, Ranatra lineatus*); Notonectidae (backswimmers) (*Notonecta glauca, Dolychoris baccarum*).

NEUROPTERA (Lace-wings)
Megaloptera: Raphidiidae (snake flies).

MECOPTERA (Scorpion flies)
Panorpidae.

LEPIDOPTERA (Butterflies and moths)
Nymphalidae (admirals, tortoiseshells etc) (*Vanessa atalanta, V. cardui, Nymphalis antiopa, Limenitis camilla, Inachis io*); Papilionidae (swallowtails) (*Papilio machaon*); Pieridae (whites, yellows) (*Colias calida, C. hyale, Aporia crataegi, Gonepteryx rhamni, Pieris napi, P. brassicae*); Lycaenidae (blues) (*Lycaena*); Sphingidae (hawk-moths) (*Macroglossum stellatarum, Deilephila, Amorpha populi, Hyles lavornica*); Noctuidae (*Agrotis fimbria*); Geometridae; Hesperiidae (skippers).

TRICHOPTERA (Caddisflies)

DIPTERA (Flies)
Stratiomyidae (soldierflies) (*Stratiomyia cenisia, S. chameleon, S. furcata*); Tabanidae (horseflies) (*Tabanus spectabilis, T. solstitialis, T. bovinus, Chrysozona*): Syrphidae (hover-flies) (*Tubifera trivittata, Eristalis memorum, Eristalomya tenax, Volucella*); Muscidae (houseflies, dungflies); Tachinidae; Asilidae (robber flies) (*Asilis, Satanas gigas*); Nemestrinidae (*Nemestrinus caucasicus*).

HYMENOPTERA (Wasps, ants and bees)
Symphyta: Tenthredinidae (sawflies) (*Rhogogaster viridis*); Siricidae (wood-wasps) (*Sirex gigas*).
Apocrita: Ichneumonoidea: Ichneumonidae (ichneumon-flies) (*Oneilella, Netelia, Larpelites*, Phaisura*, Apatetor, Atropha*, Corymbichneumon, Ichneumon*); Chalcidoidea: Pteromalidae; Bethyloidea: Chrysididae (ruby-tails) (*Stilbum cyanurum*); Scolioidea: Scoliidae (*Scolia, Campsomeris*); Tiphiidae (*Tiphia femorata*); Mutillidae (velvet-ants); Formicoidea: Formicidae (ants) (*Messor structor, Tetramorium, Formica, Myrmeca*, Camponotus*); Pompiloidea: Pompilidae (spider-hunting wasps); Vesopoidea: Vespidae (true wasps) (*Vespula vulgaris, V. germanica, V. rufa, Vespa crabro, V. orientalis, Dolichovespula saxonica, Odynerus bifasciatus, Polistes gallicus, P. foederatus, Eumenes, Ropalidia*); Sphecoidea: Sphecidae (digger wasps) (*Astatus boops, Crabro, Ammophila, Liris, Bembex rostrata, Sceliphron destillatorium, Philanthus triangulum, Stizus, Cerceris tuberculata, C. arenaria*); Apoidea (bees): Colletidae (*Prosopis annulata*); Halictidae (*Sphecodes*, Nomia*, Halictus tumulorum, H. quadricinctus*); Andrenidae (*Andrena thoracica, A. flavipes*); Melittidae (*Dasypoda plumipes*); Megachilidae (*Anthidium*); Apidae (*Tetralonia dentata, T. tricincta, Eucera clypeata, Apis mellifera, Nomada, Anthophora acervorum, A. parietina, Trigona, Xylocopa violacea, X. valga, Bombus hortorum, B.humilis, B. mastrucatus, B. terrestris, B. pomorum, B. muscorum, Ceratina cucurbitana, Oblomerus melanocephalus*).

COLEOPTERA (Beetles)

Cicindelidae (tiger beetles) (*Cicindela campestris*); Carabidae (ground beetles) (*Nebria salina, Loricera pilicornis, Amara, Broscus cephalotes, Platisma, Taphoxenus, Calosoma inquisitor, C. denticolle, Carabus, Ophonus calceatus, O. pubescens, Harpalus anxius, H. distinguendus, H. aenus, H. attenuatus, H. psittaceus, Colliurus*, Agonum impressum, Anisodactylum binotatum, Chlaenius spoliaetus, Poecilus, Calathus, Amara aenea*); Dytiscidae (water beetles) (*Colymbetes fuscus, Dytiscus marginalis, Agabus fuliginosus, Rhantus pulverosus, R. punctatus, Cybister laterimarginalis, Brychius*); Hydrophilidae (water beetles) (*Hydrous piceus, Limoxenus oblongus, Hydrophilus caraboides, Sphaeridium scarabaeoides*); Histeridae (*Pachylister inaequalis, Hister stercorarius, H. purpurascens, H. bimaculatus, H. unicinctus, Saprinus*); Silphidae (burying beetles) (*Thanatophilus terminatus, Xylodrepa quadripunctata, Silpha carinata, S. obscura, Necrophorus*); Staphylinidae (rove beetles) *Ontholestes tesselatus, Staphylinus*, Philonthus, Creophilus maxillosus*); Geotrupidae (*Lethrus apterus, Geotrupes mutator*); Scarabaeidae (dung beetles, chafers etc) (*Onthophagus amyntas, O. taurus, O. austriacus, O. vacca, O. speculifer, O. pygargus, O. nocturnus, O. haroldi, O. lemur, O. furcatus, O. fracticornis, Codocera ferruginea, Copris lunaris, Aphodius hydrochoeris, A. subterraneus, A. fossor, A. haemorrhoidalis, A. depressus, Onitis humerosus, O. damoetas, Pentodon, Gymnopleurus mopsus, G. aciculatus, Caccobius schreberi, Oniticellus fulvus, O. pallipes, Sisyphus boshniaki, Melolontha hippocastani, M. melolontha, Cetonia aurata, Amphimallon solstitialis, Riotrogus, Anomala dubia, A. metonidia, A. vitis, A. aenea, A. errans, Anisoplia segetum, A. austriaca, Anoxia pilosa, Potosia hungarica, P. cuprea, Chionesma, Epicometis hirta, Polyphylla irrorata, P. alba, Scarabaeus sacer, Oxythyrea funesta, O. cinctella, Hoplia parvula, Amphicoma vulpes, Rhizotrogus, Cyriopertha glabra, Phyllopertha horticola*); Buprestidae (*Eurythyrea, Sphenoptera, Lampra decipiens, Cyphosoma tataricum*); Elateridae (click beetles) (*Elater sanguinolentus, Lacon murinus, Athous, Cardiophorus*, Agriotes*); Dermestidae (*Dermestes laniarius*); Cleridae (*Trichodes*); Tenebrionidae (darklings) (*Blaps, Gnaptor spinimanus, Tentyria nomas*); Prionidae (*Prionus coriarius, Plagionotus arcuatus*); Lagriidae; Meloidae (oil and blister beetles) (*Cerocoma schreberi, Mylabris quadripunctata, Zonabris polymorpha, Lytta vesicatoria*); Oedomeridae (*Oedomera*); Cerambycidae (longhorns) (*Asemum striatum, Acmaeops, Dorcadion, Leptura, Acantocinus, Pogonocherus, Necydalis, Rhopalopus, Plagionotus floralis, P. arcuatus, Judolia cerambyciformis, Chlorophorus varius, Clytus arietus*); Chrysomelidae (leaf beetles) (*Donacia, Plateumaris, Cassida rubiginosa, Gallerucella luteola*); Curculionidae (weevils) (*Rhynchites auratus, Bothynoderes punctiventris, Otiorrhynchus ligustici, Cleonus piger, Sphenophorus piceus*, S. abbreviatus, Curculio, Doliopygus, Larinus, Sitona, Brachysomus, Conorhynchus, Lixus, Leucomigus candidatus*).

* Or near ally.

APPENDIX 9

Aberrant plumages

Red-throated Bee-eaters are dimorphic, a few birds per thousand having golden-yellow throats instead of red ones; long ago they were described as a distinct species, '*Merops boleslavskii*'. Both sexes can be yellow-throated, but nothing is known about the heritability and genetics of the condition. Similar yellow-throated variants occur in White-fronted Bee-eaters, even more rarely (S.T. Emlen pc), and the British Museum collection has a Black Bee-eater with a fiery throat—not the usual scarlet, but scarlet with yellow-gold barbs intermingled.

Albinism is rare amongst bee-eaters and I know of only six instances. An Oriental Little Green Bee-eater skin in the British Museum is pure creamy white except for a yellowish throat and green or brown washes on head, breast, mantle and inner primaries. A recently moulted covert feather is normal green; there is no black gorget and the trailing edge of the wing is merely brownish. A half creamy white European Bee-eater was seen in Malaŵi, a whitish Carmine in Kenya[80], and the other three examples—single Carmine, White-fronted and Red-throated Bee-eaters[20,247] are partial albinos with only a few white feathers scattered asymmetrically.

Blue and green colour in bee-eaters' plumage arises by the scattering of short-wavelength light from a cloudy cortical layer in the feather, filled with tiny vacuoles and overlying a pigmented medulla which absorbs longer wavelengths[23]. That is Tyndall's principle and such colour is termed simply 'Tyndall colour'. Sometimes structural defects occur in the feather, so that Tyndall green shows olive or brown, and blue becomes pale or whitish. Such aberrations are very scarce; but two Swallow-tailed Bee-eaters collected together in Botswana (so doubtless siblings) are an instance. They have the emerald parts of the plumage dull olive and the blue parts almost white[288].

Last, throat colour can sometimes be 'wrong'. Fledgling Southern Carmines can have blue throats instead of the proper pink; young Little Green Bee-eaters of all races occasionally have yellow throats instead of blue or green; the White-fronted Bee-eater mentioned on p. 201 has a whitish rather than a red throat, making it look rather like a Somali; and I have seen a Bay-headed with a white instead of a yellow throat.

References*

Copies of the great majority of the books and papers referred to, including many that are difficult to obtain, are held by the author at Aberdeen University and can be made available to researchers.

Titles are given in the original of west European languages but Russian, Finnish, Ukrainian, Serbian, Hungarian and Czech ones are rendered in English.

1 Abdulali, H. 1973. A catalogue of the birds in the collection of the Bombay Natural History Society. *J. Bombay Nat. Hist. Soc.* 70: 147–155.
2 Alexander, R.D. & Tinkle, D.W. (eds) 1981. *Natural Selection and Social Behavior*. Chiron Press, New York.
3 Ali, S. 1937. The ornithology of Travancore and Cochin. Part 6. *J. Bombay Nat. Hist. Soc.* 39: 3–35.
4 Ali, S. 1948. The Gujerat Satpuras in Indian ornithogeography: the highway of Malayan forms to the Western Ghats. *Gujerat Res. Soc. Monogr.* 2: 1–11.
5 Ali, S. 1954. The birds of Gujarat. *J. Bombay Nat. Hist. Soc.* 52: 374–458.
6 Ali, S. & Ripley, S.D. 1970. *Handbook of the Birds of India and Pakistan*. Oxford University Press, Oxford.
7 Alleijn, F., Braaksma, S., Peereboom Voller, J.D.G. & van Schendel, J.A.A. 1966. Een Broedgeval van de Bijeneter (*Merops apiaster*) in Nederland. *De Levende Nat.* 69: 1–11.
8 Alvarez, F. & Hiraldo, F. 1974. Estructura de las galerías de nidificación del Aberjaruco (*Merops apiaster*) en Doñana. *Doñana, Acta Vert.* 1: 61–67.
9 Ambrose, J.T. 1978. Birds, Ch. 14 (pp. 215–226) *in Honey Bee Pests, Predators and Diseases*, ed. R.A. Morse. Cornell University Press.
10 Anderson, R.H., Buys, B. & Johannsmeier, M.F. 1973. *Beekeeping in South Africa*. Dept. Agric. Techn. Services Bull. no. 394, pp. 1–191.
11 Anon. 1952. Blue-cheeked Bee-eater in Scilly: a new British bird. *Brit. Birds* 45: 225–227.
12 Anon. 1967. *New Guinea Bird Soc. Newsl.* 26: 3.
13 Anon. 1969. *New Guinea Bird Soc. Newsl.* 49: 2.
14 Anon. 1971. *Wagtail* 9: 1–52 (see p. 3).
15 Anon. 1979. *Beekeeping in Rural Development*. Commonwealth Secretariat and IBRA, London. pp. viii + 196.
16 Anon. 1981. Bird topography. *Brit. Birds* 74: 239–242.
17 Archer, G. & Godman, E.M. 1971. *The Birds of British Somaliland and the Gulf of Aden*. Vol. 3. Oliver & Boyd, Edinburgh.
18 Arnold, H.M. 1974. B.O.C. Rainbow-bird survey. *Bird Observer*, Febr. 1974: 9.
19 Ash, J.S. 1969. Spring weights of trans-Saharan migrants in Morocco. *Ibis* 111: 1–10.
20 Ash, J.S. 1978. An albinistic Carmine Bee-eater from Ethiopia. *Ostrich* 49: 91.
21 Ash, J.S., Ferguson-Lees, I.J. & Fry, C.H. 1967. B.O.U. expedition to Lake Chad, northern Nigeria, March–April 1967. *Ibis* 109: 478–486.
22 Atakishiev, T.A. 1971. [On some biological characteristics of bee pests in Azerbaidzhan.] (In Russian.) *Uchenye zapiski Kazanskogo Veterinarnogo Instituta* 109: 266–269.
23 Auber, L. 1959. The structure of feathers in Meropidae and its evolutionary significance. *Abstracts 15 Internat. Congr. Zool.*, London 1958, Sect. V, Paper 12: 1–3.
24 Avery, M. & Penny, N.D. 1978. Analysis of pellets from Blue-tailed and Blue-throated Bee-eaters in Province Wellesley, Malaysia. *Malayan Nat. J.* 32: 223–226.
25 Aylmer, G. 1944. The use of animate perches by the Carmine Bee-eater. *Ibis* 86: 554.
26 Baker, E.C.S. 1934. *The Nidification of Birds of the Indian Empire*. Vol. 3: Meropidae: 393–402. Taylor & Francis, London.
27 Bangs, O. & Penard, T.E. 1923. A new *Merops* from Java. *Proc. New England Zool. Cl.* 8: 43–44.

* There are no numbered references 166, 255, 526–529.

28 Bangs, O. & van Tyne, J. 1931. Birds of the Kelley-Roosevelts Expedition to French Indo-China. *Field Mus. Nat. Hist., Zool. Ser.*, Publ. 290, Vol. 18(3).

29 Bannerman, D.A. 1933. *The Birds of Tropical West Africa.* Vol. 3. Crown Agents, London.

30 Bannerman, D.A. 1952. *The Birds of West and Equatorial Africa.* Oliver & Boyd, Edinburgh.

31 Bannerman, D.A. 1955. *The Birds of the British Isles.* Vol. 4. Oliver & Boyd, Edinburgh.

32 Bannerman, D.A. & Bannerman, W.M. 1958. *Birds of Cyprus.* Oliver & Boyd, Edinburgh.

33 Barham, K.E.I., Conder, P.J. & Ferguson-Lees, I.J. 1956. Bee-eaters nesting in Britain, 1955. *Bird Notes* 27: 34–43.

34 Barnard, J.H. 1973. Studies of 400 Hymenoptera sting deaths in the United States. *J. Allergy Clin. Immunol.* 52: 259–264

35 Bastawde, D.B. 1976. The roosting habits of Green Bee-eater, *Merops orientalis orientalis* Latham. *J. Bombay Nat. Hist. Soc.* 73: 215.

36 Bastien, P. 1957. Un cas de nidification du guêpier *Merops apiaster* L., en Belgique. *Gerfaut* 47: 45–56.

37 Basu, P.K. 1957. Bees 'stung'. *Indian Bee J.* 19: 7.

38 Bates, G.L. 1909. Field-notes on the birds of southern Kamerun, West Africa. *Ibis* IX, 3: 1–74.

39 Bates, G.L. 1927. Notes on some birds of Cameroon and the Lake Chad region: their status and breeding-times. *Ibis* XII, 3: 1–64.

40 Bates, G.L. 1934. Birds of the southern Sahara and adjoining countries in French West Africa. Part III. *Ibis* XIII, 4: 213–239.

41 Bauer, K. 1952. Der Bienenfresser (*Merops apiaster* L.) in Österreich. *J. Orn.* 93: 290–294.

42 Baum, L. 1964. Erfolgreiche Brut des Bienenfressers (*Merops apiaster*) bei Hamburg. *J. Orn.* 105: 492–493.

43 Baum, L. & Jahn, E. 1965. Brut des Bienenfressers, *Merops apiaster*, 1964 in Schleswig-Holstein. *Corax* 1(17)2: 73–82.

44 Beesley, J.S. 1972. Birds of the Arusha National Park, Tanzania. *J. East Afr. Nat. Hist. Soc.* 132: 1–30.

45 Bell, H.L. 1969. Field notes on the birds of the Ok Tedi River drainage, New Guinea. *Emu* 69: 193–211.

46 Bell, H.L. 1970. The Rainbow-bird, *Merops ornatus*, in New Guinea. *Austral. Bird Watcher* 3: 277–278.

47 Bell, H.L. 1971. Field notes on birds of Mt Albert Edward, Papua. *Emu* 71: 13–19.

48 Bell, H.L. 1982. Abundance and seasonality of the savanna avifauna of Port Moresby, Papua New Guinea. *Ibis* 124: 252–274.

49 Bell, H.L. 1982. A bird community of lowland rain forest in New Guinea. 2. Seasonality. *Emu* 82: 65–74.

50 Belskaya, G.S. 1976. [Development, growth and food of Golden Bee-eaters in Turkmenia.] (In Russian.) *Ornitologija* 12: 125–131.

51 Belskij, N.W. 1958. [The productivity of Bee-eaters.] (In Russian.) *Ornitologija* 1: 161–164.

52 Beneš, B. & Kondělka, D. 1978. [Bee-eaters nesting in Silesia.] (In Czech.) *Čas. slez. Muz. Opava* (A), 27: 73–75.

53 Bennett, G.F. 1978. Avian Haemoproteidae. 8. The haemoproteids of the bee-eater family (Meropidae). *Can. J. Zool.* 56: 1721–1725.

54 Benson, C.W. 1960. The birds of the Comoro Islands: results of the British Ornithologists' Union Centenary Expedition 1958. *Ibis* 103b: 5–106.

55 Benson, C.W. & Benson, F.M. 1975. Studies of some Malawi birds. *Arnoldia (Rhod.)* 7(32): 1–27.

56 Benson, C.W. & Benson, F.M. 1977. *The Birds of Malaŵi.* Montfort Press, Limbe.

57 Benson, C.W., Brooke, R.K., Dowsett, R.J. & Irwin, M.P.S. 1970. Notes on the birds of Zambia: Part V. *Arnoldia (Rhod.)* 4(40): 1–59.

58 Benson, C.W., Brooke, R.K., Dowsett, R.J. & Irwin, M.P.S. 1971. *The Birds of Zambia.* Collins, London.

59 Benson, C.W. & White, C.M.N. 1957. *Check List of the Birds of Northern Rhodesia.* Department of Game and Tsetse Control, Lusaka.
60 Benton, A.W. & Morse, R.A. 1968. Venom toxicity and proteins of the genus *Apis. J. Apic. Res.* 7: 113–118.
61 Berggy, J. 1978. Birds of Madang Province. *Papua New Guinea Bird Soc. Newsl.* 148: 9–20.
62 Besson, J. 1967. Le Guêpier d'Europe (*Merops apiaster*) dans le Var en 1965. *Alauda* 35: 298–302.
63 Betts, F.N. 1947. Bird life in an Assam jungle. *J. Bombay Nat. Hist. Soc.* 46: 667–684.
64 Betts, F.N. 1966. Notes on some resident breeding birds of southwest Kenya. *Ibis* 108: 513–530.
65 Biber, O. 1971. Contribution à la biologie de reproduction et à l'alimentation du Guêpier d'Europe *Merops apiaster* en Camargue. *Alauda* 39: 209–212.
66 Birkhead, T.R. 1974. Predation by birds on wasps. *Brit. Birds* 67: 221–229.
67 Biswas, B. 1961. The birds of Nepal. Pt. 3. *J. Bombay Nat. Hist. Soc.* 58: 100–134.
68 Boddam-Whetham, A.D. 1971. Swallow-tailed Bee-eater *Merops hirundineus. Ostrich* 42: 138–139.
69 Boetticher, H. von 1935. Zur Systematik der Spinte oder Bienenfresser (Meropidae). *Kócsag* 8: 3–44.
70 Boetticher, H. von 1951. La systematique des guêpiers. *Oiseau Rev. Fr. Orn.* 5(21): 194–199.
71 Bolle, C. 1857. Mein zweiter Beitrag zur Vogelkunde der canarischen Inseln. *J. Orn.* V, 29: 305–351.
72 Borrett, R.P. 1973. Notes on the food of some Rhodesian birds. *Ostrich* 44: 145–148.
73 Boswall, J. 1970. The association of the Northern Carmine Bee-eater *Merops n. nubicus* with mammals, birds and motor vehicles in Ethiopia. *Bull. Brit. Orn. Cl.* 90: 92–96.
74 Bouet, G. 1961. *Oiseaux de l'Afrique Tropicale.* Faune Tropicale (Ancienne faune de l'Union Française) XVII. Pt. 2. Paris.
75 Britton, P.L. 1967. Weights of the Carmine Bee-eater *Merops nubicoides. Ibis* 109: 606–614.
76 Britton, P.L. 1968. Two African species pairs. *Bull. Brit. Orn. Cl.* 88: 163–166.
77 Britton, P.L. 1970. Birds of the Balovale Ditrict of Zambia. *Ostrich* 41: 145–190.
78 Britton, P.L. 1970. Some non-passerine bird weights from East Africa. (Part II). *Bull. Brit. Orn. Cl.* 90: 152–154.
79 Britton, P.L. (ed.) 1980. *Birds of East Africa, their Habitat, Status and Distribution.* East Afr. Nat. Hist. Soc., Nairobi.
80 Britton, P.L. & Britton, H. 1978. Two albinistic birds in coastal Kenya. *Bull. East Afr. Nat. Hist. Soc.* 1978: 9.
81 Britton, P.L. & Dowsett, R.J. 1969. More weights of the Carmine Bee-eater. *Bull. Brit. Orn. Cl.* 89: 85–86.
82 Britton, P.L. & Harper, J.F. 1969. Some new distributional records for Kenya. *Bull. Brit. Orn. Cl.* 89: 162–165.
83 Broekhuysen, G.J. 1967. Bird migration in the most southern part of the African continent. *Vogelwarte* 24: 6–16.
84 Broekhuysen, G.J. 1974. Third report on migration in southern Africa. *Ostrich* 45: 235–238.
85 Brooke, R.K. 1965. Notes, chiefly distributional, on some birds in Kafue National Park. *Puku* (Occ. Pap. Dept. Game & Fisheries, Zambia) 3: 59–65.
86 Brooke, R.K. 1965. Ornithological notes on the Furancungo District of Mozambique. *Arnoldia (Rhod.)* 2(10): 1–12.
87 Brooke, R.K. 1968. Notes on some birds in Mozambique. *Ostrich* 39: 180–184.
88 Brooke, R.K. 1971. Breeding and breeding season notes on the birds of Mzimbiti and adjacent low-lying areas of Mozambique. *Ann. Natal Mus.* 21: 55–69.
89 Brown, J.L. 1975. *The Evolution of Behavior.* W.W. Norton Inc., New York.
90 Brown, J.L. 1978. Avian communal breeding systems. *Ann. Rev. Ecol. Syst.* 9: 123–155.
91 Brown, L.H. 1948. Notes on birds of the Kabba, Ilorin and N. Benin Provinces of Nigeria. *Ibis* 90: 525–538.

92 Brown, L. H. & Britton, P. L. 1980. *The Breeding Seasons of East African Birds.* East Africa Natural History Society, Nairobi.

93 Brunel, J. & Thiollay, J.M. 1969. Liste préliminaire des oiseaux de Côte-d'Ivoire. *Alauda* 37: 230–254.

94 Bryant, D.M. 1983. Leg exposure by bee-eaters and other species. *Brit. Birds* 76: 139–140.

94A Bryant, D.M. 1983. Heat stress in tropical birds: behavioural thermoregulation during flight. *Ibis*: 313–323.

94B Bryant, D.M. & Hails, C.J. 1983. Energetics and growth patterns of three tropical bird species. *Auk* 100: 425–439.

95 Bundy, G. 1976. *The Birds of Libya.* British Ornithologists' Union, London.

96 Bundy, G. In press. *The Birds of Eastern Saudi Arabia.* Aramco.

97 Bundy, G. & Warr, E. 1980. A check-list of the birds of the Arabian Gulf States. *Sandgrouse* 1: 4–49.

98 Burley, N. 1981. The evolution of sexual indistinguishability. Pp. 121–137 in R.D. Alexander & D.W. Tinkle (eds.) *Natural Selection and Social Behavior.* Chiron Press, New York.

99 Burton, P.J.K. 1977. Feeding behaviour in the Paradise Jacamar and the Swallow-wing. *Living Bird* 15 (1976): 223–238.

100 Burton, P.J.K. 1978. The intertarsal joint of the Harrier-Hawks *Polyboroides* spp. and the Crane Hawk *Geranospiza caerulescens. Ibis* 120: 171–177.

101 Burton, P.J.K. In press. Anatomy and evolution of the feeding apparatus in the avian orders Coraciiformes and Piciformes. *J. Zool.,* London

102 Butler, A.L. 1905. A contribution to the ornithology of the Egyptian Soudan. *Ibis* VIII, 19: 301–330.

103 Buys, B. 1975. A survey of honeybee pests in South Africa. *Proc. 1 Congr. Entomol. Soc. s. Afr.* 1975 (ed. H.J. Durr, J.H. Gilliomee & S. Neser), pp. 185–189.

104 Cade, T.J. 1967. Ecological and behavioral aspects of predation by the northern shrike. *Living Bird* 6: 43–86.

105 Cairns, J. 1957. Penang bee-eaters. *Malayan Nat. J.* 11: 114–120.

106 Callegari, E. 1956. Osservazioni su di una merops africana, il *Melittophagus bullockoides,* ed alcune considerazioni sul mimetismo aggressivo degli insetti. *Riv. Ital. Orn.* 26(ser. 2): 138–141.

107 Callegari, E. 1970. Breeding in captivity of the European Bee-eater, the Carmine Bee-eater, and of a hybrid between the two. *Avicult. Mag.* 76: 186–188.

108 Cano, A. 1960. Sobre nidificacion communal y alimentacion del Abejaruco (*Merops apiaster*). *Ardeola* 6: 324–326.

109 Cansdale, G.S. 1979. Fishing bee-eaters. *Niger. Field* 44: 82.

110 Carruthers, R.K. 1975. Banding and observations of Rainbow Bee-eaters. *Austral. Bird Bander* 13: 71–74.

111 Carter, C. 1978. Responses of Little Bee-eaters to a Black-throated Honeyguide entering their nest hole. *Scopus* 2: 23.

112 Carter, C. & Robinson, G.P. 1981. The occurrence of both Red-throated and White-fronted bee-eaters in the Virunga Park, eastern Zaïre. *Scopus* 5: 80.

113 Cave, F.O. 1946. Some further notes on *Merops-Ardeotis* perching associations. *Ibis* 88: 236–238.

114 Cave, F.O. & Macdonald, J.D. 1955. *Birds of the Sudan.* Oliver & Boyd, Edinburgh.

115 Cawkell, E.M. 1965. Notes on Gambian birds. *Ibis* 107: 535–540.

116 Cawkell, E.M. & Moreau, R.E. 1963. Notes on birds in The Gambia. *Ibis* 105: 156–178.

117 Chandler, A.C. 1916. A study of the structure of feathers, with reference to their taxonomic significance. *Univ. Calif. Publ. Zool.* 13: 243–446.

118 Chapin, J.P. 1939. The Birds of the Belgian Congo. Vol. 2. *Bull. Amer. Mus. Nat. Hist.* 75: 1–632.

119 Chaplin, A. 1937. *Merops apiaster. Avicult. Mag.* ser 5(2): 103–104.

120 Charlemagne, N.V. 1954. [A short report on the consumption of Hymenoptera by birds.] (In Russian.) *Zool. Zh.* 33: 1420–1422.

121 Charles, J.K. 1976. The bee-eaters of Ginting. *Malayan Nat.* 2: 18–20.

122 Cheke, R.A., Fishpool, L.D.C. & Forrest, G.A. 1980. *Oedaleus senegalensis* (Krauss) (Orthoptera: Acrididae: Oedipodinae): an account of the 1977 outbreak in West Africa and notes on eclosion under laboratory conditions. *Acrida* 9: 107–132.

123 Chisholm, A.H. 1971. Further notes on tool-using by birds. *Victorian Nat.* 88: 342–343.

124 Chubb, E.C. 1914. A descriptive list of the Millar Collection of South African birds' eggs. *Ann. Durban Mus.* 1: 29–106.

125 Clancey, P.A. 1953. Miscellaneous taxonomic notes on African birds, 3. *Durban Mus. Novit.* 4(4): 57–59.

126 Clancey, P.A. 1962. Miscellaneous taxonomic notes on African birds, 18. *Durban Mus. Novit.* 6(13): 149–160.

127 Clancey, P.A. 1964. *The Birds of Natal and Zululand.* Oliver & Boyd, Edinburgh.

128 Clancey, P.A. 1967. A new race of the Little Bee-eater from the South West Arid district of Africa. *Bull. Brit. Orn. Cl.* 87: 166–167.

129 Clancey, P.A. 1971. Miscellaneous taxonomic notes on African birds, 32. *Durban Mus. Novit.* 9(5): 39–44.

130 Clancey, P.A. 1980. On birds from the mid-Okavango valley on the South West African/Angola border. *Durban Mus. Novit.* 12(9): 87–127.

131 Clapham, C.S. 1964. The birds of the Dahlac Archipelago. *Ibis* 106: 376–388.

132 Clay T. 1950. A preliminary survey of the distribution of the Mallophaga ('feather lice') on the Class Aves (birds). *J. Bombay Nat. Hist. Soc.* 49: 430–443

133 Coates, B.J. 1974. *New Guinea Bird Soc. Newsl.* 95.

134 Cobb, F.K. 1979. Honey Buzzards at wasps' nest. *Brit. Birds* 72: 59–64.

134A Collett, J. 1982. Birds of the Cradock District. *Southern Birds* 9: 1–65.

135 Collier, F. 1933. Migration and other problems. *Niger. Field* 2: 45.

135A Colston, P. & Curry-Lindahl, K. In press. *The Birds of the Mt Nimba Region in Liberia.*

136 Comrie-Smith, E. 1930. Notes on the Rainbow-bird. *Emu* 30: 64–66.

137 Conacher, G. 1970. Note on two White Storks each carrying Carmine Bee-eater. *Newsl. Ethiop. Wildl. Nat. Hist. Soc.* 37.

138 Conant, R.A. 1981. Diving behaviour in a flock of Carmine Bee-eaters *Merops nubicus* in Kalabo District. *Bull. Zambian Orn. Soc.* 12: 61–62.

139 Coultas, W.F. 1935. Manuscript of journals and letters, vol. 4, of William F. Coultas, *Whitney South Seas Expedition, October 1933–March 1935.* Amer. Mus. Nat. Hist.: unpubl.

140 Courtney, J. 1971. Breeding of the Rainbowbird at Swan Vale, NSW. *Emu* 71: 172–174.

141 Craig, A. & Burman, C. 1974. Whitefronted Bee-eater *Merops bullockoides*. *Ostrich* 45: 137.

141A Crick, H.Q.P. 1984. *Weight Changes, Foraging, and the Role of Helpers in Red-throated Bee-eaters.* Unpubl. Ph.D. thesis, Aberdeen University, pp. 389.

142 Crick, H.Q.P. & Fry, C.H. 1980. Level-ground nesting by *Merops bulocki*. *Malimbus* 2: 73–74.

143 Cronin, E.W. & Sherman, P.W. 1976. A resource-based mating system: the Orange-rumped Honeyguide. *Living Bird* 15: 5–32.

143A Crowe, T.W. & Crowe, A.A. 1982. Patterns of distribution, diversity and endemism in Afrotropical birds. *J. Zool.* London 198: 417–442.

144 Cruon, R. & Vielliard, J. 1975. Notes d'ornithologie française. *Alauda* 43: 167–184.

145 Cunningham-van Someren, G.R. 1970. Animated perches and feeding associations of birds in the Sudan. *Bull. Brit. Orn. Cl.* 90: 120–122.

146 Cunningham-van Someren, G.R. 1982. *Museum Avifauna News* (Nat. Mus. Kenya Dept. Ornithol.) 1982: 50.

147 Curry-Lindahl, K. 1981. *Bird Migration in Africa.* 2 vols. Academic Press, London.

148 Cyrus, D. & Robson, N. 1980. *Bird Atlas of Natal.* University of Natal Press, Pietermaritzburg.

149 D'Albertis, L. 1880. *New Guinea: What I Did and What I Saw.* 1: 325.

150 Dams, L.R. 1977. Spanish rock-art depicting honey-gathering during the Mesolithic. *Nature,* London 268(5617): 228–230.

151 Dawson, W.R. 1925. The Bee-eater (*Merops apiaster*) from the earliest times, and a further note on the Hoopoe. *Ibis* XII(1): 590–593.

151A Dean, W.R.J. & Huntley, M.A. In press. An updated list of the birds of Angola.

152 Dean, W.R.J. & MacDonald, A.W. 1981. A review of African birds feeding in association with mammals. *Ostrich* 52: 135–155.

153 Debout, C., Debout, E. & Debout, G. 1981. Premières nidifications normandes du guêpier (*Merops apiaster*). *Cormoran* 23: 199–210.

154 Deignan, H.G. 1955. Eastern Asiatic races of the bee-eater, *Merops philippinus* L. *Bull. Brit. Orn. Cl.* 75: 57–59.

155 Dejaifve, P.A. 1981. Quelques données sur la migration automnale des Guêpiers d'Europe, *Merops apiaster*, dans les Pyrénées orientales. *Gerfaut* 71: 619–620.

156 Delacour, J. & Mayr, E. 1946. *Birds of the Philippines*. The Macmillan Company, New York.

157 Dement'ev, G.P. & Gladkov, N.A. (eds.) 1951–1954. *Birds of the Soviet Union*, Vol. I. Israel Program for Scientific Translation, Jerusalem, 1966.

158 Demong, N.J. & Emlen, S.R. 1975. An optical scope for examining nest contents of tunnel-nesting birds. *Wilson Bull.* 87: 550–551.

159 Devillers, P. 1977. Projet de nomenclature française des oiseaux du monde. 5. Trogonidés aux Picidés. *Gerfaut* 67: 469–489.

160 Diamond, A.W. & Hamilton, A.C. 1980. The distribution of forest passerine birds and Quaternary climatic change in tropical Africa. *J. Zool.*, London 191: 379–402.

161 Diamond, J.M. & LeCroy, M. 1979. Birds of Karkar and Bagabag Islands, New Guinea. *Bull. Amer. Mus. Nat. Hist.* 164: 469–531.

162 Dickson, V. 1943. A visit to Maskan and Auha Islands in the Persian Gulf, off Kuwait. *J. Bombay Nat. Hist. Soc.* 11: 258–264.

163 Dobbs, K.A. 1959. Some birds of Sokoto, northern Nigeria. *Niger. Field* 24: 102–119 & 185–191.

164 Dolgushin, I.A., Korelov, M.N., Kuzmina, M.A., Gavrilov, E.I., Gavrin, V.F., Kovshar, A.F., Borodikhin, E.F. & Rodionov, E.F. 1960–1972. [*The Birds of Kazakhstan.*] Vol. 3 (1970) (In Russian.) Akad. Nauk Kazak SSR, Alma-Ata.

165 Donnelly, A. & Donnelly, P. 1977. Carmine Bee-eaters roosting up the Mida Creek. *Bull. E. Afr. Nat. Hist. Soc.* 1977: 61–62.

167 Douthwaite, R.J. & Fry, C.H. 1982. Food and feeding behaviour of the little bee-eater *Merops pusillus* in relation to tsetse fly control by insecticides. *Biol. Conserv.* 23: 71–78.

168 Dowsett, R. J. 1968. Migrants at Malamfatori, Lake Chad, spring 1968. *Bull. Niger. Orn. Soc.* 5: 53–56.

169 Draffan, R.D.W., Garbett, S.T. & Malone, G.J. In press. Birds of the Torres Strait: an annotated list and biogeographical analysis. *Emu.*

170 Dragesco, J. 1960. Notes biologiques sur quelques oiseaux d'Afrique equatoriale. *Alauda* 28: 262–273.

171 Dragesco, J. 1961. Oiseaux des savanes equatoriale. *Oiseau Rev. Fr. Orn.* 31: 261–271.

172 Dresser, H.E. 1884–1886. *A Monograph of the Meropidae, or Family of the Bee-eaters.* Published by the author, London, pp xx + 144, 34 plates.

173 DuPont, J.E. 1971. *Philippine Birds.* Delaware Mus. Nat. Hist., Delaware.

174 Dupuy, A.R. 1970. Données sur les migrations transsahariennes du printemps 1966. *Alauda* 38: 278–285.

175 Dupuy, A.R. 1976. Données nouvelles concernant la reproduction de quelques éspèces aviennes au Sénégal. *Oiseau Rev. Fr. Orn.* 46: 47–62.

176 Dyer, M. 1979. *The Adaptive Significance of Co-operative Breeding in the Red-throated Bee-eater Merops bulocki (Vieillot) and Other Bee-eaters.* Unpubl. Ph.D. thesis, Aberdeen University, pp. 170.

177 Dyer, M. 1980. Notes on prey-capture by Blue-cheeked Bee-eaters. *Malimbus* 2: 76.

178 Dyer, M. 1983. Effect of nest helpers on growth of Redthroated Bee-eaters. *Ostrich* 54: 43–46.

179 Dyer, M. & Crick, H.Q.P. 1983. Observations on Whitethroated Bee-eaters breeding in Nigeria. *Ostrich* 54: 52–55.

180 Dyer, M. & Demeter, A. 1981. Notes on the provisioning rates of Bee-eaters (*Merops apiaster*) in north-east Hungary. *Aquila* 88: 87–90.

181 Dyer, M. & Fry, C.H. 1980. The origin and role of helpers in bee-eaters. *Acta 17 Congr. Internat. Orn.*, Berlin 1978 (ed. R. Nöhring). Vol. II: 862–868. Verlag D.O.-G., Berlin.

182 Dyer, M., Fry, C.H. & Hendrick, J.A. 1981. Breeding of Black-headed Bee-eaters in Nigeria. *Malimbus* 4: 43–45.

183 Eates, K.R. 1939. The status and nidification of the Persian Bee-eater (*Merops persicus persicus* Pall.) in Sind. *J. Bombay Nat. Hist. Soc.* 40: 756–759.

184 Ebbutt, D., Horwood, M.T., Sharland, R.E. & Smith, V.W. 1964. Check-list of the birds of Plateau Province over 3,000 feet. *Bull. Niger. Orn. Soc.* 1(3): 9–14.

185 Elgood, J.H. 1982. *The Birds of Nigeria.* British Ornithologists' Union, London.

186 Elgood, J.H., Fry, C.H. & Dowsett, R.J. 1973. African migrants in Nigeria. *Ibis* 115: 1–45, 375–411.

187 Elliott, C.C.H. 1972. An ornithological survey of the Kidepo National Park, northern Uganda. *J. East Afr. Nat. Hist. Soc.* 28(129): 1–31.

188 Elmosa, H.M. & Al-Rubae, A. 1972. Notes on beekeeping in Iraq. *Amer. Bee J.* 112: 17–18.

189 Emlen, S.T. 1979. Fiscal attacks upon White-fronted Bee-eaters. *Scopus* 3: 101–102.

190 Emlen, S.T. 1981. Altruism, kinship, and reciprocity in the White-fronted bee-eater. Pp. 217–230 in R.D. Alexander & D.W. Tinkle (eds.) *Natural Selection and Social Behavior.* Chiron Press, New York.

191 Emlen, S.T. 1982. The evolution of helping. I. An ecological constraints model. *Amer. Nat.* 119: 29–39.

192 Emlen, S.T. 1982. The evolution of helping. II. The role of behavioral conflict. *Amer. Nat.* 119: 39–53.

193 Emlen, S.T., Demong, N.H. & Hegner, R.E. 1980. Bee-eaters: an alternative route to cooperative breeding? *Acta 17 Congr. Internat. Orn.*, Berlin 1978 (ed. R. Nöhring). Vol. II: 895–901 Verlag D.O.–G., Berlin.

193A Emlen, S.T. & Vehrencamp, S.L. 1983. Cooperative breeding strategies among birds. Ch. 4 (pp. 93–120) in A.H. Brush & G.A. Clark (eds.) *Perspectives in Ornithology.* Cambridge University Press.

194 Erard, C. 1966. Le baguage des oiseaux en 1966. *Bull. Centre Rech. Migrat. Mammif. Oiseaux* 20: 1–66.

195 Esmaili, M. 1974. Bee-eaters—a problem for beekeepers in Iran. *Amer. Bee J.* 114: 136–137.

196 Etchécopar, R.D. & Hüe, F. 1967. *The Birds of North Africa.* Oliver & Boyd, Edinburgh.

197 Etchécopar, R.D. & Hüe, F. 1978. *Les Oiseaux de Chine, de Mongolie et de Corée:· Non Passeraux.* Editions Pacifique, Tahiti.

198 Every, B. 1982. Observations on the European Bee-eater, summer 1981/2. *Bee-eater* (Newsl. E. Cape Wild Bird Soc.) 33: 25–29.

199 Faaborg, J. 1982. Trophic and size structure of West Indian bird communities. *Proc. Nat. Acad. Sci. USA* 79: 1–10.

200 Farkas, T. 1962. Contribution to the bird fauna of Barberspan. *Ostrich* suppl. 4: 1–39.

201 Feduccia, A. 1977. A model for the evolution of perching birds. *Syst. Zool.* 26: 19–31.

202 Field, G. (in prep.) *Birds of Sierra Leone.*

203 Filewood, L.W.C. 1970. *New Guinea Bird Soc. Newsl.* 60: 2.

204 Filewood, L.W.C. 1971. *New Guinea Bird Soc. Newsl.* 71: 2.

205 Filewood, L.W.C., Hough, K., Morris, I.C. & Peters, D.E. 1978. Helpers at the nest of the Rainbow Bee-eater. *Emu* 78: 43–44.

206 Finch, B.W. 1980. Bensbach. *Papua New Guinea Bird Soc. Newsl.* 171–172: 10–38.

207 Finch, R.S. 1971. The European Bee-eater. *Honeyguide* 65: 19–20.

208 Fintha, I. 1968. Beobachtungen über den Bienenfresser (*Merops apiaster*), seine Brut-verhältnisse, seine Nahrung an der Szamos. *Aquila* 75: 102–109 (preceded on pp. 93–102 by the same paper in Hungarian).

209 Fischthal, J.H. 1977. Some digenetic trematodes of birds from central and west Africa. *Rev. Zool. Afr.* 91: 676–680.

210 Fitzgerald, O. 1970. The population structure of a White-fronted Bee-eater colony. *Honeyguide* 63: 13–15.

211 Fleming, R.L. & Traylor, M.A. 1961. Notes on Nepal birds. *Fieldiana Zool.* 35: 443–487.

212 Fleming, R.L. & Traylor, M.A. 1968. Distributional notes on Nepal birds. *Fieldiana Zool.* 53: 147–203.

213 Fogden, M. 1976. *Sarawak Mus. J.*: 263.

214 Fraser, W. 1982. Feeding associations of Carmine Bee-eaters with other animals. *Bokmakierie* 34: 18.

215 Friedmann, H. 1930. Birds collected by the Childs Frick Expedition to Ethiopia and Kenya Colony. *Bull. U.S. Nat. Mus.* 153: 1–516.

216 Friedmann, H. 1966. A contribution to the ornithology of Uganda. *Bull. Los Angeles County Mus. Nat. Hist., Science* 3: 1–55.

217 Friedmann, H. & Kern, J. 1956. The problem of cerophagy or wax-eating in the honey-guides. *Quart. Rev. Biol.* 31: 19–30.

218 Friedmann, H. & Stager, K.F. 1967. Results of the 1966 Cheney Expedition to the Samburu District, Kenya. *Los Angeles County Mus. Contrib. Sci.* 130: 1–34.

219 Friedmann, H. & Williams, J.G. 1969. The birds of the Sango Bay forests, Buddu County, Masaka District, Uganda. *Los Angeles County Mus. Contrib. Sci.* 162: 1–48.

220 Friedmann, H. & Williams, J.G. 1971. The birds of the lowlands of Bwamba, Togo Province, Uganda. *Los Angeles County Mus. Contrib. Sci.* 211: 1–70.

221 Fry, C.H. 1964. White-throated Bee-eater eating oil-palm nut fibres. *Bull. Niger. Orn. Soc.* 1(3): 16.

222 Fry, C.H. 1966. *Some Aspects of the Biology of African Bee-eaters (Meropidae) with Particular Reference to Merops bulocki (Vieillot).* Unpubl. Ph.D. thesis, Ahmadu Bello University, pp. 264.

223 Fry, C.H. 1967. Lipid levels in an intratropical migrant. *Ibis* 109: 118–120.

224 Fry, C.H. 1967. Studies of bee-eaters. *Niger. Field* 32: 4–16.

225 Fry, C.H. 1969. The recognition and treatment of venomous and non-venomous insects by small bee-eaters. *Ibis* 111: 23–29.

226 Fry, C.H. 1969. The evolution and systematics of bee-eaters (Meropidae). *Ibis* 111: 557–592.

227 Fry, C.H. 1970. Convergence between jacamars and bee-eaters. *Ibis* 112: 257–259.

228 Fry, C.H. 1970. Birds in Wasa National Park, Cameroun. *Bull. Niger. Orn. Soc.* 7: 1–23.

229 Fry, C.H. 1971. Migration, moult and weights of some birds in Northern Guinea savanna in Nigeria and Ghana. *Ostrich* suppl. 8: 239–263.

230 Fry, C.H. 1972. The social organisation of bee-eaters and co-operative breeding in hot-climate birds. *Ibis* 114: 1–14.

231 Fry, C.H. 1973. The biology of African bee-eaters. *Living Bird* 11 (1972): 75–112.

232 Fry, C.H. 1974. Vocal mimesis in nestling Greater Honey-guides. *Bull. Brit. Orn. Cl.* 94: 58–59.

233 Fry, C.H. 1975. An undescribed form of *Merops orientalis*. *Bull. Brit. Orn. Cl.* 95: 133–135.

234 Fry, C.H. 1977. The evolutionary significance of co-operative breeding in Birds. pp. 127–135 in B. Stonehouse & C. Perrins (eds.) *Evolutionary Ecology.* Macmillan, London.

235 Fry, C.H. 1978. Meropidae. Pp. 303–311 (Maps 315–324) in D.W. Snow (ed.) *An Atlas of Speciation in African Non-Passerine Birds.* British Museum (Natural History), London.

236 Fry, C.H. 1980. Survival and longevity among tropical land-birds. *Proc. 4 pan-Afr. Orn. Congr.*, Seychelles 1976: 333–343.

237 Fry, C.H. 1980. The evolutionary biology of kingfishers (Alcedinidae). *Living Bird* 18 (1979–1980): 113–160.

238 Fry, C.H. 1980. The origin of Afrotropical kingfishers. Appendix by A.G. Knox: Feather protein evidence of the relationship of *Halcyon* species. *Ibis* 122: 57–74.

239 Fry, C.H. 1981. The diet of large green bee-eaters *Merops superciliosus* supersp. and the question of bee-eaters fishing. *Malimbus* 3: 31–38.

240 Fry, C.H. 1981. On the breeding season of *Merops persicus* in West Africa. *Malimbus* 3: 52.

241 Fry, C.H. 1981. The residential status of the Madagascar Bee-eater *Merops superciliosus* in Africa. *Scopus* 5: 41–45.

242 Fry, C.H. 1982. Water-diving behaviour of Carmine Bee-eaters. *Ostrich* 53: 244–245.

243 Fry, C.H. 1983. Honeybee predation by bee-eaters, with economic considerations. *Bee World* 64: 65–78.

244 Fry, C.H. 1983. Birds in savanna ecosystems. Pp. 337–357 in F. Bourlière (ed.) *Tropical Savannas.* Elsevier Scient. Publ. Co., Amsterdam.

245 Fry, C.H. In press. Material Supplied for *Merops apiaster* European Bee-eater. pp. in S.

Cramp & K.E.L. Simmons (eds.) *Handbook of the Birds of Europe, the Middle East and North Africa: The Birds of the Western Palearctic.* Oxford University Press, Oxford.

246 Fry, C.H. In press. Bee-eaters: beekeepers' benefactors? '*Birds and Man*' symp. S. Afr. Orn. Soc., Johannesburg 1983.

247 Fry, C.H. & Crick, H.Q.P. 1980. An albinistic example of *Merops bulocki. Malimbus* 2: 73.

248 Fry, C.H., Dyer, M. & Crick, H.Q.P. 1984. Monitoring adult and nestling bee-eater weights. *Proc. 5 pan-Afr. Orn. Congr.*, Lilongwe 1980.

249 Fry, C.H., Ferguson-Lees, I.J. & Ash, J.S. 1969. Mite lesions in Sedge Warblers and bee-eaters in Africa. *Ibis* 111: 611–612.

249A Fry, C.H. & Gilbert, D.J. 1983. Food of the Black-headed Bee-eater. *Bull. Brit. Orn. Cl.* 103: 119–123.

250 Gallagher, M. & Woodcock, W. 1980. *The Birds of Oman.* Quartet Books, London.

251 Galton, D. 1971. *Survey of a Thousand Years of Beekeeping in Russia.* Bee Res. Soc., London. Pp. 1–90.

252 Gamauf, A. 1981. Ein Brutvorkommen des Bienenfressers (*Merops apiaster*) im südlichen Burgenland. *Natur u. Umwelt Burgenland* 4: 3–4.

252A Ganguli, U. 1975. *A Guide to the Birds of the Delhi Area.* New Delhi.

253 Garland, I. 1970. Swallow-tailed Bee-eater *Merops hirundineus* at Mtunzini. *Natal Bird Cl. News Sheet* 186.

254 Gass, M.D.I. 1963. The bee-eaters of Ghana. *Niger. Field* 28: 30–34.

256 Gee, J.P. 1969. White-fronted Bee-eater *Melittophagus bullockoides* at Libreville, Gabon. *Bull. Niger. Orn. Soc.* 6: 34–35.

257 Gee, J.P. & Heigham, J.B. 1977. The birds of Lagos, Nigeria. *Bull. Niger. Orn. Soc.* 13: 43–52, 103–132.

258 Gehlhaar, H. & Klebb, W. 1979. Wandert der Bienenfresser bei uns ein? *Falke* 26: 88–91.

259 Gehlhaar, H. & Klebb, W. 1980. Wandert der Bienenfresser bei uns ein? Nachtrag 1977/1978. *Falke* 27: 352–353.

260 Géroudet, P. 1966. Nidification du Guêpier *Merops apiaster* dans le Pays de Genève. *Nos Oiseaux* 28: 319–320.

261 Gillet, H. 1960. Observations sur l'avifaune du Massif de l'Ennedi (Tchad). *Oiseau Rev. Fr. Orn.* 30: 45–82, 99–134.

262 Gilliard, E.T. & LeCroy, M. 1967. Results of the 1958–1959 Gilliard New Britain expedition. 4. Annotated list of birds of the Whiteman Mountains, New Britain. *Bull. Amer. Mus. Nat. Hist.* 135: 175–216.

263 Glenister, A.G. 1971. *The Birds of the Malay Peninsula.* Oxford University Press.

264 Glutz von Blotzheim, U.N. & Bauer, K.M. 1980. *Handbuch der Vögel Mitteleuropas.* 9 Columbiformes-Piciformes. Akademische Verlagsgesellschaft Wiesbaden.

265 Good, A.I. 1952. *The Birds of French Cameroon.* Sér. Sciences Naturelles, Mém. Inst. Française d'Afr. Noire, Dakar.

266 Goodwin, D. 1952. Dominant and submissive behaviour of Bee-eaters. *Brit. Birds* 45: 32–33.

267 Gore, M.E.J. 1981. *Birds of The Gambia.* British Ornithologists' Union, London.

268 Gough, M.M. 1972. The carmine bee-eaters of the Luangwa Valley. *Black Lechwe* 10: 23–26.

269 Grant, C. 1945. Drone bees selected by birds. *Condor* 47: 261–263.

269A Gregory, P.A. 1983. Water-diving behaviour of bee-eaters. *Bokmakierie* 35: 68.

270 Grimwood, I. 1964. The Northern Carmine Bee-eater *Merops nubicus* Gmelin using animal perches. *Bull. Brit. Orn. Cl.* 84: 105–106.

271 Grozdanić, S. 1955. [The Bee-eater (*Merops apiaster*): biological research.] (In Serbian with German summary.) *Zborn. Matice srp., Ser. prir. Nauk* No. 8: 1–24.

272 Guichard, K.M. 1947. Birds of the inundation zone of the River Niger, French Soudan. *Ibis* 89: 450–489.

273 Guichard, K.M. 1955. The birds of Fezzan and Tibesti. *Ibis* 97: 393–424.

274 Guthrie, T.H. 1969. Rainbowbirds "dipping" for food. *Austral. Bird. Watcher* 3: 175–176.

275 Guy, R.D. 1972. The honey hunters of southern Africa. *Bee World* 53: 159–166.

276 Gwinner, E. 1961. Über die Entstachelungshandlung des Neuntöters (*Lanius collurio*). *Vogelwarte* 21: 36–47.

277 Hachler, E.M. 1958. [On the nesting of Bee-eaters (*Merops apiaster*) in southern Moravia.] (In Czech with German summary.) *Sylvia* 15: 239–246.

277A Hahn, V. 1981. Zur sozialen Organisation des Bienenfressers *Merops apiaster*. *J. Orn.* 122: 429–434.

277B Hahn, V. 1982. Rufduett des Bienenfressers (*Merops apiaster*). *J. Orn.* 123: 55–62.

277C Hahn, V. 1982. Beobachtungen zum Sozialverhalten des Bienenfressers. *Gefiederte Welt* 106: 327–329.

278 Hall, B.P. & Moreau, R.E. 1970. *An Atlas of Speciation in African Passerine Birds*. British Museum (Natural History), London.

278A Hall, D.G. 1983. Birds of Mataffin, Eastern Transvaal. *Southern Birds* 10: 1–55.

279 Hall, H. 1981. Perched swallows feeding from hogweed. *Brit. Birds* 74: 98 (and see following editorial comment).

280 Hamilton, W.D. 1964. The genetical evolution of social behaviour. I and II. *J. Theoret. Biol.* 7: 1–16, 17–32.

281 Hanmer, D.B. 1980. Mensural and moult data on six species of bee-eater in Moçambique and Malaŵi. *Ostrich* 51: 25–38.

282 Hanmer, D.B. 1982. Mortality rate of the Little Bee-eater. *Ostrich* 53: 241–242.

283 Harber, D.D. 1964. Report on rare birds in Great Britain in 1963. *Brit. Birds* 57: 261–281.

284 Harris, R. 1979. The wet season feeding ecology and daily activity of the Red-throated Bee-eater (*Merops bulocki*) in northern Ghana, July/August 1978. *Unpubl. Manuscript*, Aberdeen University, 46 pp.

285 Hartley, P.H.T. 1966. Breeding behaviour of Blue-cheeked Bee-eater, *Merops superciliosus*. Abstracts 14 Internat. Orn. Congr. Oxford 1966, p. 68.

286 Harwin, R.M. 1959. Observations from a Bulawayo garden. *Ostrich* 30: 97–104.

287 Harwin, R.M. 1976. European Bee-eater recovery. *Ostrich* 47: 230.

288 Harwin, R.M. & Rockingham-Gill, D.V. 1981. Aspects of the biology of the southern races of the Swallow-tailed Bee-eater. *Honeyguide* 106: 4–10.

289 Hegner, R.E. 1981. *Territoriality, Foraging Behaviour, and Breeding Energetics of the White-fronted bee-eater (Merops bullockoides) in Kenya*. Unpubl. Ph.D. thesis, Cornell University, pp. 1–322.

290 Hegner, R.E. 1982. Central place foraging in the whitefronted bee-eater. *Anim. Behav.* 30: 953–963.

291 Hegner, R.E., Emlen, S.T. & Demong, N.J. 1982. Spatial organization of the white-fronted bee-eater. *Nature*, London 298: 264–266.

292 Hegner, R.E., Emlen, S.T., Demong, N.T. & Miller, C.E. 1979. Helpers at the nest in the White-fronted Bee-eater. *Scopus* 3: 9–13.

293 Heim de Balsac, H. & Mayaud, N. 1962. *Les Oiseaux du Nord-Ouest de l'Afrique*. Paul Lechevalier, Paris.

293A Helbig, A. 1982. Zur Nahrungsökologie eines norddeutschen Bienenfresser (*Merops apiaster*)-Paares mit Überlegungen zum Aufreten im nördlichen Mitteleuropa. *Die Vogelwelt* 103: 161–175.

294 Hendrick, J. 1980. 'That bird' *Bombylonax greweri* (sic) (Cassin). *Elaeis* (Journal of Igalaland) 2: 63–66.

295 Henry, G.M. 1971. *A Guide to the Birds of Ceylon*. 2nd ed. Oxford University Press, London.

296 Herbert, D.A. 1963. Bee-eating by Kookaburras. *Queensland Nat.* 17: 30.

297 Hernandez-Pachéco, E. 1924. Las pinturas prehistoricas de la Cueva de la Araña. *Mem. Com. Invest. Paleont., Madrid* No. 34.

298 Herrera, C.M. & Ramirez, A. 1974. Food of Bee-eaters in southern Spain. *Brit. Birds* 67: 159–164.

299 Hespenheide, H.A. 1975. Selective predation by two swifts and a swallow in Central America. *Ibis* 117: 82–99.

299A Hillman, J.C. 1983. *An Ecological Survey of Management Recommendations for*

Bangangai Game Reserve, Southwest Ludon, with Special Reference to the Bongo Antelope. Pp. 116. New York Zoological Society.

300 Hogg, P. 1950. Some breeding records from the Anglo-Egyptian Sudan. *Ibis* 92: 574–578.

301 Holmes, D.A. 1972. Bird notes from the plains south of Lake Chad. *Bull. Niger. Orn. Soc.* 9: 47–55, 76–84 & 28–37.

302 Holmes, D.A. & Wright, J.O. 1968–1969. The birds of Sind: a review. *J. Bombay Nat. Hist. Soc.* 65: 533–556; 66: 8–30.

303 Hopson, A.J. 1964. Preliminary notes on the birds of Malamfatori, Lake Chad. *Bull. Niger. Orn. Soc.* 1: 7–15.

304 Hopson, J. & Hopson, A.J. 1977. Breeding Carmine and White-throated Bee-eaters in the vicinity of Ferguson's Gulf, Turkana. *Bull. East Afr. Nat. Hist. Soc.* 1977: 2–3.

305 Horn, H.S. & May, R.M. 1977. Limits to similarity among coexisting competitors. *Nature,* London 270: 660–661.

306 Horwood, M.T. 1964. Notes on some West African bee-eaters. *Bull. Niger. Orn. Soc.* 1(1): 2–5.

307 Hüe, F. & Etchécopar, R.D. 1970. *Les Oiseaux du Proche et du Moyen Orient.* N. Boubée & Cie., Paris.

308 Hume, A.O. & Davison, W. 1978. A revised list of the birds of Tenasserim. *Stray Feathers* 6: 1–524.

309 Husain, M.A. & Bhalla, H.R. 1937. The bird enemies of the cotton leaf roller (*Sylepta derogata* Fb.) at Khanewal, Multan (Punjab). *Indian J. Agric. Sci.* 7: 785–792.

310 Hutson, H.P.W. 1947. On the migrations of *Merops apiaster* Linnaeus and *Merops superciliosus* Linnaeus in the Middle East and India. *Ibis* 89: 291–300.

311 Hutson, H.P.W. & Bannerman, D.A. 1930–1932. The birds of northern Nigeria. Part III. *Ibis* XIII, 1: 147–203.

312 Irwin, M.P.S. 1982. *The Birds of Zimbabwe.* Quest, Salisbury.

313 Irwin, M.P.S. & Benson, C.W. 1966. Notes on the birds of Zambia, Part II. *Arnoldia (Rhod.)* 2(37): 1–21.

314 Irwin, M.P.S. & Benson, C.W. 1967. Notes on the birds of Zambia, Part III. *Arnoldia (Rhod.)* 3(4): 1–30.

315 Irwin, M.P.S., Niven, P.N.F. & Winterbottom, J.M. 1969. Some birds of the lower Chobe River area, Botswana. *Arnoldia (Rhod.)* 4(21): 1–3.

316 Jackson, F.J. 1938. *The Birds of Kenya Colony and the Uganda Protectorate.* 3 vols. Gurney & Jackson, London.

317 Jackson, H.D. 1969. Notes on a collection of birds from the Khwae River, Botswana. *Arnoldia (Rhod.)* 4(24): 1–9.

318 Jackson, T.H.E. 1945. Some *Merops-Ardeotis* perching associations in northern Kenya. *Ibis* 87: 284–286.

319 James, F.F. 1968. Further notes on the Rainbow Birds at "Lilydale House" Batesford. *Bird Observer* 438: 5.

320 Jánossy, D. 1974. Die mittelpleistozäne Vogelfauna von Hundsheim (Niederösterreich). *Österr. Akad. Wiss. Math.-Naturwiss.* 182: 211–258.

321 Jazenja, O.S. 1966. [The food of bee-eaters on the middle Dnieper.] (In Ukrainian). Pp. 140–146 in *Ekologija ta Istorija Chrebetnich fauni Ukraini,* Kiev.

322 Jenn, R.A.Y. 1973. Ravages of the bee-eater. *Amer. Bee J.* 113: 21.

323 Jennings, M.C. 1981. *The Birds of Saudi Arabia: a Check List.* Published by the author, Cambridge, England: pp. 109.

324 Jensen, J.V. & Kirkeby, J. 1980. *The Birds of The Gambia.* Aros Nature Guides, Aarhus.

325 Jensen, L. 1959. Notes on the European Bee-eater *Merops apiaster.* *Ostrich* 30: 86–87.

326 Jilka, A. & Ursprung, J. 1980. Zur Stimme des Bienenfressers (*Merops apiaster*) und ihrer Rolle im sozialen Verkehr der Artgenossen. *Egretta* 23: 8–19.

327 Jones, P.J. 1979. The moult of the Little Bee-eater in northwestern Botswana. *Ostrich* 50: 183–185.

328 Jubb, R.A. 1968. Nesting of Carmine Bee-eaters interrupted. *Bokmakierie* 20: 70.

329 Keith, S. 1968. Notes on birds of East Africa, including additions to the avifauna. *Amer. Mus. Novit.* 2321, pp. 1–15.

330 Kemp, A. (in prep.) *Bird Atlas of Transvaal.*

331 Kendall, R.L. 1969. An ecological history of the Lake Victoria basin. *Ecol. Monogr.* 39: 121–176.

332 Kepler, A.K. 1977. *Comparative Study of Todies (Todidae): with Emphasis on the Puerto Rican Tody, Todus mexicanus.* Publ. Nuttall Orn. Cl. 16. Cambridge, Mass.

333 Khacher, L.J. 1975. The Bluecheeked Bee-eater *Merops superciliosus*, its status in Kutch and Saurashtra. *J. Bombay Nat. Hist. Soc.* 72: 543–544.

334 Khanmamedov, A.I. & Gasanova, Z.R. 1969. [Towards the ecology of Golden Bee-eaters in Azerbaijan.] (In Russian.) *Collected Works Orn. USSR* 2: 680–682.

335 King, B., Woodcock, M. & Dickinson, E.C. 1975. *A Field Guide to the Birds of South-East Asia.* Collins, London.

336 Klapste, J. 1980. Rainbow Bee-eater: playful behaviour, and other observations. *Austral. Bird Watcher* 8: 252–253.

337 Klapste, J. 1982. Notes on the Celebes Bee-eater *Meropogon forsteni*. *Austral. Bird Watcher* 9: 252–259.

338 Knox, A.G. 1980. Feather protein as a source of avian taxonomic information. *Comp. Biochem. Physiol.* 65B: 45–54.

339 Koenig, L. 1950. Untersuchungen über Beuteschema und Nahrungserwerb des Bienenfressers. *Zool. Inform. Biol. Stat. Wilhelminenberg* 2.

340 Koenig, L. 1951. Beiträge zu einem Aktionssystem des Bienenfressers (*Merops apiaster* L.). *Zeitschr. Tierpsychol.* 8: 169–210.

341 Koenig, L. 1953. Beobachtungen am afrikanischen Blauwangenspint (*Merops superciliosus chrysocercus*) in freier Wildbahn und Gefangenschaft, mit Vergleichen zum Bienenfresser (*Merops apiaster* L.). *Zeitschr. Tierpsychol.* 10: 180–204.

342 Koenig, L. 1956. Zum Vorkommen einiger Spinte zwischen Tessalit und Niamey (Französisch-Westafrika). *J. Orn.* 97: 384–402.

343 Koenig, L. 1958. Pflege und Zucht von Bienenfressern. *Gefiederte Welt* 82: 181–185.

344 Koenig, L. 1959. Die Brutfürsorge des heimischen Bienenfressers. *Mitt. Biol. Stat. Wilhelminenberg* 2: 50–54.

345 Koenig, L. 1960. *Merops apiaster* (Meropidae) Jugendentwicklung. Pp. 7. *Encyclopaedia Cinematographica*, Inst. Wiss. Film. Göttingen.

346 Koenig, L. 1968. Bunte Räritaten. Europäischer, australische und Afrikanische Bienenfresser brüten im die Voliere. *Vogel Kosmos* 12: 400–416.

347 Koenig, L. 1969. Der Nahrungsverbrauchjunger *Melittophagus bullockoides* (Meropidae) während der Entwicklungszeit. *Österr. Akad. Wiss. Math.-Naturwiss.* 178: 323–336.

348 Koenig, L. 1970. *Merops ornatus* (Meropidae) Graben einer Nisthöhle. Pp. 8. *Encyclopaedia Cinematographica*, Inst. Wiss. Film, Göttingen.

349 Koenig, W.D. & Pitelka, F.A. 1981. Ecological factors and kin selection in the evolution of cooperative breeding in birds. Pp. 261–280 in R.D. Alexander & D.W. Tinkle (eds.) *Natural Selection and Social Behavior.* Chiron Press, New York.

350 König, C. & von Wicht, U. 1973. Eine erfolgreiche Brut des Bienenfressers (*Merops apiaster*) in Hegau. *Anz. Orn. Ges. Bayern* 12: 52–56.

351 Korelov, M.N. 1948. [Information on the ecology and economic significance of Golden Bee-eaters.] (In Russian.) *Izvestia Acad. Nauk Kazakhstan SSR., Zool. ser.* 51(7): 107–123.

352 Korodi Gál, J. & Libus, A. 1968. Beiträge zur Kenntnis der Brutnahrung des Bienenfressers (*Merops apiaster* L.). *Zool. Abh. Ber. Mus. Tierk. Dresden* 29: 95–102.

353 Kowalski, S. & Kowalski, H. 1957. Nidification du Guêpier d'Europe à Noirmoutier (Vendée) en 1956. *Oiseau Rev. Fr. Orn.* 5(27): 378–381.

354 Kozák, V. 1958. [Breeding of Bee-eaters (*Merops apiaster*) at Převov in Moravia.] (In Czech with German summary.) *Sylvia* 15: 247–250.

355 Kracht, W. 1968. Zur Haltung von Bienenfressern. *Gefiederte Welt* 92: 97–98.

356 Kraft, J.A. & Korelov, M.N. 1938. [Concerning chemical methods in the struggle with *Merops apiaster* L. in apiaries in Uzbekistan.] (In Russian.) *Bull. Univ. Asie Centr.* 22: 165–168.

356A Krebs, J.R. & Avery, M.I. In press. Test of central place foraging in a single-prey loader. [*Merops apiaster.*] *J. Anim. Ecol.*

357 Krimmer, M., Piechocki, R. & Uhlenhaut, K. 1974. Über die Ausbreitung des Bienenfressers und die ersten Brutnachweise 1973 in der DDR. *Falke* 21: 42–51, 95–101.

358 Kulesza, G. In press. Adaptive radiation in the higher nonpasserines: Piciformes and Coraciiformes.
359 Kumerloeve, H. 1968. Recherches sur l'avifaune de la République Arabe Syrienne essai d'un aperçu. *Alauda* 36: 190–207.
360 Kumerloeve, H. 1972. Liste comparée des oiseaux nicheurs de Turquie méridionale, Syrie et Liban. *Alauda* 40: 353–366.
361 Kuznetsov, L.A. 1979. [Golden Bee-eaters in the Perm region.] (In Russian.) *Ornitologija* 14: 192.
362 Lack, D. 1968. *Ecological Adaptations for Breeding in Birds*. Methuen, London.
363 Lamarche, B. 1980. Liste commentée des oiseaux du Mali. *Malimbus* 2: 121–158.
364 Lamothe, L. 1979. Diet of some birds in *Araucaria* and *Pinus* forests in Papua New Guinea. *Emu* 79: 36–37.
365 Lane, S.G. 1963. Notes on banding Rainbow Birds. *Austral. Bird Bander* 1: 59–61.
366 Larsen, A.A. 1949. Yuglende Biaeder i Danmark. *Dansk Orn. Foren. Tidsskr.* 43: 129–149.
367 Latif, A. & Yunus, C.M. 1950. The Common or Green Bee-eater as an enemy of honeybees. *Bee World* 31: 91–92.
368 Laurence, G. & Mohammed. I. 1975. Notes on a bird pest of honeybees in Trinidad. *J. Agric. Soc. Trinidad* 75: 258.
369 Lavrovskiy, V.V. & Priklonskiy, S.G. 1974. [A trap for birds nesting in burrows.] (In Russian with English summary.) *Zool. Zh.* 53: 1869–1870.
370 Lea, A.M. & Gray, J.T. 1935. The food of Australian birds. *Emu* 25: 63–98.
371 Leuthold, W. 1973. Is the Somali Bee-eater extending its range? *Bull. East Afr. Nat. Hist. Soc.* (July 1973): 101.
372 Lindgren, E. 1970. *New Guinea Bird Soc. Newsl.* 59: 1.
373 Livingstone, D.A. 1975. Late Quaternary climatic change in Africa. *Ann. Rev. Ecol. Syst.* 6: 249–280.
374 Lombard, A.L. 1965. Notes sur les oiseaux de Tunisie. *Alauda* 33: 1–33, 206–235.
375 Lomont, H. 1946. L'extension du *Merops apiaster* L. en Camargue. *Bull. Mus. Hist. Nat. Marseille* 6: 81–88.
376 Lopez Gordo, J.L. 1975. Sobre la migración posnupcial del Abejaruco (*Merops apiaster*) en el Estrecho de Gibraltar. *Ardeola* 21: 615–625.
377 Lorber, P. 1982. Late breeding of bee-eaters in a drought year. *Honeyguide* 111/112: 58–59.
378 Louette, M. 1981. *The Birds of Cameroon, an Annotated Check-List*. A.W.L.S.K., Paleis der Akademiën, Brussels.
379 Loveridge, A. 1928. Notes on East African birds (chiefly nesting-habits and stomach-contents) collected in 1926. *Proc. Zool. Soc.* London 73: 71–79.
380 Lynes, H. 1925. On the birds of north and central Darfur, with notes on the west-central Kordofan and North Nuba Provinces of British Sudan (IV). *Ibis* XII(1): 344–416.
381 Mackworth-Praed, C.W. 1946. Animate perch associations. *Ibis* 88: 132.
382 Mackworth-Praed, C.W. & Grant, C.H.B. 1957–1973. *African Handbook of Birds*. Ser. I, Birds of Eastern and North Eastern Africa (2nd ed.); Ser. II, Birds of the Southern Third of Africa, Ser. III, Birds of West Central and Western Africa. 6 vols. Longmans, London.
383 Madoc, G.C. 1956. *An Introduction to Malayan Birds*. Malayan Nature Soc., Kuala Lumpur.
384 Maes, V. & Louette, M. 1983. Breeding of Black-headed Bee-eater in Zaire. *Malimbus* 5: 55.
385 Malbrant, R. 1952. *Faune du Centre Africain Français*. Lechevalier, Paris.
386 Malbrant, R. 1954. Contribution a l'étude des oiseaux du Borkou-Ennedi-Tibesti. *Oiseau Rev. Fr. Orn.* 5(24): 1–47.
387 Mann, C.F. 1976. Some recent changes in our knowledge of bird distribution in East Africa. *J. East Afr. Nat. Hist. Soc.* 157: 1–24.
388 Mařan, J. 1958. [On the food of Bee-eaters (*Merops apiaster*).] (In Czech with German summary.) *Sylvia* 15: 254.
389 Marchant, S. 1942. Some birds of the Owerri Province, S. Nigeria. *Ibis* 84: 137–196.
390 Marchant, S. 1953. Notes on the birds of south-eastern Nigeria. *Ibis* 95: 38–69.

391 Marchant, S. 1963. The breeding of some Iraqi birds. *Ibis* 105: 516–557.
392 Marien, D. 1950. Notes on some Asiatic Meropidae (birds). *J. Bombay Nat. Hist. Soc.* 49: 151–164.
393 Mason, C.W. & LeFroy, H.M. 1912. The food of birds in India. *Mem. Dept. Agric. India* 3: 1–166.
394 Mateo, M.P.M. 1978. Malofagos parasitos de Coraciformes. *Rev. Iber. Parasitol.* 38: 385–402.
395 Matousek, B. 1951. [Biology of the Bee-eater in Slovakia.] (In Czech with English summary.) *Sylvia* 13: 122–125.
395A Maurer, D.R. & Raikow, R.J. 1981. Appendicular myology, phylogeny, and classification of the avian Order Coraciiformes (including Trogoniformes). *Ann. Carnegie Mus.* 50 (18): 417–434.
396 Mayr, E. 1945. *Birds of the Southwest Pacific*. Macmillan, New York.
397 McAtee, W.L. 1932. Effectiveness in nature of the so-called protective adaptations in the animal kingdom, chiefly as illustrated by the food habits of Nearctic birds. *Smithson. Misc. Coll.* 85(7): 1–201.
398 McClure, H.E. 1974. *Migration and Survival of the Birds of Asia*. USAMC (SEATO), Bangkok.
399 McCulloch, D. 1961. Probable courtship behaviour of Little Bee-eater. *Bokmakierie* 13: 39.
400 McKay, C. 1969. Notes on *Myrops* (sic) *Ornatus* Latham. *Australas. Beekeeper* 71: 105–106.
401 McLachlan, G.R. & Liversidge, R. (revisers) 1978. *Roberts Birds of South Africa*. John Voelcker Bird Book Fund, Cape Town.
402 Medway, Lord & Wells, D.R. 1976. *The Birds of the Malay Peninsula*. Vol. V: Conclusion, and Survey of Every Species. H.F. & G. Witherby Ltd., London.
403 Mees, G.F. 1970. Birds of the Inyanga National Park, Rhodesia. *Zool. Verhandelingen.* 109: 1–19.
404 Mees, G.F. 1982. Birds from the lowlands of southern New Guinea (Merauke and Koembe). *Zool. Verhandelingen* 191: 1–188 + 4 plates.
405 Meinertzhagen, R. 1930. *Nicolls' The Birds of Egypt*. Oliver & Boyd, Edinburgh.
406 Meinertzhagen, R. 1954. *Birds of Arabia*. Oliver & Boyd, Edinburgh.
407 Meinertzhagen, R. 1959. *Pirates and Predators*. Oliver & Boyd, Edinburgh.
408 Méric, J-D. 1973. Moineau soulcie nichant dans un trou de Guêpier. *Alauda* 41: 161–163.
409 Meyer, A.B. 1879–1885. *Abbildungen von Vögel-Skeletten herausgegeben mit Unterstützung des Generaldirection der Königl.* Sammlungen für Kunst und Wiss. Dresden. Pt. i (1879), Pl. 5, pt. ix (1885), Pl. 84.
410 Michener, C.D. 1974. *The Social Behavior of the Bees*. Harvard University Press, Cambridge, Mass.
411 Miller, W. DeW. 1924. Further notes on ptilosis. *Bull. Amer. Mus. Nat. Hist.* 50: 305–331.
412 Miller, W. DeW. 1924. Variations in the structure of the aftershaft and their taxonomic value. *Amer. Mus. Novit.* 140: 1–7.
413 Milton, M. 1970. Metabeleland notes. *Honeyguide* 61: 7–8.
414 Misonne, X. 1956. Notes sur les oiseaux de la Syrie et de l'Iran. II. Liste des oiseaux nicheurs de la région de Tell-Abiad, N.E. de la Syrie. *Gerfaut* 46: 195–197.
415 Molesworth, B.D. 1950. The nesting of the Chestnut-headed Bee-eater. *Malayan Nat. J.* 5: 76–78.
416 Molesworth, B.D. 1952. Further notes on the nesting of the Chestnut-headed Bee-eater. *Malayan Nat. J.* 7: 148.
417 Moltoni, E. 1928. Descrizione di un nuovo Meropidae (Aves) dell' Eritrea. *Atti. Soc. Ital. Sci. Nat.* 67: 179–181.
418 Moltoni, E. & Ruscone, G.C. 1940–1944. *Gli Uccelli dell' Africa Orientale Italiana*. Museo Civico di Storia Naturale, Milan.
419 Moreau, R.E. 1927. Some notes from the Egyptian oases. *Ibis* XII(3): 210–245.
420 Moreau, R.E. 1938. Bird migration over the north-western part of the Indian Ocean, the Red Sea and the Mediterranean. *Proc. Zool. Soc.* London (A) 108: 1–26.
421 Moreau, R.E. 1941. The ornithology of Siwa Oasis, with particular reference to the results of the Armstrong College expedition, 1935. *Bull. Inst. Egypte* 23: 247–261.

422 Moreau, R.E. 1961. Problems of Mediterranean-Saharan migration. *Ibis* 103A: 373–427 & 580–623.

423 Moreau, R.E. 1966. *The Bird Faunas of Africa and its Islands.* Academic Press, London.

424 Moreau, R.E. 1972. *The Palaearctic-African Bird Migration Systems.* Academic Press, London.

425 Morel, G.J. 1972. Liste commentée des oiseaux du Sénégal et de la Gambie. Typescript, pp. 139. *ORSTOM*, Dakar.

426 Morel, G.J. & Morel, M.-Y. 1962. La reproduction des oiseaux dans une région semi-aride: la vallée du Sénégal. *Alauda* 30: 161–203.

427 Morel, G.J. & Morel, M.-Y. 1982. Dates de reproduction des oiseaux de Sénégambie. *Bonn. Zool. Beitr.* 33: 249–268.

428 Morel, G.J. & Roux, F. 1966. Les migrateurs palearctiques au Sénégal. I. Non Passereaux. *Terre et Vie* 1: 19–72.

429 Morris, I.C. 1976. Observations on the Rainbow Bird *Mirops* (*sic*) *ornatus* in the Warby Ranges. *Victorian Nat.* 93: 152–154.

430 Morris, I.C. 1977. More observations of Rainbow Bee-eaters *Merops ornatus* in the Warby Ranges. *Victorian Nat.* 94: 158–160.

431 Morse, R.A. & Ghent, R.L. 1959. Protective measures against stinging insects. *New York Stat. J. Med.* 59: 1546–1548.

432 Morse, R.A. & Laigo, F.M. 1969. The Philippine Spine tailed Swift, *Chaetura dubia* McGregor as a honey bee predator. *Philipp. Entomol.* 1: 138–143.

433 Mountfort, G. 1957. Nest-hole excavation by the Bee-eater. *Brit. Birds* 50: 263–267.

434 Mountfort, G. 1958. *Portrait of a Wilderness.* Hutchinson, London.

435 Muller, K.A. 1976. Rainbow bee-eater. P. 328 *in Reader's Digest Complete Book of Australian Birds.* Reader's Digest Services Pty Ltd, Sydney.

436 Murie, J. 1873. On the Upupidae and their relationships. *Ibis* 15: 181–211.

437 Neelakantan, K.K. 1948. On the breeding of the Blue-tailed Bee-eater (*Merops superciliosus javanicus*) in Rajahmundri, East Godavari District. *J. Bombay Nat. Hist. Soc.* 47: 741–742.

438 Nelson, J.B. 1980. *Seabirds Their Biology and Ecology.* Hamlyn, London.

439 Newby, J. 1980. The birds of the Ouadi Rime-Ouadi Achim Faunal Reserve, a contribution to the study of the Chadian avifauna. Part 2. *Malimbus* 2: 29–50.

440 Nicholls, C.A. & Rook, D.A. 1962. Preparation of bees for consumption by a captive bee-eater (*Merops ornatus*). *West. Austral. Nat.* 8: 84–86.

441 Nickerson, B. 1958. Some observations on the Carmine Bee-eater *Merops nubicus* Gmelin in the French Sudan. *Ibis* 100: 454–457.

442 Nikolaus, G. 1982. Further notes on some birds new to south Sudan. *Scopus* 6: 1–4.

443 North, M.E.W. 1944. The use of animate perches by the Carmine Bee-eater and other African species. *Ibis* 86: 171–176.

444 O'Connor, R.J. 1978. Growth strategies in nestling passerines. *Living Bird* 16 (1977): 209–240.

445 Olioso, G. 1974. Moineau soulcie *Petronia petronia* pris à parti par des Guêpiers d'Europe *Merops apiaster*. *Alauda* 42: 502.

446 Oosthuizen, J.H. & Markus, M.B. 1969. The haematozoa of South African birds. III. The Carmine Bee-eater *Merops nubicoides* Des Murs and Pucheran. *Zool. Afr.* 4: 99–100.

447 Orejuela, J.E. 1977. Comparative biology of Turquoise-browed and Blue-crowned Motmots in the Yucatan Peninsula, Mexico. *Living Bird* 16 (1977): 193–208.

448 Osmolovskaja, V.I. & Formosov, A.N. 1955. [On the food habits of the bee-eater in the lower Volga and south-east Ciscaucasia.] (In Russian.) *Trudy Inst. Georgia.* (Leningrad) 66: 274–286.

449 Pagden, H.T. 1958. The Bay-headed Bee-eater. *Malayan Nat. J.* 13: 90–91.

450 Pager, H. 1971. *Ndedema.* Akademische Druck- u. Verlagsanstalt, Graz.

451 Pager, H. 1973. Rock paintings in southern Africa showing bees and honey hunting. *Bee World* 54: 61–68.

452 Pager, H. 1976. Cave paintings suggest honey hunting activities in ice age times. *Bee World* 57: 9–14.

453 Pakenham, R.H.W. 1979. *The Birds of Zanzibar and Pemba.* British Ornithologists' Union, London.

454 Parslow, J.L.F. 1972. An early record of a Blue-cheeked Bee-eater *Merops superciliosus* in the Isles of Scilly. *Bull. Brit. Orn. Cl.* 92: 57–59.

455 Pateff, P. 1942. Die von der Kgl. Ornithologischen Zentrale in Sofia beringten und rückgemeldeten Vögel. *Mitt. Naturwiss. Inst. Sofia* 15: 235–251.

456 Pearson, R. 1978. *Climate and Evolution.* Academic Press, London.

457 Pek, L.W. & Fedjanina, T.F. 1961. [Food of birds of Kirghiziya. Pp. 59–118 in A.I. Yanushevich, *The Birds of Kirghiziya*, Vol. 3.] (In Russian.) Acad. Sci. Kirghiz S.S.R.

458 Pelchen, H. 1978. European Bee-eaters wintering in Nairobi. *Bull. East Afr. Nat. Hist. Soc.* 1978: 58–59.

459 Pérez Chiscano, J.L. 1975. Avifauna de los cultivos de regadíos del Guadiana (Badajoz). *Ardeola* 21: 753–794.

460 Peters, J.L. 1955. *Check-List of Birds of the World.* V. Harvard University Press, Cambridge, Mass.

461 Petrov, V.S. 1954. [Concerning the feeding ecology of Golden Bee-eaters.] (In Russian.) *Works Sci. Invest. Inst. Biol. & Biol. Faculty Kharkov University* (Ukraine) 20: 171–180.

462 Pettet, A. 1969. Feeding association of *Aerops albicollis* and *Cinnamopteryx castaneofuscus* with the squirrel *Funisciurus anerythrus. Ibis* 111: 98–101.

463 Phillips, W.W.A. 1963. The birds of the Maldive Islands, Indian Ocean. *J. Bombay Nat. Hist. Soc.* 60: 546–584.

464 Phillips, W.W.A. 1979. Nests and eggs of Ceylon birds. X. *Ceylon J. Sci. (Bio. Sci.)* 13: 131–158.

465 Phisalix, M. 1935. Action comparée du venin d'abeilles sur vertebrés et en particulier sur les éspèces venimeuses. *Annls. Sci. Nat. Zool.* 18: 67–95.

466 Pineau, J. & Giraud-Audine, M. 1974. Notes sur les migrateurs traversant l'extreme nord-ouest du Maroc. *Alauda* 42: 159–188.

467 Pitman, C.R.S. 1929. The economic importance of birds in Uganda and parts of Kenya colony from the point of view of locust destruction. *Bull. Soc. Roy. Entomol. d'Égypte* 13: 93–103.

468 Pocock, T.N. 1961. Some notes on Giant Kingfisher *Megaceryle maxima*, Turnstone *Arenaria interpres*, Swallow-tailed Bee-eater *Melittophagus hirundineus* and Yellow Wagtail *Motacilla flava. Ostrich* 32: 183.

469 Potter, E.F. 1970. Anting in wild birds, its frequency and probable purpose. *Auk* 78: 692–713.

470 Prigogine, A. 1980. Etude de quelques contacts secondaires au Zaïre oriental. *Gerfaut* 70: 305–384.

471 Priklonskiy, S.G. 1970. [Peculiarities of relationship of Golden Bee-eaters with their breeding range at its northern border.] (In Russia.) *Proc. 7 pre-Baltic Orn. Congr.* 1: 83–85.

472 Priklonskiy, S.G. & Lavrovskiy, V.V. 1974. [On the ecology of Golden Bee-eaters and perspectives on their protection in central reaches of the Oka River.] (In Russian.) *Proc. 6 All-Union Orn. Congr.* 2: 106–108.

473 Rand, A.L. 1936. The distribution and habits of Madagascar birds. *Bull. Amer. Mus. Nat. Hist.* 72: 145–499.

474 Randík, A. 1958. [Colonies of the Bee-eater (*Merops apiaster*) in the environs of Levice.] (In Czech with English summary.) *Sylvia* 15: 255–258.

475 Randík, A. 1961. [The postembryonic development of Bee-eaters (*Merops apiaster* L.)] (In Czech with German summary.) *Zool. Listy* 10: 59–67.

476 Rasmussen, E.V. 1977. Danske forekomster af Haerfugl *Upupa epops* 1968–1975, Biaeder *Merops apiaster* og Ellekrage *Coracias garrulus* 1970–1975. *Dansk. Orn. Foren. Tidsskr.* 71: 37–42.

477 Reid, J.C. 1974. Bienenfresser-Beobachtungen im östlichen Österreich. *Egretta* 1: 15–22.

478 Remaudière, G. 1954. Etude écologique de *Locusta migratoria migratorioides* Rch & Frm. (Orthoptera, Acrididae) dans la zone d'inondation du Niger en 1950. *Locusta* 2: 1–248.

479 Reng, O. & Broch-Christensen, M. 1968. Biaederen ynglende i Østjylland i 1966. *Dansk. Orn. Foren. Tidsskr.* 62: 142–143.

480 Reynolds, J.F. 1965. Bee-eaters and rollers diving into water. *East Afr. Wildl. J.* 3: 129.
481 Reynolds, J.F. 1974. Nursery help for bee-eaters. *Wildlife* 16: 256–259.
482 Richardson, F. 1965. Breeding and feeding habits of the Black Wheatear *Oenanthe leucura* in southern Spain. *Ibis* 107: 1–16.
483 Riley, J.H. 1938. Birds from Siam and the Malay Peninsula in the United States National Museum collected by Drs Hugh M. Smith & William L. Abbott. *Bull. U.S. Nat. Mus.* 172: 1–581.
484 Ripley, S.D. 1949. Avian relicts and double invasions in peninsular India and Ceylon. *Evol.*, Pa. 3: 150–159.
485 Ripley, S.D. 1964. A systematic and ecological study of birds of New Guinea. *Bull. Peabody Mus. Nat. Hist.* 19: 1–87.
486 Risberg, L. 1979. Fågelrapport för 1976. *Vår Fågelvärld* 38: 266–285.
487 Rivoire, A. 1947. Contribution a l'étude du *Merops apiaster*. *Oiseau Rev. Fr. Orn.* 17: 23–43.
488 Robin, P. 1968. L'avifaune de l'Iriki (sud-Marocain). *Alauda* 36: 237–253.
489 Robinson, G.B. & Robinson, J.M. 1975. European Bee-eaters feeding young in Zambia. *Bull. Zambian Orn. Soc.* 7: 107.
490 Roff, C. & Brimblecombe, A.R. 1963. Pests of honeybees and bee-hives. *Queensl. Agric. J.* 89: 540–545.
491 Rowan, M K. 1967. European Bee-eater *Merops apiaster* in the Cape Province: apparent change in status. *Ostrich* 38: 158–159.
491A Rowley, I. 1983. Commentary [on co-operative breeding and survival]. Pp. 127–133 in A.H. Brush & G.A. Clark (eds.) *Perspectives in Ornithology*. Cambridge University Press.
492 Roy, M.B. 1968. Occurrence of the European Bee-eater *Merops apiaster* Linnaeus, at Mettur Dam, Salem District, Madras. *J. Bombay Nat. Hist. Soc.* 65: 776.
493 Royds, T.F. 1918. *The Beasts, Birds and Bees of Virgil*. Blackwell, London.
494 Ruttner, F. 1976. African races of honeybees. *Proc. 25 Internat. Beekeeping Congr.*, Grenoble, 1975, ed. E.V. Harnaj & R. Borneck: 325–344.
495 Ruttner, F. 1977. The problem of the Cape Bee (*Apis mellifera capensis* Escholtz): parthenogenesis—size of population—evolution. *Apidologie* 8: 281–294.
496 Ruttner, F. 1977. The present knowledge of the taxonomy of African races of bees. Pp. 50–54 in D.J.C. Fletcher (ed.) *African Bees: Taxonomy, Biology and Economic Use*. Proc. Apimondia Int. Symp., Pretoria, 1976.
497 Ruwet, J.-C. 1965. *Les Oiseaux des Plaines et du Lac-Barrage de la Lufira Supérieure (Katanga Méridional)*. Liège, éditions F.U.L.R.E.A.C., pp. 265.
498 Sackl, P. 1981. Zur Ernährungsbiologie des Bienenfressers, *Merops apiaster* L., 1758, im südlichen Búrgenland. *Natur u. Umwelt Burgenland* 4: 5–12.
499 Sage, B.L. 1960. Bee-eaters diving into water. *Brit. Birds* 53: 222.
500 Sagitov, A.K. & Fundukchiev, S.E. 1980. [Information on the breeding of *Merops superciliosus*.] (In Russian.) *Zool. Zh.* 5: 88–89.
501 Salvan, J. 1967–1969. Contribution à l'étude des oiseaux du Tchad. *Oiseau Rev. Fr. Orn.* 37: 255–284, 38: 53–85, 127–150, 249–273, 39: 38–69.
501A Savin, Yu. G. & Gistsov, A.P. 1983. [Moult and weights of Golden and Green Bee-eaters during autumn migration in the western Tyan-Shan. Pp. 197–202 in A.F. Kovshar, E.I. Gavrilov & V.V. Khrokov (eds.) *Migrations of Birds in Asia* Vol. 8.] (In Russian.) Nauke Publ. House, Kazak SSR.
502 Schmidt, E. 1980. Bird-banding of the Hungarian Ornithological Institute—31. Report on bird-banding (1978). *Aquila* 87: 131–139.
503 Schouteden, H. 1962. La faune ornithologique des districts de la Mongala et de l'Ubangi. *Document. Zool. Mus. Roy. Afr. Centr.*, Tervuren, No. 3 (see p. 60).
504 Schuefele, U. & Ullrich, B. 1973. Schwarzstirnwürger (*Lanius minor*) entstacheln Hymenopteren. *Anz. Orn.*, Bayern 12: 142–144.
505 Schumann, G. 1971. Brut des Bienenfressers *Merops apiaster* 1971 in Nordhessen. *Luscinia* 41: 153–159.
506 Sclater, W.L. & Mackworth-Praed, C. 1919. A list of the birds of the Anglo-Egyptian Sudan, based on the collections of Mr. A.L. Butler, Mr. A. Chapman and Capt. H.

Lynes, R.N., and Major Cuthbert Christy, R.A.M.C. (T.F.). Part III. *Ibis* XI, 1: 628–707.

507 Seale, J.D. 1975. *New Guinea Bird Soc. Newsl.* 113: 8.

508 Serle, W. 1939. Field observations on some northern Nigerian birds. *Ibis* XIV(3): 654–699.

509 Serle, W. 1943. Further field observations on northern Nigerian birds. *Ibis* 85: 264–300, 413–437.

510 Serle, W. 1950. A contribution to the ornithology of the British Cameroons. *Ibis* 92: 342–376.

511 Serle, W. 1954. A second contribution to the ornithology of the British Cameroons. *Ibis* 96: 47–80.

512 Serle, W. 1957. A contribution to the ornithology of the eastern region of Nigeria. *Ibis* 99: 371–418, 628–685.

513 Serle, W. 1958. Some breeding records of birds at Sapele, western Nigeria. *Niger. Field* 23: 70–75.

514 Short, L.L. 1979. Burdens of the picid hole-excavating habit. *Wilson Bull.* 91: 16–28.

515 Short, L.L. & Horne, J.F.M. 1981. Bird observations along the Egyptian Nile. *Sandgrouse* 3: 43–61.

516 Shufeldt, R.W. 1903. On the osteology and systematic position of the kingfishers (Halcyones). *Amer. Nat.* 37: 697–725.

517 Sibley, C.G. 1960. The electrophoretic patterns of avian egg-white proteins as taxonomic characters. *Ibis* 102: 215–284.

518 Sibley, C.G. & Ahlquist, J.E. 1972. A comparative study of the egg white proteins of non-passerine birds. *Bull. Peabody Nat. Hist. Mus. Yale* 39: 1–276.

519 Sim, L. 1979. *Birds of Wondo Genet.* Orgut-Swedforest Consortium, Stockholm.

519A Sinclair, I. 1983. S.A.O.S. Rarities Committee report. *Bokmakierie* 35: 35–40.

520 Skarén, U. 1955. [The Bee-eater, *Merops apiaster* L., in Lappee.] (In Finnish.) *Orn. Fenn.* 32: 29.

521 Skead, C.J. 1967. Ecology of birds in the Eastern Cape Province. *Ostrich* Suppl. 7: 1–103.

522 Slater, P. 1970. *A Field Guide to Australian Birds. Non-Passerines.* Rigby Ltd., Adelaide.

523 Sloane, J. 1916. The Golden Merops (*Merops ornatus*). *Emu* 16: 99–100.

524 Smit, F.G.A.M. 1977. An unusual form of the stick-tight flea *Echidnophaga gallinacea. Rev. Zool. Afr.* 91: 198–199.

525 Smith, K. D. 1955. The winter breeding season of land-birds in eastern Eritrea. *Ibis* 97: 480–507.

530 Smith, K.D. 1957. An annotated check list of the birds of Eritrea. *Ibis* 99: 1–26, 307–337.

531 Smith, K.D. 1968. Spring migration through southeast Morocco. *Ibis* 110: 452–492.

532 Smith, V.W. 1966. Breeding records for the Plateau Province over 3,000 feet, 1957–1966. *Bull. Niger. Orn. Soc.* 3: 78–90.

533 Smith, V.W. 1966. Birds seen on a trans-Saharan overland crossing in spring 1966. *Bull. Niger. Orn. Soc.* 3: 50–62.

534 Smithers, R.H.N. 1964. *A Check List of the Birds of the Bechuanaland Protectorate and the Caprivi Strip.* Trustees Nat. Mus. S. Rhodesia, Causeway.

535 Smithers, R.H.N., Irwin, M.P.S. & Paterson, M.L. 1957. *A Check List of the Birds of Southern Rhodesia.* Rhodesian Ornithological Society, Salisbury.

536 Smythies, B.E. 1953. *The Birds of Burma.* Oliver & Boyd, Edinburgh.

537 Smythies, B.E. 1981. *The Birds of Borneo* (3rd ed. revised by Earl of Cranbrook). Sabah Soc. and Malayan Nature Soc., Kuala Lumpur.

538 Snow, D.W. (ed.). 1978. *An Atlas of Speciation in African Non-Passerine Birds.* British Museum (Natural History), London.

539 Spoerry, A. 1976. Notes on Carmine Bee-eaters seen nesting in Ileret on the 8th May 1974. *Bull. East Afr. Nat. Hist. Soc.* 1976: 126–128.

540 Steyn, P. & Brooke, R.K. 1971. Cold induced mortality of birds in Rhodesia during November 1968. Proc. 3 pan-Afr. Orn. Congr., Pretoriuskop 1969, *Ostrich* Suppl. 8: 271–282.

541 Storr, G.M. 1973. List of Queensland birds. *Special Publ. Western Austral. Mus.* 5: 1–177.

542 Stresemann, E. 1940. Die Vögel von Celebes. III. *J. Orn.* 88: 389–467.

543 Sueur, F. le 1957. Bee-eaters breeding in the Channel Islands in 1956. *Brit. Birds* 50: 361–364.

544 Sutton, R.W.W. 1964. Notes on birds seen in Ghana in 1964. *Bull. Niger. Orn. Soc.* 2: 55–62, 102–107.

545 Sutton, R.W.W. 1970. Bird records from Ghana in 1967 and 1968/69. *Bull. Niger. Orn. Soc.* 7: 53–56, 76–93.

546 Swift, J.J. 1959. Le Guêpier d'Europe *Merops apiaster* L. en Camargue. *Alauda* 27: 97–143.

547 Szederkényi, N., Faust, R., Varga, G., Tárnoky, E., Dékány, D. & Koltay, P. 1956. [Damage to bees by bee-eaters.] (In Hungarian.) *Méhészet*, Budapest 3(7): 125–126.

548 Szijj, J. 1952–1955. [Bee-eater colonies in Hungary in 1949.] (In Hungarian.) *Aquila* 59–62: 185–190.

549 Tapfer, D. 1957. Über die Verbreitung und Brutbiologie des Bienenfressers in Ungarn. *Falke* 4: 3–5.

550 Tapfer, D. 1978. *Publ. Mus. Com. Vesprimiensis Rer. Nat.* 13.

551 Taylor, P.B. 1979. Palaearctic and intra-African migrant birds in Zambia: a report for the period May 1971 to December 1976. *Zambian Orn. Soc. Occ. Pap.* 1: 1–169.

552 Telleria, J.L. 1979. La migration postnuptiale du Guêpier d'Europe *Merops apiaster* L. au detroit de Gibraltar en 1977. *Alauda* 47: 139–150.

553 Ten Kate, C.G.B. 1967. Ornithologie van Nederland, 1965. *Limosa* 40: 14–58.

554 Thesiger, W. & Meynell, M. 1935. On a collection of birds from Danakil, Abyssinia. *Ibis* V(13): 774–807.

555 Thiollay, J.M. 1970. L'exploitation par les oiseaux des essaimages de fourmis et termites dans une zone de contact savane-forêt en Côte d'Ivoire. *Alauda* 38: 255–273.

556 Thiollay, J.M. 1971. Les guêpiers et rolliers d'une zone de contact savane-forêt en Cote d'Ivoire. *Oiseau Rev. Fr. Orn.* 41: 148–162.

557 Thiollay, J.M. 1971. L'exploitation des feux de brousse par les oiseaux en Afrique occidentale. *Alauda* 39: 54–72.

558 Thiollay, J.M. 1978. Ecologie des migrateurs tropicaux dans une zone préforestière de Côte d'Ivoire. *Terre et Vie* 27: 268–296.

559 Thomsen, P. & Jacobsen, P. 1979. *The Birds of Tunisia.* Publ. by the authors. Copenhagen.

560 Thonglongya, K. 1968. A new martin of the genus *Pseudochelidon* from Thailand. *Thai. Nat. Sci. Papers, Fauna Ser.* 1: 1–10.

561 Ticehurst, C.B., Buxton, P.A. & Cheesman, R.E. 1922. The birds of Mesopotamia. *J. Bombay Nat. Hist. Soc.* 28: 381–427.

562 Ticehurst, C.B., Cox, P. & Cheesman, R.E. 1926. Additional notes on the avifauna of Iraq. *J. Bombay Nat. Hist. Soc.* 31: 91–119.

563 Took, J.M.E. 1963. Bee-eaters diving into water. *Ostrich* 34: 176.

564 Tostain, O. 1978. Nidification du Guêpier d'Europe *Merops apiaster* et observations de la Cisticole des joincs *Cisticola juncidis* en Seine-et-Marne. *Oiseau Rev. Fr. Orn.* 48: 184.

565 Traylor, M.A. 1963. Check-list of Angolan birds. *Publ. Cult. Cia. Diament. Angola*, No. 61: 1–250.

566 Traylor, M.A. & Archer, A.L. 1982. Some results of the Field Museum 1977 Expedition to south Sudan. *Scopus* 6: 5–12.

567 Traylor, M.A. & Parelius, D. 1967. A collection of birds from the Ivory Coast. *Fieldiana, Zool.* 51: 91–117.

568 Tree, A.J. 1961. Bee-eaters diving into water. *Brit. Birds* 54: 286–282.

569 Tree, A.J. 1963. Little Bee-eaters *Merops pusillus* dust-bathing. *Ostrich* 34: 179.

570 Tree, A.J. 1971. Notes on Palaearctic migrants in the Eastern Cape. *Ostrich* 42: 198–204.

571 Turner, A.K. 1981. Lepidopteran larvae in the diet of the Swallow. *Bird Study* 28: 65.

572 Tutman, I. 1949–50. [Great Tits and bees.] (In Serbian with English summary.) *Larus*, Zagreb 3: 281–304.

573 Urban, E.K. & Brown, L.H. 1971. *A Checklist of the Birds of Ethiopia.* Haile Sellassie I University Press, Addis Ababa.

574 Ursprung, J. 1979. Zur Ernährungsbiologie ostösterreichischer Bienenfresser (*Merops apiaster*). *Egretta* 22: 4–17.

575 Valverde, J.A. 1953. Le Guêpier d'Europe dans le bassin du Duero (Espagne). *Nos Oiseaux* 22: 7–10.

576 Van Someren, V.G.L. 1945. The use of animate perches. *Ibis* 87: 109.

577 Van Someren, V.G.L. 1956. Days with birds. *Fieldiana, Zool.* 38: 1–520.

578 Vaurie, C. 1959. Systematic notes on Palearctic birds. No. 38. Alcedinidae, Meropidae, Upupidae, and Apodidae. *Amer. Mus. Novit.* 1971: 1–25.

579 Vernon, C.J. 1968. A year's census of Marandellas, Rhodesia: *Ostrich* 39: 12–24.

580 Verschuren, J. 1966. Contribution à l'ornithologie. Exploration du Parc National de la Garamba. *Inst. Parcs Nat. Congo*, Brussels, Fasc. 49: 13–28.

581 Vielliard, J. 1972. Données biogéographiques sur l'avifaune d'Afrique centrale. II. *Alauda* 40: 63–92.

582 Vincent, J. 1934. The birds of northern Portuguese East Africa. Comprising a list of, and observations on, the collections made during the British Museum Expedition of 1931–32. *Ibis* XIII (4): 757–799.

583 Vuilleumier, F. 1977. Suggestions pour des recherches sur la spéciation des oiseaux en Iran. *Terre et Vie* 31: 468–470.

584 Waldenström, A. 1976. Biätaren *Merops apiaster* häckande på Öland 1976. *Calidris* 5: 99–103.

585 Walsh, J.F. 1968. Notes on bee-eaters in the Borgu area. *Bull. Niger. Orn. Soc.* 5: 10–13.

586 Ward, P. 1971. Development of our natural resources versus the Carmine Bee-eater. *Honeyguide* 66: 36–37.

587 Waterman, M.H. 1965. Notes on the Rainbow Bird in South Australia. *Austral. Bird Bander* 3: 49.

588 Waterman, M.H. & Llewellyn, L.C. 1968. Further notes on White-backed Swallows and Rainbow-birds. *Austral. Bird Bander* 6: 8–9.

589 Watson, J. 1981. *Population Ecology, Food and Conservation of the Seychelles Kestrel (Falco araea) on Mahé.* Unpubl. Ph.D. thesis, Aberdeen University, pp. 248.

590 Wells, D.R. & Walsh, F. 1969. Birds of northern and central Borgu. *Bull. Niger. Orn. Soc.* 6: 1–25, 63–93.

591 Wheeler, R. 1973. Rainbowbirds taking tadpoles. *Austral. Bird Watcher* 5: 48.

592 Whistler, H. 1949. *Popular Handbook of Indian Birds* (4th ed.). Oliver & Boyd, Edinburgh.

593 Whistler, H. & Kinnear, N.B. 1932–1935. The Vernay scientific survey of the Eastern Ghats (ornithological section). *J. Bombay Nat. Hist. Soc.* 35: 505–524 and (Part X) 37: 751–763.

594 White, C.M.N. 1965. *A Revised Check List of African Non-Passerine Birds.* Department of Game and Fisheries, Lusaka.

595 White, C.M.N. & Bruce, M.D. In press. *A Checklist of the Birds of Wallacea (Sulawesi, the Moluccas and Lesser Sunda Islands).* British Ornithologists' Union, London.

596 White, F.N., Bartholomew, G.A. & Kinney, J.L. 1978. Physiological and ecological correlates of tunnel nesting in the European Bee-eater, *Merops apiaster. Physiol. Zool.* 51: 140–154.

597 Wildash, P. 1968. *Birds of South Vietnam.* Charles E. Tuttle Co., Rutland, Vermont.

598 Willis, E.O. 1969. On the behaviour of five species of *Rhegmatorhina*, ant-following antibirds of the Amazon basin. *Wilson Bull.* 81: 363–395.

599 Willis, E.O. & Oniki, Y. 1978. Birds and army ants. *Ann. Rev. Ecol. Syst.* 9: 243–263.

600 Wilson, J.H. 1970. R.O.S. Carmine Bee-eater research project—progress report. *Honeyguide* 64: 10.

601 Winterbottom, J.M. 1942. A contribution to the ornithology of Barotseland. *Ibis* XIV, 6: 337–389.

602 Winterbottom, J.M. 1959. Courtship feeding in European Bee-eater. *Ostrich* 30: 44.

603 Winterbottom, J.M. 1959. Notes on the status of some birds in Northern Rhodesia. *Ostrich* 30: 1–12.

604 Winterbottom, J.M. 1960. Southern limit of the range of the Swallow-tailed Bee-eater *Merops hirundineus* Licht. *Ostrich* 31: 27.

605 Winterbottom, J.M. 1962. Some manuscript notes of S.F. Townsend for the period 1878–1925. *Ostrich* 33: 66–71.

606 Winterbottom, J.M. 1966. Results of the Percy Fitzpatrick Institute—Wind-

hoek State Museum joint ornithological expeditions: 5. Report on the Birds of the Kaokoveld and Kunene River. *Cimbebasia* 19: 1–170.

607 Witherby, H.F., Jourdain, F.C.R., Ticehurst, N.F. & Tucker, B.W. 1938–1941. *The Handbook of British Birds*. H.F. & G. Witherby Ltd., London.

608 Woldhek, S. 1979. *Bird Killing in the Mediterranean*. European Committee for Prevention of Mass Destruction of Migratory Birds, Zeist, Netherlands. pp. 62.

609 Yakubanis, V.N. & Litvak, M.D. 1962. [Feeding of the Golden Bee-eater in the Dniester area, Moldavia. *Collected Essays on problems in ecology of practical significance regarding the birds of Moldavia.*] (In Russian.) Pp 49–55.

610 Zimmerman, D.A. 1972. The avifauna of the Kakamega Forest, Western Kenya, including a bird population study. *Bull. Amer. Mus. Nat. Hist.* 149: 255–339.

611 Zusi, R.L. 1978. Remarks on the generic allocation of *Pseudochelidon sirintarae*. *Bull. Brit. Orn. Cl.* 98: 13–15.

Index